S.G.

$100\% \; HNO_3 - 1.51$
$100\% \; H_2SO_4 - 1.83$

THE CHEMISTRY OF
POWDER AND EXPLOSIVES

The Chemistry of
Powder and Explosives

BY

TENNEY L. DAVIS, Ph.D.

Emeritus Professor of Organic Chemistry
Massachusetts Institute of Technology
Director of Research and Development
National Fireworks, Inc.

VOLUME II

NEW YORK

JOHN WILEY & SONS, Inc.

London: CHAPMAN & HALL, Limited

1943

PREFACE

This second volume preserves the point of view of the first volume and fulfils the plan which was outlined in its preface. In its preparation I have been aided by the information and criticism of many friends. I wish to make grateful acknowledgment of my indebtedness to Dr. E. Berl, to Dr. Émile Monnin Chamot, to the U. S. Bureau of Mines, to the Atlas Powder Company, to E. I. du Pont de Nemours and Company, to the Hercules Powder Company, to the Trojan Powder Company, and to the Western Cartridge Company for pictures, to the Williams and Wilkins Company of Baltimore for permission to cite and to quote from Symmes' translation of Naoúm's "Nitroglycerine and Nitroglycerine Explosives," to Sir Isaac Pitman & Sons, Limited, of London, for permission to cite and to quote from MacDonald's "Historical Papers on Modern Explosives" published originally by Whittaker & Co., whose business this firm later took over, and to the *Journal of the American Chemical Society*, to *Industrial and Engineering Chemistry*, to *Army Ordnance*, and to the U. S. Bureau of Mines for permission to cite and to quote from their publications. My thanks are also due to Dr. C. G. Storm who has read the manuscript and has made many helpful suggestions and to Dr. Joseph Ackerman, Jr., who has read the proof.

Tenney L. Davis

Norwell, Massachusetts
21 November 1942

CONTENTS

CHAPTER V

NITRIC ESTERS

Nitric esters or *organic nitrates* contain the nitrate radical, —O—NO$_2$, attached to a carbon atom, or, to express the same idea in a different way, they contain the nitro group, —NO$_2$, attached to an oxygen atom which is attached to a carbon. In *nitro compounds*, strictly so called, the nitro group is attached directly to a carbon; in *nitroamines* or *nitramines* it is attached to an amino nitrogen atom, that is, to a nitrogen which is attached to a carbon. In the nitric esters and in the nitroamines alike, a single atom stands between the nitro group and the carbon atom of the organic molecule. Substances of the two classes are alike in their most characteristic reaction, namely, they are formed by the reversible nitration of alcohols and amines respectively.

During the nitration of glycerin by the action of strong nitric acid or of strong mixed acid upon it, nitro groups are introduced in place of three of the hydrogen atoms of the original molecule. There is therefore a certain propriety in thinking of the product as a nitro compound, and a reasonable warrant for the common practice of calling it by the name of trinitroglycerin or, more commonly, of *nitroglycerin*. The hydrogen atoms which are replaced were attached to oxygen atoms; the product is really a nitric ester, and its proper name is *glyceryl trinitrate*. Similarly, the substances which are commonly called nitroglycol, nitrostarch, nitrosugar, nitrolactose, nitrocotton, etc., are actually nitric esters.

The physical properties of the nitric esters resemble in a general way the physical properties of the alcohols from which they are derived. Thus, methyl and ethyl nitrate, like methyl and ethyl alcohol, are volatile liquids; nitroglycerin is a viscous oil, more viscous and less volatile than glycol dinitrate as glycerin is more viscous and less volatile than glycol. Nitrocellulose from fibrous cellulose yields a tough and plastic colloid, but nitro-starch remains from the evaporation of its solutions as a mass which is brittle and friable.

Methyl Nitrate

Methyl nitrate is a powerful explosive although its physical properties are such that it is not of practical use, and it is of interest only because it is the simplest of the nitric esters. Like ethyl and n-propyl nitrates, it may be prepared by the careful distillation of the alcohol with concentrated nitric acid (d. 1.42) from which, however, the last traces of nitrous acid must first have been removed by the addition of urea. It may also be prepared by adding the alcohol to strong mixed acid at low temperature, stirring, and separating and washing the product without distillation, by a process similar to that which is used for the preparation of nitroglycerin and nitroglycol except that the volatility of the product requires the stirring to be done by mechanical means and not by compressed air. It is a colorless limpid liquid somewhat less viscous than water, boiling point 65–66°, specific gravity 1.2322 at 5°, 1.2167 at 15°, and 1.2032 at 25°. Its vapors have a strongly aromatic odor resembling that of chloroform, and cause headache if they are inhaled. It dissolves collodion nitro-cotton to form a jelly from which the methyl nitrate evaporates readily.

Methyl nitrate has a slightly higher energy content than nitro-glycerin and a slightly greater explosive effect. Naoúm [1] reports that 10 grams of methyl nitrate in the Trauzl test with water tamping caused an expansion of 615 cc., while 10 grams of nitro-glycerin under the same conditions gave 600 cc. Methyl nitrate is very much more sensitive to initiation than nitroglycerin, a fact which, like its higher velocity of detonation, is probably associated with its lower viscosity. It is less sensitive than nitro-glycerin to the mechanical shock of the drop test. In the small lead block test, or lead block compression test, 100 grams of methyl nitrate under slight confinement in a shell of sheet lead 1 mm. thick and tamped with thin cork plates, gave a compres-

[1] Phokion Naoúm, "Nitroglycerine and Nitroglycerine Explosives," trans. E. M. Symmes, Baltimore, The Williams and Wilkins Company, 1928, p. 205.

sion of 24.5 mm. while nitroglycol similarly gave 30 mm. and nitroglycerin 18.5 mm.

Methyl nitrate is easily inflammable and burns in an open dish with a large non-luminous flame. Its vapors explode when heated to about 150°.

Berthelot [2] measured the velocity of detonation of methyl nitrate in tubes of such small diameter that the maximum velocity of detonation was not secured, but he was able to make certain interesting inferences both as to the effect of the envelope and as to the effect of the physical state of the explosive. Some of his results are summarized in the table below. The data indicate

Tube of	Internal Diameter, Millimeters	External Diameter, Millimeters	Velocity of Detonation, Meters per Second
Rubber, canvas covered	5	12	1616
Glass	3	12	2482
Glass	3	7	2191
Glass	5	7	1890
Britannia metal	3	12.6	1230
Steel	3	15	2084
Steel	3	15	2094

that with tubes of the same internal diameter the velocity of detonation is greater in those cases in which the rupture of the tube is more difficult; it is greater in the tubes which have thicker walls and in the tubes which are made of the stronger materials. The extent to which the velocity of detonation builds up depends in some measure upon the pressure which builds up before the container is ruptured. By comparing these results with those from other explosive substances, Berthelot was able to make further inductions.

In fact, nitroglycerin in lead tubes 3 mm. internal diameter gave velocities in the neighborhood of 1300 meters per second, while dynamite in similar metallic tubes attained 2700 meters per second. This sets in evidence the influence of the structure of the explosive substance upon the velocity of propagation of the explosion, pure nitroglycerin, a viscous liquid, transmitting the shock which determines the detonation much more irregularly than the silica impregnated in

[2] *Mém. poudres,* **4,** 13 (1891); *Ann. chim. phys.,* **23,** 485 (1901).

a uniform manner with the same liquid. Mica dynamite according to my observations produces effects which are still more considerable, a fact which could be foreseen from the crystalline structure of the mica, a substance which is less deformable than amorphous silica.

This last induction is confirmed by observations on nitromannite, a crystalline solid which appears by reason of this circumstance better suited than liquid methyl nitrate for transmitting detonation. It has in fact given practically constant velocities of 7700 meters per second in lead tubes of 1.9 mm. internal diameter at a density of loading of 1.9. Likewise picric acid, also crystalline, 6500 meters per second. . . .

The influence of the structure of the explosive substance on the course of the detonation being thus made evident, let us cite new facts which show the effect due to the containing envelope. . . . Compressed guncotton at such densities of loading as 1.0 and 1.27 in lead tubes 3.15 mm. internal diameter gave velocities of 5400 meters per second, while at a density of loading of practically one-half less (0.73) in a lead tube 3.77 mm. internal diameter, a velocity of 3800 meters per second was observed—a difference which is evidently due to the reduced continuity of the material. In supple cordeau, slightly resistant, formed by a single strand or braid, with a density of loading of 0.65, the velocity falls even to 2400 meters per second. But the feeble resistance of the envelope may be compensated by the mass of the explosive which opposes itself, especially in the central portion of the mass, to the instantaneous escape of the gas. Abel, in fact, with cartridges of compressed guncotton, of ten times the diameter of the above-mentioned cordeau, placed end to end, in the open air, has observed velocities of 5300 to 6000 meters per second.[3]

Other Alkyl Nitrates

Ethyl nitrate is a colorless liquid of agreeable odor, boiling point 87°, specific gravity (15°/15°) 1.1159 at 15°, and 1.1044 (25°/25°) at 25°. It has a less favorable oxygen balance than methyl nitrate, and is much less sensitive to initiation than the latter substance. It has only about 48% of the energy content of nitroglycerin, but its lower viscosity tends to give it a higher initial velocity of detonation than nitroglycerin and it performs about 58% as well as nitroglycerin in the sand test.[4] A No. 8

[3] *Mém. poudres*, **4**, 18–19 (1891).
[4] Naoúm, *op. cit.*, p. 207.

blasting cap will not detonate ethyl nitrate unless the explosive is tamped or confined. Mixed with fuller's earth in the proportion 70/30 or 60/40, it yields a brisant explosive which may be detonated without confinement.

n-Propyl nitrate, like ethyl nitrate, can be prepared by mixing the alcohol with nitric acid of density 1.42 or thereabouts, and carefully distilling the mixture. Ethyl alcohol and *n*-propyl alcohol, which contain the methylene group, are easily oxidized; if they are added to nitric acid of greater strength than density 1.42, or if they are added to strong mixed acid, they are likely to react with explosive violence and the abundant production of nitrous fumes, no matter how efficient the cooling. *n*-Propyl nitrate has a pleasant ethereal odor, boiling point 110.5°, specific gravity (15°/15°) 1.0631 at 15°, and (25°/25°) 1.0531 at 25°. It is less sensitive to detonation than ethyl nitrate. Ten grams in a Trauzl block, with water tamping and with a No. 8 blasting cap, detonated only partially and gave an expansion of 45 cc., or 15 cc. more than the cap alone, but 10 grams of it, mixed with 4 grams of fuller's earth to form a moist powder and exploded with a No. 8 cap, gave a sharp explosion and a net expansion of 230 cc.[5]

Isopropyl nitrate, b.p. 101–102°, specific gravity 1.054 at 0°, 1.036 at 19°, is prepared by the interaction of isopropyl iodide and silver nitrate. The hydrogen atom which is attached in isopropyl alcohol to the carbon atom carrying the hydroxyl group is so easily oxidized that it is not feasible to prepare the compound by the action of nitric acid on the alcohol.

Nitroglycerin (Glyceryl trinitrate, NG)

Nitroglycerin was first prepared late in the year 1846 or early in 1847 by the Italian chemist, Ascanio Sobrero (1812–1888), who was at the time professor of applied chemistry at the University of Torino. Sobrero had studied medicine in the same city, and in 1834 had been authorized to practice as a physician. After that he studied with Pelouze in Paris and served as his assistant in his private laboratory from 1840 to 1843. In 1843 he left Paris, studied for several months with Liebig at Giessen, and returned to Torino where he took up the duties of a teacher and in 1845

[5] *Ibid.*, p. 209.

built and equipped a modest laboratory of his own. The earliest printed account of nitroglycerin appears in a letter which Sobrero wrote to Pelouze and which Pelouze caused to be published in *L'Institut* of February 15, 1847.[6] In the same month Sobrero presented to the Academy of Torino a paper, *Sopra alcuni nuovi composti fulminanti ottenuti col mezzo dell'azione dell'acido*

FIGURE 51. Ascanio Sobrero (1812-1888). First prepared nitroglycerin, nitromannite, and nitrolactose, 1846-1847.

nitrico sulle sostanze organiche vegetali,[7] in which he described nitroglycerin, nitromannite, and nitrated lactose. Later in the year he presented another paper, *Sulla Glicerina Fulminante o Piroglicerina,* before the chemistry section of the Ninth Italian Scientific Congress at Venice.[8]

Sobrero found that, if concentrated nitric acid or strong mixed acid is added to glycerin, a violent reaction ensues and red fumes

[6] *L'Institut,* **15,** 53 (1847).
[7] *Mem. Acad. Torino,* [2] **10,** 195 (1847).
[8] *Proc. Ninth Ital. Sci. Congr.,* **3,** 105 (1848).

are evolved, but that, if syrupy glycerin is added to a mixture of two volumes of sulfuric acid (*d.* 1.84) and one volume of nitric acid (*d.* 1.50) with stirring while the mixture is kept below 0°, then the results are entirely different, the glycerin dissolves, and the solution when poured into water gives an oily precipitate of nitroglycerin. He collected the oil, washed it with water until free from acid, dried in a vacuum over sulfuric acid, and procured a transparent liquid of the color and appearance of olive oil. (Pure nitroglycerin is water-white.) Sobrero reported a value for the density which is very close to that which is now generally accepted, observed the ready solubility of nitroglycerin in alcohol and its reprecipitation by water, and reported a number of its chemical reactions—its comportments with acid and with alkali, that

It detonates when brought into contact with metallic potassium, and evolves oxides of nitrogen in contact with phosphorus at 20° to 30°C., but at higher temperatures it ignites with an explosion. . . . When heated, nitroglycerin decomposes. A drop heated on platinum foil ignites and burns very fiercely. It has, however, the property of detonating under certain circumstances with great violence. On one occasion a small quantity of an ethereal solution of nitroglycerin was allowed to evaporate in a glass dish. The residue of nitroglycerin was certainly not more than 2 or 3 centigrams. On heating the dish over a spirit lamp a most violent explosion resulted, and the dish was broken to atoms. . . . The safest plan for demonstrating the explosive power of nitroglycerin is to place a drop upon a watch glass and detonate it by touching it with a piece of platinum wire heated to low redness. Nitroglycerin has a sharp, sweet, aromatic taste. It is advisable to take great care in testing this property. A trace of nitroglycerin placed upon the tongue, but not swallowed, gives rise to a most violent pulsating headache accompanied by great weakness of the limbs.

For many years Sobrero kept in his laboratory and guarded jealously a sample of the original nitroglycerin which he had prepared in 1847. In 1886 he washed this material with a dilute solution of sodium bicarbonate and took it to the Nobel-Avigliana factory, of which he was a consultant, where he gave verbal testimony of its authenticity and where it has since been stored in one of the magazines. Molinari and Quartieri [9] in a book published in 1913 state that the sample, consisting of about 200 cc. under water in a bottle, was at that time unaltered and that analyses gave values for nitrogen in the neighborhood of 18.35%, close to the theoretical.

Sobrero seems originally to have thought more highly of the solid crystalline nitromannite, which he thought might be used in percussion caps, than of the liquid nitroglycerin, but a spontaneous explosion of 400 grams of the former substance in the laboratory of the arsenal of Torino in 1853 and the extensive damage which resulted caused him to lose interest in the material. After Nobel's invention of dynamite and of the blasting cap had made the use of nitroglycerin safe and practical, Sobrero attempted in 1873 to establish a factory to be operated by Italian capital for the manufacture of an explosive called *melanina,* which was a kind of dynamite formed by absorbing nitroglycerin in a mixture of powdered charcoal and the silicious earth of Santa Fiora in Tuscany.[10] The project did not succeed. Shortly afterwards Sobrero accepted a position as consultant to the Nobel-Avigliana factory, a position which paid a generous salary during his life and a pension to his widow after his death. The high regard in which he was held by the Nobel company is indicated further by the bust of him which was unveiled in 1879 in the Avigliana factory.

Glycerin (glycerol) is a by-product of soap manufacture. All natural fats, whether of animal or vegetable origin, whether solid like beef suet or liquid like olive oil, are glyceryl esters of long-chain fatty acids containing an even number of carbon atoms. When they are warmed with an aqueous solution of strong alkali, they are saponified; soap, which is the alkali salt of the acids of the fats, is formed, and glycerin is produced which remains dissolved in the liquid. Glycerin is also formed from fats by the action of steam; the fatty acids, insoluble in water and generally of higher melting point than the fats, are formed at the same time.

Glycerin is a viscous liquid, colorless and odorless when pure, and possessing a sweet taste. It is hygroscopic, will absorb more

[9] Molinari and Quartieri, "Notizie sugli Esplodenti in Italia," Milano, 1913, p. 15.
[10] *Ibid.,* p. 33.

than half its own weight of moisture from the air, and does not evaporate. Glycerin will solidify in a freezing mixture, and when once frozen melts again at about 17°. It boils at atmospheric pressure at 290° with slight decomposition, and is best purified by distillation in vacuum. Its specific gravity is 1.265 at 15°. Perfectly pure and colorless glycerin yields a water-white nitroglycerin. Dynamite glycerin is a distilled product of high purity, density 1.262 or higher, and contains at least 99% of glycerin and less than 1% of water. It varies in color from pale yellow to dark brown, generally has a faint odor resembling that of burnt sugar, and yields a nitroglycerin of a pale yellow or pale brown color. The explosives makers consider a test nitration on a laboratory scale to be the surest way of estimating the quality of a sample of dynamite glycerin.

Small amounts of glycerin are produced during an ordinary alcoholic fermentation, but the quantity is greatly increased if a considerable amount of sodium sulfite is present. A commercial process based upon this principle was developed and used in Germany during the first World War, when the supply of glycerin from fats was insufficient to fill the needs of the explosives manufacturers, and similar processes have been used to some extent elsewhere and since that time. At the beginning of the second World War an effort was made to increase the production of whale oil for the manufacture of glycerin. Modern methods— harpoons shot from guns, fast Diesel-propelled steel ships—resulted immediately in a tremendous slaughter of whales, and whale oil again has become difficult to procure. Recent advances in synthetic chemistry make it probable that glycerin in the future will be prepared in large quantity from petroleum.

Cracking gas, which is produced when heavy petroleum is cracked to produce gasoline, consists in large part of olefins, particularly ethylene and propylene, and is being used more and more for the manufacture of such materials as glycol and glycerin, glycol dinitrate and nitroglycerin, mustard gas, ethanolamine and pentryl. The olefins under ordinary conditions combine with two atoms of chlorine, adding them readily to the unsaturated linkage, and thereafter react with chlorine no further. It has been found that chlorine does not add to hot propylene in the gas phase, but substitutes instead, one of the hydrogen atoms of the methyl group being replaced and allyl chloride being formed. This at a lower temperature adds chlorine normally to form 1,2,3-trichloropropane which gives glycerin on hydrolysis.

$$
\begin{array}{ccccc}
CH_3 & CH_2\!-\!Cl & CH_2\!-\!Cl & CH_2\!-\!OH & CH_2\!-\!ONO_2 \\
| & | & | & | & | \\
CH \longrightarrow & CH \longrightarrow & CH\!-\!Cl \longrightarrow & CH\!-\!OH \longrightarrow & CH\!-\!ONO_2 \\
\| & \| & | & | & | \\
CH_2 & CH_2 & CH_2\!-\!Cl & CH_2\!-\!OH & CH_2\!-\!ONO_2
\end{array}
$$

Nitroglycerin is formed and remains in solution if glycerin is added to a large excess of strong nitric acid. Heat is evolved, and

FIGURE 52. Nitroglycerin Nitrating House. (Courtesy E. I. du Pont de Nemours and Company, Inc.)

cooling is necessary. The nitroglycerin is thrown out as a heavy oil when the solution is diluted with water. A further quantity of the substance is procured by extracting the dilute acid liquors with chloroform. Naoúm [11] reports that 100 grams of glycerin treated in this manner with 1000 grams of 99% nitric acid yields 207.2 grams of nitroglycerin analyzing 18.16% nitrogen (calc. 18.50% N) and containing a small amount of dinitroglycerin (glyceryl dinitrate). The yield of the trinitrate may be improved by the addition to the nitric acid of dehydrating agents such as phosphorus pentoxide, calcium nitrate, or strong sulfuric acid.

[11] Op. cit., pp. 25, 26.

Thus, if 100 grams of glycerin is added with cooling to a solution of 150 grams of phosphorus pentoxide in the strongest nitric acid, phosphoric acid precipitates as a heavy syrupy layer and the supernatant acid liquid on dilution yields about 200 grams of nitroglycerin. The yield is substantially the same if the glycerin is first dissolved in the nitric acid alone and if the phosphorus pentoxide is added afterwards. One hundred grams of glycerin in 500 grams of the strongest nitric acid, 400 grams of anhydrous

FIGURE 53. Nitroglycerin Nitrator. (Courtesy E. I. du Pont de Nemours and Company, Inc.)

calcium nitrate being added and the mixture allowed to stand for some hours, gives on drowning and purification 220 grams of nitroglycerin which contains about 10% of glyceryl dinitrate.

All these methods are too expensive, for the excess of nitric acid is lost or has to be recovered from dilute solution. A process in which the nitroglycerin comes out as a separate phase without the spent acid being diluted is preferable—and it is indeed true that the addition of strong sulfuric acid to a solution of glycerin in strong nitric acid completes the esterification and causes the nitroglycerin to separate out. Since the strongest nitric acid is expensive to manufacture, and since a mixture of less strong nitric acid with oleum (sulfuric acid containing free sulfur trioxide) may be identical in all respects with a mixture of strong nitric and strong sulfuric acids, glycerin is universally nitrated in commercial practice by means of acid already mixed, and the nitroglycerin is procured by means of gravity separation of the phases. One hundred parts by weight of glycerin yield 225 to 235 parts of nitroglycerin.

One part of glycerin is nitrated with about 6 parts of mixed acid, made up by the use of oleum and containing about 40.0%

FIGURE 54. Interior of Nitroglycerin Storage House. (Courtesy E. I. du Pont de Nemours and Company, Inc.)

of nitric acid, 59.5% of sulfuric acid, and 0.5% of water. The nitration in this country is carried out in cast iron or steel nitrators, in Europe in nitrators of lead. The glycerin is commonly added from a cock, controlled by hand, in a stream about the size of a man's finger. The mixture is stirred by compressed air, and the temperature is controlled carefully by means of brine coils, there being usually two thermometers, one in the liquid, one in the gas phase above it. In Great Britain the temperature of the nitration mixture is not allowed to rise above 22°C., in this country generally not above 25°. If the temperature for any reason gets out of control, or if the workman sees red fumes through the window in the nitrator, then the charge is dumped quickly into a drowning tank and the danger is averted. The safety precautions which are everywhere exercised are such that the explosion of a nitroglycerin plant is a rare occurrence. After all the glycerin has been added to the nitrator, agitation and cooling are continued until the temperature drops to about 15°,

FIGURE 55. Nitroglycerin Buggy. (Courtesy Hercules Powder Company.) For transporting nitroglycerin from the storage house to the house where it is mixed with the other ingredients of dynamite. Note the absence of valves and the use of wooden hose clamps as a safety precaution.

and the mixture is then run off to the *separator* where the nitroglycerin rises to the top. The spent acid contains 9 to 10% of nitric acid, 72 to 74% of sulfuric acid, and 16 to 18% of water.

The nitroglycerin from the separator contains about 10% of its weight of dissolved acid (about 8% nitric and about 2% sulfuric). Most of this is removed by a *drowning wash* or *prewash* carried out, in Europe with water at about 15°, in this country with water at 38° to 43°, while the mixture is agitated with compressed air. The higher temperature reduces the viscosity of the nitroglycerin and increases greatly the efficiency of the washing. The nitroglycerin is heavier than water and sinks rapidly to the bottom. It is washed again with water, then with sodium carbonate solution (2 or 3%), and then with water until the washings give no color with phenolphthalein and the nitroglycerin itself is neutral to litmus paper. In this country the nitroglycerin is sometimes given a final wash with a concentrated solution of common salt. This reduces the moisture which is suspended in it, to about the same extent as the filtration to which it is commonly subjected in European practice. The nitroglycerin then goes to storage tanks in a heated building where there is no danger of freezing. It has a milky appearance at first, but this quickly disappears. After one day of storage it generally contains not more than 0.3 or 0.4% of moisture, and this amount does not interfere with its use for the manufacture of dynamite.

Pure nitroglycerin is odorless at ordinary temperatures, but has a faint and characteristic odor at temperatures above 50°. Its specific gravity is 1.6009 at 15° and 1.5910 at 25°.[12] It contracts on freezing. Its vapor pressure has been reported by Marshall and Peace [13] to be 0.00025 mm. at 20°, 0.00083 mm. at 30°, 0.0024 at 40°, 0.0072 at 50°, 0.0188 at 60°, 0.043 at 70°, 0.098 at 80°, and 0.29 mm. at 93.3°. About 5 cc. of nitroglycerin passes over with one liter of water in a steam distillation. Snelling and Storm [14] heated nitroglycerin at atmospheric pressure in a distillation apparatus behind an adequate barricade. They reported that

> Nitroglycerin begins to decompose at temperatures as low as 50° or 60°C. . . . At a temperature of about 135°C. the decomposition of nitroglycerin is so rapid as to cause the liquid to become of a strongly reddish color, owing to the absorption of the nitrous fumes resulting from that which is decomposed; and at a temperature of about 145°C. the evolution of decomposition products is so rapid that, at atmospheric pressures, ebullition begins, and the liquid

12 Perkin, *J. Chem. Soc.*, **55**, 685 (1879).
13 *J. Soc. Chem. Ind.*, **109**, 298 (1916).
14 *U. S. Bur. Mines Tech. Paper* 12, "The Behavior of Nitroglycerine When Heated," Washington, 1912.

"boils" strongly. This "boiling" is due in part to the evolution of decomposition products (mainly oxides of nitrogen and water vapor) and in part to the actual volatilization of nitroglycerin itself.

FIGURE 56. C. G. Storm. Author of numerous articles and government publications on the properties, testing, and analysis of smokeless powder and high explosives. Explosives Chemist at Navy Powder Works, 1901-1909, at U. S. Bureau of Mines, 1909-1915; Directing Chemist, Aetna Explosives Company, 1915-1917; Major and Lieutenant-Colonel, Ordnance Department, 1917-1919; Research Chemist, Trojan Powder Company, 1919; Chief Explosives Chemical Engineer, Office of the Chief of Ordnance, War Department, 1919-1942; since early in 1942, Technical Director, National Fireworks, Inc.

. . . At temperatures between 145° and 215°C. the ebullition of nitroglycerin becomes more and more violent; at higher temperatures the amount of heat produced by the decomposing liquid becomes proportionately greater, and at about 218°C. nitroglycerin explodes.[15]

When nitroglycerin is maintained at a temperature between 145° and 210°C., its decomposition goes on rapidly, accompanied by much volatilization, and under these conditions nitroglycerin may be readily distilled. The distillate consists of nitroglycerin, nitric acid, water, and other decomposition products. The residue that remains after heating nitroglycerin under such conditions for some time probably consists mainly of glycerin, with small amounts of dinitroglycerin, mononitroglycerin, and other decomposition products. These substances are far less explosive than ordinary nitroglycerin, and accordingly by heating nitroglycerin slowly it can be caused to "boil" away until the residue consists of products that are practically non-explosive. In a number of experiments nitroglycerin was thus heated, and a copious residue was obtained. By carefully raising the temperature this residue could be made to char without explosion.

Belyaev and Yuzefovich [16] heated nitroglycerin and other explosives in vacuum, and procured the results summarized in the following table. The fact that ignition temperatures are fairly

	B.P. (2 mm.) EXPERIMENTAL, °C.	B.P. (50 mm.) EXPERIMENTAL, °C.	B.P. (760 mm.) MOST PROBABLE VALUE, °C.	IGNITION TEMPERATURE, °C.
Methyl nitrate	...	5	66	...
Glycol dinitrate	70	125	197 ± 3	195–200
TNT	190	245–250	300 ± 10	295–300
Picric acid	195	255	325 ± 10	300–310
TNB	175	250	315 ± 10	...
PETN	160	180	200 ± 10	215
Nitroglycerin	125	180	245 ± 5	200

close to probable boiling points indicates that high concentrations of vapor exist at the moment when the substances ignite. The authors point out that TNT, PETN, and picric acid neither detonate nor burn in vacuum and suggest that this is probably

[15] Munroe had found the "firing temperature" of nitroglycerin to be 203 to 205°, *J. Am. Chem. Soc.*, **12**, 57 (1890).

[16] *Comp. rend. acad. sci. U.S.S.R.*, **27**, 133 (1940).

because the boiling points in vacuum are considerably below the ignition temperatures.

Nitroglycerin crystallizes in two forms, a stable form, dipyramidal rhombic crystals, which melt or freeze at 13.2–13.5°, and a labile form, glassy-appearing triclinic crystals, m.p. 1.9–2.2°. It does not freeze readily or quickly. When cooled rapidly, it becomes more and more viscous and finally assumes the state of a hard glassy mass, but this is not true freezing, and the glassy mass becomes a liquid again at a temperature distinctly below the melting point of the crystalline substance. Nitroglycerin in dynamite freezes in crystals if the explosive is stored for a considerable length of time at low temperatures, the form in which it solidifies being determined apparently by the nature of the materials with which it is mixed.[17] If liquid nitroglycerin is cooled strongly, say to −20° or −60°, stirred with a glass rod, and seeded with particles of one or the other form, then it crystallizes in the form with which it has been seeded. If the solid is melted by warming, but not warmed more than a few degrees above its melting point, it will on being cooled solidify in the form, whether labile or stable, from which it had been melted. If, however, it is warmed for some time at 50°, it loses all preference for crystallizing in one form rather than in the other, and now shows the usual phenomena of supercooling when it is chilled. Crystals of the labile form may be preserved sensibly unchanged for a week or two, but gradually lose their transparency and change over to the stable form. Crystals of the stable form cannot be changed to the labile form except by melting, warming above the melting point, and seeding with the labile form.

Nitroglycerin is miscible in all proportions at ordinary temperatures with methyl alcohol, acetone, ethyl ether, ethyl acetate, glacial acetic acid, benzene, toluene, nitrobenzene, phenol, chloroform, and ethylene chloride, and with homologous nitric esters such as dinitroglycerin, dinitrochlorohydrin, nitroglycol, and trimethyleneglycol dinitrate. Absolute ethyl, propyl, isopropyl, and amyl alcohols mix with nitroglycerin in all proportions if they are hot, but their solvent power falls off rapidly at lower temperatures. One hundred grams of absolute ethyl alcohol dissolves

[17] Hibbert, *Z. ges. Schiess- u. Sprengstoffw.*, **9**, 83 (1914).

37.5 grams of nitroglycerin at 0°, 54.0 grams at 20°. One hundred grams of nitroglycerin on the other hand dissolves 3.4 grams of ethyl alcohol at 0°, 5.5 grams at 20°.

Nitroglycerin dissolves aromatic nitro compounds, such as dinitrotoluene and trinitrotoluene, in all proportions when warm. When the liquids are cooled, 100 grams of nitroglycerin at 20° still holds in solution 35 grams of DNT or 30 grams of TNT. Both nitroglycerin and the polynitro aromatic compounds are solvents or gelatinizing agents for nitrocellulose.

Nitroglycerin dissolves in concentrated sulfuric acid with the liberation of its nitric acid, and may therefore be analyzed by means of the nitrometer (see below).

Nitroglycerin is destroyed by boiling with alcoholic sodium or potassium hydroxide, but glycerin is not formed; the reaction appears to be in accordance with the following equation.

$$C_3H_5(ONO_2)_3 + 5KOH \longrightarrow$$
$$KNO_3 + 2KNO_2 + H\text{—}COOK + CH_3\text{—}COOK + 3H_2O$$

This however is not the whole story, for resinous products, oxalic acid, and ammonia are also formed. If the reaction with caustic alkali is carried out in the presence of thiophenol, some glycerin is formed and the thiophenol is oxidized to diphenyl sulfide. Alkali sulfides, K_2S, KHS, and CaS, also yield glycerin.

Nitroglycerin vapors cause severe and persistent headache. A workman who is exposed to them constantly soon acquires an immunity. If he is transferred to another part of the plant, he may retain his immunity by paying a short visit every few days to the area in which the nitroglycerin is being used. Workmen appear to suffer no ill effects from handling the explosive continually with the naked hands. Nitroglycerin relaxes the arteries, and is used in medicine under the name of *glonoin*. *Spirit of glonoin* is a 1% solution of nitroglycerin in alcohol. The usual dose for angina pectoris is one drop of this spirit taken in water, or one lactose or dextrose pellet, containing $\frac{1}{100}$ grain (0.0006 gram) of nitroglycerin, dissolved under the tongue.

Nitroglycerin is not easily inflammable. If a small quantity is ignited, it burns with a slight crackling and a pale green flame— and may be extinguished readily before all is burned. If a larger amount is burned in such manner that the heat accumulates and the temperature rises greatly, or if local overheating occurs as by burning in an iron pot, then an explosion ensues. The explosion of nitroglycerin by heat is conveniently demonstrated by heating a stout steel plate to dull redness, removing the source of heat, and allowing the nitroglycerin to fall drop by drop slowly onto the plate while it is cooling. At first the drops assume the spheroidal condition when they strike the plate and deflagrate or burn with a flash, but when the plate cools somewhat each drop yields a violent explosion.

Nitroglycerin is very sensitive to shock, and its sensitivity is greater if it is warm. A drop of the liquid on a steel anvil, or a drop absorbed by filter paper and the paper placed upon the anvil, is detonated by the blow of a steel hammer. The shock of iron striking against stone, or of porcelain against porcelain, also explodes nitroglycerin, that of bronze against bronze less readily, and of wood against wood much less so. Stettbacher [18] reports drop tests with a 2-kilogram weight: mercury fulminate 4.5 cm., lead azide 9 cm., nitroglycerin 10–12 cm., blasting gelatin 12–15 cm., and tetryl 30–35 cm. He also reports the observations of Kast and Will and of Will that nitroglycerin at 90° requires only half as much drop to explode it as nitroglycerin at ordinary temperature, while the frozen material requires about three times as much.

Nitroglycerin and nitroglycerin explosives, like all other high explosives, show different velocities of detonation under different conditions of initiation and loading. They are sometimes described as having low and high velocities of detonation. Berthelot found for nitroglycerin a velocity of 1300 meters per second in lead or tin tubes of 3 mm. internal diameter. Abel [19] found 1525 meters per second in lead pipe 30 mm. internal diameter, while Mettegang [20] found 2050 meters per second in iron pipes of the same internal diameter. Comey and Holmes [21] working with pipes of 25–37.5 mm. internal diameter found values varying from 1300–1500 to 8000–8500 meters per second, and, with especially strong detonators, they regularly found velocities between 6700

[18] Stettbacher, "Die Schiess- und Sprengstoffe," Leipzig, 1919, p. 124.
[19] Phil. Trans., 156, 269 (1866); 157, 181 (1867).
[20] Internat. Congr., 2, 322 (1903).
[21] Z. ges. Schiess- u. Sprengstoffw., 8, 306 (1913).

and 7500 meters per second. Naoúm [22] reports that blasting gelatin (92–93% NG, 7–8% collodion nitrocotton) has a low velocity of 1600–2000 meters per second and a high velocity of about 8000. Blasting gelatin filled with air bubbles always shows the higher velocity, while clear and transparent blasting gelatin almost always shows the lower velocity of detonation. Frozen dynamite is more difficult to initiate, but always detonates at the high velocity.[23]

Certain properties of nitroglycerin and of other explosives, reported by Brunswig,[24] are tabulated below and compared in a manner to show the relative power of the substances. The spe-

	Specific Volume, Liters	Explosion Temperature, °C.	Heat of Explosion, Calories	Characteristic Product
Nitroglycerin	712	3470	1580	1,125,000
Nitromannite	723	3430	1520	1,099,000
Blasting gelatin (93% NG, 7% NC)	710	3540	1640	1,164,000
75% Guhr dynamite	628	3160	1290	810,000
Nitrocotton (13% N)	859	2710	1100	945,000
Picric acid	877	2430	810	710,000
Black powder	285	2770	685	195,000
Ammonium nitrate	937	2120	630	590,000
Mercury fulminate	314	3530	410	129,000

cific volume is the volume, at 0° and 760 mm., of the gaseous products of the explosion. This number multiplied by the heat of explosion gives the *characteristic product* which Berthelot considered to be a measure of the mechanical work performed by the explosion. The mechanical work has also been estimated, differently, in kilogram-meters by multiplying the heat of explosion by 425, the mechanical equivalent of heat.

Naoúm [25] reports the results of his own experiments with nitroglycerin and with other explosives in the Trauzl lead block test (sand tamping), 10-gram samples, as shown below. The Trauzl test is essentially a measure of brisance, but for explosives of similar

22 *Op. cit.,* p. 145.
23 Herlin, *Z. ges. Schiess- u. Sprengstoffw.,* **9,** 401 (1914).
24 Brunswig, "Explosivstoffe," 1909, cited by Naoúm, *op. cit.,* p. 152.
25 *Op. cit.,* p. 156.

velocities of detonation it supplies a basis for the comparison of their total energies.

	EXPANSION, CUBIC CENTIMETERS
Nitroglycerin	550
Nitromannite	560
Compressed guncotton (13.2% N)	420
Blasting gelatin	580
65% Gelatin dynamite	410
75% Guhr dynamite	325
Tetryl	360
Picric acid	300
Trinitrotoluene	285
Mercury fulminate	150

For several years after the discovery of nitroglycerin, the possibility of using it as an explosive attracted very little interest. Indeed, it first came into use as a medicine, and the first serious study on its preparation, after the work of Sobrero, was made by J. E. de Vrij, professor of chemistry in the Medical School at Rotterdam, and published in the Dutch journal of pharmacy, *Tijdschrift voor wetensch. pharm.*, in 1855. The next significant work was done by Alfred Nobel who in 1864 patented [26] improvements both in the process of manufacturing nitroglycerin and in the method of exploding it. No liquid explosive had been successful in practical use. Nobel believed that he had solved the difficulty by taking advantage of the property of nitroglycerin of exploding from heat or from the shock of an explosion. A small glass vessel containing black powder was to be immersed in the nitroglycerin and exploded. Another method was by the local heat of an electric spark or of a wire electrically heated under the surface of the nitroglycerin. And another was the percussion cap. Nobel used black powder first in glass bulbs, later in hollow wooden cylinders closed with cork stoppers, then a mixture of black powder and mercury fulminate, and later fulminate in small lead capsules and finally in the copper detonators which are still in general use. The invention of the blasting cap depended upon the discovery of the phenomenon of initiation, and signalized the beginning of a new era in the history of

[26] Brit. Pat. 1813 (1864).

explosives. Blasting caps were used first for the safe and certain explosion of the dangerous liquid nitroglycerin, but presently they were found to be exactly what was needed for the explosion of the safer and less sensitive dynamites which Nobel also invented.

The first establishment for the manufacture of nitroglycerin in industrial quantities was a laboratory set up by Alfred Nobel and his father, Immanuel Nobel, probably in the autumn of 1863, near the latter's home at Heleneborg near Stockholm. An explosion which occurred there in September, 1864, cost the life of Alfred's younger brother, Emil, and of four other persons. The manufacture of nitroglycerin was prohibited within the city area, but the explosive was already in practical use for the tunnelling operations of the State Railway, and it was desirable to continue its manufacture. The manufacture was removed to a pontoon moored in Malar Lake and was continued there during the late autumn of 1864 and during the following winter until March, 1865, when it was transferred to a new factory, the first real nitroglycerin factory in the world, at Winterwik near Stockholm. Later in the same year the Nobel company commenced manufacturing nitroglycerin in Germany, at a plant near Hamburg, and within a few years was operating explosives factories in the United States and in all the principal countries of Europe.[27]

The first considerable engineering operation in the United States to be accomplished by means of nitroglycerin was the blasting out of the Hoosac tunnel in Massachusetts. The work had been progressing slowly until George M. Mowbray,[28] an "operative chemist" of North Adams, was engaged to manufacture nitroglycerin at the site of the work and to supervise its use. Twenty-six feet of tunnel was driven during May, 1868, 21 during June, 47 during July when the use of nitroglycerin commenced, 44 during August, and 51 feet during September. Mowbray profited by the observation of W. P. Granger that frozen nitroglycerin could not be detonated, and accordingly transported his

[27] Cf. Schück and Sohlman, "The Life of Alfred Nobel," London, William Heinemann, Ltd., 1929.

[28] His experiences and methods are told in a very interesting manner in his book, "Tri-Nitro-Glycerine, as Applied in the Hoosac Tunnel," third edition, rewritten, New York and North Adams, 1874.

material in safety in the frozen condition.[29] He described an explosion which occurred in December, 1870, in which the life of a foreman was lost, and another in March, 1871, in which a large amount of frozen nitroglycerin failed to explode.

The new magazine had hardly been completed, and stored with nitroglycerine, when, on Sunday morning, at half past six o'clock, March twelfth, 1871, the neighborhood was startled by another explosion of sixteen hundred pounds of nitroglycerine. The cause of this last explosion was continuous overheating of the magazine. . . . The watchman con-

[29] During the severe winter of 1867 and 1868, the Deerfield dam became obstructed with ice, and it was important that it should be cleared out without delay. W. P. Granger, Esq., engineer in charge, determined to attempt its removal by a blast of nitroglycerine. In order to appreciate the following details, it must be borne in mind that the current literature of this explosive distinctly asserted that, when congealed, the slightest touch or jar was sufficient to explode nitroglycerine. Mr. Granger desired me to prepare for him ten cartridges, and, as he had to carry them in his sleigh from the west end of the tunnel to the east end or Deerfield dam, a distance of nine miles over the mountain, he requested them to be packed in such a way that they would not be affected by the inclement weather. I therefore caused the nitroglycerine to be warmed up to ninety degrees, warmed the cartridges, and, after charging them, packed them in a box with sawdust that had been heated to the same temperature; the box was tied to the back of the sleigh, with a buffalo robe thrown over it. In floundering across the divide where banks, road, hedge and water courses were indistinguishable beneath the drifted snow, horse, sleigh and rider were upset, the box of cartridges got loose, and were spread indiscriminately over the snow. After rectifying this mishap, picking up the various contents of the sleigh, and getting ready to start again, it occurred to Mr. Granger to examine his cartridges; his feelings may be imagined when he discovered the nitroglycerine frozen solid. To have left them behind and proceeded to the dam, where miners, engineers and laborers were waiting to see this then much dreaded explosive, would never do; so accepting the situation, he replaced them in the case, and, laying it between his feet, proceeded on his way, thinking a heap but saying nothing. Arrived, he forthwith attached fuse, exploder, powder and some guncotton, and inserted the cartridge in the ice. Lighting the fuse, he retired to a proper distance to watch the explosion. Presently a sharp crack indicated that the fuse had done its work, and, on proceeding to the hole drilled in the ice, it was found that fragments of the copper cap were imbedded in the solid cylinder of congealed nitroglycerine, which was driven through and out of the tin cartridge into the anchor ice beneath, but not exploded. A second attempt was attended with like results. Foiled in attempting to explode the frozen nitroglycerine, Mr. Granger thawed the contents of another cartridge, attached the fuse and exploder as before; this time the explosion was entirely successful. From that day I have never transported nitroglycerine except in a frozen condition, and to that lesson are we indebted for the safe transmission of more than two hundred and fifty thousand pounds of this explosive, over the roughest roads of New Hampshire, Vermont, Massachusetts, New York, and the coal and oil regions of Pennsylvania, in spring wagons with our own teams.

Mowbray, *op. cit.,* pp. 45–46.

fessed he had neglected to examine the thermometer, made
his fire under the boiler, and gone to bed. . . . Fortunately,
this accident involved no damage to life or limb, whilst a
very instructive lesson was taught in the following circumstance: Within twelve feet of the magazine was a shed, sixteen feet by eight, containing twelve fifty-pound cans of
congealed nitroglycerine ready for shipment. This shed was
utterly destroyed, the floor blasted to splinters, the joists
rent to fragments, the cans of congealed nitroglycerine driven
into the ground, the tin of which they were composed perforated, contorted, battered, and portions of tin and nitroglycerine sliced off but not exploded. Now, this fact proves one
of two things: Either that the tri-nitroglycerine made by
the Mowbray process, differs from the German nitroglycerine
in its properties, or the statements printed in the foreign
journals, as quoted again and again, that nitroglycerine,
when congealed, is more dangerous than when in the fluid
state, are erroneous.[30]

Mowbray used his nitroglycerin in the liquid state, either
loaded in cylindrical tin cannisters or cartridges, or poured
directly into the bore hole, and exploded it by means of electric
detonators. The electric detonators were operated by means of a
static electric machine which caused a spark to pass between
points of insulated wire; the spark set fire to a priming mixture
made from copper sulfide, copper phosphide, and potassium
chlorate; and this fired the detonating charge of 20 grains of
mercury fulminate contained in a copper capsule, the whole
being waterproofed with asphaltum varnish and insulated electrically with gutta-percha. The devices were so sensitive that they
could be exploded by the static electricity which accumulated on
the body of a miner operating a compressed air drill, and they
required corresponding precautions in their use.

Liquid nitroglycerin is still used as an explosive to a limited
extent, particularly in the blasting of oil wells, but its principal
use is in the manufacture of dynamite and of the propellants,
ballistite and cordite.

Dinitroglycerin (Glyceryl dinitrate)

Dinitroglycerin does not differ greatly from nitroglycerin in
its explosive properties. It is appreciably soluble in water, and
more expensive and more difficult to manufacture than nitrogly-

---

[30] *Ibid.*, pp. 44–45.

cerin. It mixes with the latter substance in all proportions and lowers its freezing point, and was formerly used in Germany in such mixtures in non-freezing dynamites. It has now been superseded entirely for that purpose by dinitrochlorohydrin which is insoluble in water, and cheaper and more convenient to manufacture.

Dinitroglycerin is never formed alone by the nitration of glycerin but is always accompanied by the trinitrate or the mononitrate or both. If the nitration is carried out in a manner to give the best yields of the dinitrate, then considerable trinitrate is formed: if the process is modified to reduce the yield of trinitrate, then the yield of dinitrate is also reduced and some mononitrate is formed. If 3 or 4 parts by weight of nitric acid is added slowly to 1 part of glycerin, so that the glycerin or its nitrated product is always in excess, then the dinitrate is the principal product. If the order of mixing is reversed, so that the glycerin dissolves first in the strong nitric acid, then the yield of trinitrate is more considerable. Dinitroglycerin is formed if glycerin is added to mixed acid which is low in nitric acid or high in water, or which contains insufficient sulfuric acid for the necessary dehydrating action. It is also one of the products of the hydrolysis of nitroglycerin by cold concentrated (95%) sulfuric acid, the trinitrate by this reagent being in part dissolved and in part converted to the dinitrate, the mononitrate, and to glyceryl sulfate according to the relative amount of sulfuric acid which is used. Dinitroglycerin is separated from its mixture with nitroglycerin and obtained pure by treating the oil with about 15 volumes of water, separating the insoluble trinitrate, extracting the aqueous solution with ether, washing the ether with dilute sodium carbonate solution, and evaporating. The resulting dinitroglycerin gives a poor heat test because of the peroxide which it contains from the ether. Material which gives an excellent heat test may be procured by evaporating the aqueous solution in vacuum.

The dinitroglycerin obtained by the nitration of glycerin is a colorless, odorless oil, more viscous and more volatile than nitroglycerin. It causes the same kind of a headache. It has a specific gravity of 1.51 at 15°, boils at 146–148° at 15 mm. with only slight decomposition, and solidifies at −40° to a glassy solid which melts if the temperature is raised to −30°. It is readily soluble in alcohol, ether, acetone, and chloroform, somewhat less soluble than nitroglycerin in benzene, and insoluble in carbon tetrachloride and ligroin. It consists of a mixture of the two possible structural isomers, the 1,2- or α,β-dinitrate, known also as "dinitroglycerin F," and the 1,3- or α,α'-dinitrate or "dinitroglycerin K." Both are uncrystallizable oils, and both are hygroscopic and take up about 3% of their weight of moisture from the air. They are separated by virtue of the fact that the α,α'-dinitrate forms a hydrate [31] with one-third of a molecule of water, $C_3H_6O_7N_2 + \frac{1}{3} H_2O$, water-clear prisms, m.p. 26°. No hydrate of the α,β-dinitrate has ever been isolated in the state of a crystalline solid. If a test portion of the moist mixture of the isomers is mixed with fuller's earth and chilled strongly, it deposits crystals; and if these are used for seeding the principal quantity of the moist dinitroglycerin, then the hydrate of the α,α'-dinitrate crystallizes out. It may be recrystallized from water, or from alcohol, ether, or benzene without losing its water of crystallization, but it yields the anhydrous α,α'-dinitrate if it is dried over sulfuric acid or warmed in the air at 40°.

The chemical relationships between the mononitroglycerins and dinitroglycerins supply all the evidence which is needed for inferring the identities of the isomers. Of the two mononitrates, the β-compound obviously cannot yield any α,α'-dinitrate by nitration; it can yield only the α,β-. That one of the two isomers which yields only one dinitrate is therefore the β-mononitrate, and the dinitrate which it yields is the α,β-dinitrate. The α-mononitrate on the other hand yields both the α,β- and the α,α'-dinitrates.

Nitroglycide

[31] Will, Ber., 41, 1113 (1908).

Both of the dinitroglycerins on treatment with 30% sodium hydroxide solution at room temperature yield nitroglycide, and this substance on boiling with water gives α-mononitroglycerin, a series of reactions which demonstrates the identity of the last-named compound.

Dinitroglycerin is a feeble acid and gives a wine-red color with blue litmus, but none of its salts appear to have been isolated and characterized. It does not decompose carbonates, but dissolves in caustic alkali solutions more readily than in water. One hundred parts of water alone dissolves about 8 parts at 15° and about 10 parts at 50°.

Dinitroglycerin gelatinizes collodion nitrocotton rapidly at ordinary temperature. The gel is sticky, less elastic, and more easily deformed than a nitroglycerin gel. Unlike the latter it is hygroscopic, and becomes softer and greasier from the absorption of moisture from the air. Water dissolves out the dinitroglycerin and leaves the nitrocellulose as a tough, stiff mass.

Dinitroglycerin has about the same sensitivity to initiation as nitroglycerin, only slightly less sensitivity to shock, and offers no marked advantages from the point of view of safety. It shows a greater stability in the heat test, and a small amount can be evaporated by heat without explosion or deflagration. It gives off red fumes above 150°, and at 170° decomposes rapidly with volatilization and some deflagration, or in larger quantities shows a tendency to explode.

Naoúm [32] reports that a 10-gram sample of dinitroglycerin in the Trauzl test with water tamping gave a net expansion of about 500 cc., or 83.3% as much as the expansion (600 cc.) produced by 10 grams of nitroglycerin under the same conditions. He points out that the ratio here is almost the same as the ratio between the heats of explosion, and that in this case the Trauzl test has supplied a fairly accurate measure of the relative energy contents of the two explosives. In the small lead block test the effect of the greater brisance and higher velocity of detonation of nitroglycerin becomes apparent; 100 grams of dinitroglycerin gave a compression of 21 mm. while the same amount of nitroglycerin gave one of 30 mm.

[32] *Op. cit.*, p. 170.

Mononitroglycerin (Glyceryl mononitrate)

Mononitroglycerin is a by-product in the preparation of dinitroglycerin and is separated from the latter substance by its greater solubility in water. It is usually obtained as a colorless oil, density 1.417 at 15°, more viscous than dinitroglycerin and less viscous than nitroglycerin. This oil is a mixture of the two isomers which are crystalline when separate but show little tendency to crystallize when they are mixed. α-Mononitroglycerin when pure consists of colorless prisms, m.p. 58–59°, specific gravity 1.53 at 15°; it yields both of the dinitrates on nitration. The β-compound crystallizes in dendrites and leaflets, m.p. 54°, and is more readily soluble in ether than the α-compound; it yields only the α,β-dinitrate on nitration. Both isomers boil at 155–160° at 15 mm.

Mononitroglycerin resembles glycerin in being very hygroscopic and miscible in all proportions with water and alcohol, and in being only slightly soluble in ether, but it differs from glycerin in being freely soluble in nitroglycerin. It does not form a satisfactory gel with collodion cotton. Its aqueous solution reacts neutral. It appears to be perfectly stable on moderate heating, but decomposes to some extent at 170°, gives off gas, and turns yellow.

Mononitroglycerin is insensitive to shock. In the form of oil it is not detonated by a No. 8 blasting cap in the Trauzl test. If the oil is absorbed in fuller's earth, 10 grams gives a net expansion of 75 cc. The crystalline material, however, detonates easily; 10 grams gives an expansion of 245 cc. It is interesting to compare these results, reported by Naoúm,[33] with the results which the same author reports for nitroglycide which is the anhydride of mononitroglycerin. Ten grams of liquid nitroglycide with water tamping and a No. 8 detonator gave a net expansion of 430 cc.; 10 grams absorbed in fuller's earth, with sand tamping, gave 310 cc.; and 10 grams gelatinized with 5% collodion nitrocotton, with sand tamping, gave 395 cc.

Nitroglycide

This substance cannot be prepared by the nitration of glycide, for the action of acids upon that substance opens the ethylene

[33] *Ibid.,* pp. 174, 177.

oxide ring, and mononitroglycerin is formed. Nitroglycide was first prepared by Naoúm [34] in 1907 by shaking dinitroglycerin at room temperature with a 30% aqueous solution of sodium hydroxide. The clear solution presently deposited a colorless oil, and this, washed with water and dried in a desiccator, constituted a practically quantitative yield of nitroglycide.

Nitroglycide is a very mobile liquid with a faint but pleasant aromatic odor, specific gravity 1.332 at 20°. It does not freeze at −20°. It boils at 94° at 20 mm., and with some decomposition at 174–175° at atmospheric pressure. It is not hygroscopic but is distinctly soluble in water, 5 grams in 100 cc. at 20°. Ether will extract nitroglycide from the cool aqueous solution; if the solution is boiled, however, the nitroglycide is hydrated to mononitroglycerin. Nitroglycide is miscible in all proportions with alcohol, ether, acetone, ethyl acetate, and nitroglycerin. It gelatinizes collodion nitrocotton and even guncotton rapidly at ordinary temperature. It explodes in contact with concentrated sulfuric acid. If dissolved in dilute sulfuric acid and then treated with strong sulfuric acid, it gives off nitric acid. It is converted into dinitroglycerin and nitroglycerin by the action of nitric acid. It dissolves in concentrated hydrochloric acid with the evolution of considerable heat, and the solution on dilution with water gives a precipitate of monochlorohydrin mononitrate. Nitroglycide reduces ammoniacal silver nitrate slowly on gentle warming; glycide reduces the same reagent in the cold.

When heated rapidly in a test tube nitroglycide explodes with a sharp report at 195–200°. It is more easily detonated than liquid nitroglycerin. Naoúm believes that its great sensitivity results mainly from the easy propagation of the wave of detonation by a liquid of low viscosity.[35] He points out further that mononitroglycerin has 69.5% of the energy content (i.e., heat of explosion) of nitroglycide, but as a crystal powder in the Trauzl test it gives only about 62% as much net expansion, whence it is to be inferred that nitroglycide has the higher velocity of detonation. Nitroglycide has only 52% of the energy content of nitroglycerin, but produces 72% as much effect in the Trauzl test. It is therefore "relatively more brisant than nitroglycerin."

[34] *Ibid.*, p. 176.
[35] *Ibid.*, p. 178.

Dinitrochlorohydrin (Glycerin chlorohydrin dinitrate)

Among the various substances which may be used in admixture with nitroglycerin for the purpose of lowering its freezing point, dinitrochlorohydrin is preferred in Germany but has not found favor in the United States. Since dinitrochlorohydrin is distinctly safer to prepare than nitroglycerin, it is most commonly prepared by itself, that is, by the nitration of chlorohydrin which is substantially pure and contains not more than a small amount of glycerin. The product is used directly for the preparation of certain explosives, or it is mixed with nitroglycerin for the manufacture of non-freezing dynamites.

Chlorohydrin is prepared by autoclaving glycerin with concentrated hydrochloric acid or by treating it at moderate temperature with sulfur chloride. In the former process, in order to avoid the formation of dichlorohydrin, only enough hydrochloric acid is used to convert about 75% of the glycerin. The product is procured by a vacuum distillation. The monochlorohydrin, which consists almost entirely of the α-compound, comes over between 130° and 150° at 12–15 mm. and the unchanged glycerin between 165° and 180°. It is nitrated with the same mixed acid as is used for the preparation of nitroglycerin; less acid is needed of course, less heat is produced, and the process is safer and more rapid.

$$
\begin{array}{ccc}
CH_2\text{—OH} & CH_2\text{—Cl} & CH_2\text{—Cl} \\
| & | & | \\
CH\text{—OH} \longrightarrow & CH\text{—OH} \longrightarrow & CH\text{—ONO}_2 \\
| & | & | \\
CH_2\text{—OH} & CH_2\text{—OH} & CH_2\text{—ONO}_2
\end{array}
$$

If a mixture of chlorohydrin and glycerin is nitrated, the resulting mixture of nitrates contains relatively more nitroglycerin than the original mixture contained of glycerin, for the relative increase of molecular weight during the nitration of glycerin is greater.

Commercial dinitrochlorohydrin is usually yellowish or brownish in color, specific gravity about 1.541 at 15°. It boils at atmospheric pressure with decomposition at about 190°. It may be distilled at 13 mm. at 121.5°, or at 10 mm. at 117.5°, but some decomposition occurs for the distillate is acid to litmus.

Dinitrochlorohydrin is non-hygroscopic, distinctly more volatile than nitroglycerin, and it has similar physiological effects. It can be frozen only with great difficulty, shows a strong tendency to supercool, and can be kept for a long time at $-20°$ without depositing crystals. The solubility of dinitrochlorohydrin and nitroglycerin in each other is so great that only small quantities of nitroglycerin can be frozen out from the mixtures, even after seeding, at winter temperatures. A mixture of 75 parts of nitroglycerin and 25 parts of dinitrochlorohydrin is practically nonfreezing, and yields a dynamite which is not significantly less strong than one made from straight nitroglycerin.

Dinitrochlorohydrin does not take fire readily, and, if ignited, burns rather slowly without detonating and with but little of the sputtering which is characteristic of nitroglycerin mixtures. "Even larger quantities of pure dinitrochlorohydrin in tin cans burn without explosion when in a fire, so that liquid dinitrochlorohydrin is permitted on German railroads in tin cans holding 25 kg., as a safe explosive for limited freight service in the 200 kg. class, while liquid nitroglycerin is absolutely excluded." [36] Dinitrochlorohydrin is more stable toward shock than nitroglycerin. Naoúm, working with a pure sample, was not able to secure a first-rate explosion in the drop test.[37] A 2-kilogram weight dropped from a height of 40 cm. or more gave a very slight partial decomposition and a slight report, from a height of 75 cm. or more, a somewhat more violent partial deflagration but in no case a sharp report, and even a 10-kilogram weight dropped from a height of 10 or 15 cm. gave a very weak partial decomposition. The substance, however, is detonated readily by fulminate. It gives in the Trauzl test a net expansion of 475 cc., or 79% of the 600-cc. expansion given by nitroglycerin, although its heat of explosion is only about 71% of the heat of explosion of nitroglycerin.

Dinitrochlorohydrin produces hydrogen chloride when it explodes. This would tend to make it unsuitable for use in mining explosives were it not for the fact that the incorporation into the explosives of potassium or sodium nitrate sufficient to form chloride with the chlorine of the dinitrochlorohydrin prevents it altogether—and this amount of the nitrate is usually present anyway for other reasons.

[36] Naoúm, *ibid.*, p. 187.
[37] *Ibid.*, p. 188.

Acetyldinitroglycerin (monoacetin dinitrate) and formyldi-nitroglycerin (monoformin dinitrate) have been proposed by Vender [38] for admixture with nitroglycerin in non-freezing dyna-mite. The former substance may be prepared [39] by nitrating monoacetin or by acetylating dinitroglycerin. The latter sub-stance may be procured already mixed with nitroglycerin by warming glycerin with oxalic acid, whereby monoformin (gly-ceryl monoformate) is formed, and nitrating the resulting mix-ture of monoformin and glycerin. Formyldinitroglycerin has apparently not yet been isolated in the pure state. These sub-stances are satisfactory explosives but are more expensive to manufacture than dinitrochlorohydrin over which they possess no distinct advantage, and they have not come into general use.

Tetranitrodiglycerin (Diglycerin tetranitrate)

If glycerin is heated with a small amount of concentrated sulfuric acid, ether formation occurs, water splits out, and digly-cerin and polyglycerin are formed. If the heating is carried out in the absence of acids, and in such a way that the water which is formed is allowed to escape while the higher-boiling materials are condensed and returned, especially if a small amount of alkali, say 0.5%, or of sodium sulfite is present as a catalyst, then the principal product is diglycerin and not more than a few per cent of polyglycerin is formed. It is feasible for example to convert glycerin into a mixture which consists of 50–60% di-glycerin, 4–6% polyglycerin, and the remainder, 34–46%, un-changed glycerin. The diglycerin is ordinarily not isolated in the pure state. The mixture, either with or without the addition of glycerin, is nitrated directly to form a mixture of tetranitro-diglycerin and nitroglycerin which is used for the manufacture of non-freezing dynamite.

Diglycerin when obtained pure by a vacuum distillation is a water-white liquid, more viscous and more dense than glycerin, sweet-tasting, very hygroscopic, b.p. 245–250° at 8 mm. It is nitrated with the same mixed acid as glycerin, although a smaller

[38] *Z. ges. Schiess- u. Sprengstoffw.*, **2**, 21 (1907). *Fourth Internat. Congr.* **2**, 582 (1906).
[39] Ger. Pat. 209,943 (1906); Brit. Pat. 9791 (1906); French Pat. 372,267 (1906); Swiss Pat. 50,836 (1910); U. S. Pat. 1,029,519 (1912).

amount is necessary. Salt solutions are always used for washing the nitrated product, otherwise the separation of the phases is extremely slow.

$$
\begin{array}{ccc}
\text{CH}_2-\text{OH} & \text{CH}_2-\text{OH} & \text{CH}_2-\text{ONO}_2 \\
| & | & | \\
\text{CH}-\text{OH} & \text{CH}-\text{OH} & \text{CH}-\text{ONO}_2 \\
| & | & | \\
\text{CH}_2-\text{O}\lceil\text{H}\rceil & \text{CH}_2 & \text{CH}_2 \\
& \searrow & \searrow \\
& O & O \\
\text{CH}_2-\lceil\text{OH}\rceil & \text{CH}_2\nearrow & \text{CH}_2\nearrow \\
| & | & | \\
\text{CH}-\text{OH} & \text{CH}-\text{OH} & \text{CH}-\text{ONO}_2 \\
| & | & | \\
\text{CH}_2-\text{OH} & \text{CH}_2-\text{OH} & \text{CH}_2-\text{ONO}_2
\end{array}
$$

Tetranitrodiglycerin is a very viscous oil, non-hygroscopic, insoluble in water, and readily soluble in alcohol and in ether. It has not been obtained in the crystalline state. It is not a good gelatinizing agent for collodion cotton when used alone. Its mixture with nitroglycerin gelatinizes collodion cotton more slowly than nitroglycerin alone but gives a satisfactory gel. It is less sensitive to mechanical shock than nitroglycerin, about the same as dinitroglycerin, but is readily exploded by fulminate. According to Naoúm [40] 75% tetranitrodiglycerin guhr dynamite gave in the Trauzl test a net expansion of 274 cc. or 85.6% of the expansion (320 cc.) produced by 75% nitroglycerin guhr dynamite.

Nitroglycol (Ethylene glycol dinitrate, ethylene dinitrate)

Nitroglycol first found favor in France as an ingredient of non-freezing dynamites. It has many of the advantages of nitroglycerin and is safer to manufacture and handle. Its principal disadvantage is its greater volatility. Formerly the greater cost of procuring glycol, which is not as directly accessible as glycerin but has to be produced by synthesis from ethylene, was an impediment to its use, but new sources of ethylene and new methods of synthesis have reduced its cost and increased its accessibility.

Ethylene was formerly procured from alcohol (itself produced from raw material which was actually or potentially a foodstuff) by warming with sulfuric acid, by passing the vapors over heated coke impregnated with phosphoric acid, or by comparable methods. Ethylene combines with bromine to give ethylene dibromide,

[40] *Op. cit.*, p. 201.

which yields glycol by hydrolysis, but bromine is expensive. Ethylene also combines readily with chlorine, but, even if care is exercised always to have the ethylene present in excess, substitution occurs, and tri- and tetrachloroethane are formed along with the ethylene dichloride, and these do not yield glycol by hydrolysis. Ethylene is now produced in large quantities during the cracking of petroleum. Its comportment with chlorine water has been found to be much more satisfactory for purposes of synthesis than its comportment with chlorine gas. Chlorine water contains an equilibrium mixture of hydrogen chloride and hypochlorous acid.

$$Cl_2 + H_2O \leftrightarrows HCl + HOCl$$

Ethylene adds hypochlorous acid more readily than it adds either moist chlorine or hydrogen chloride. Bubbled into chlorine water, it is converted completely into ethylene chlorohydrin, and by the hydrolysis of this substance glycol is obtained. Ethylene chlorohydrin is important also because of its reaction with ammonia whereby mono-, di-, and triethanolamine are formed, substances which are used in the arts and are not without interest for the explosives chemist. Ethylene may be oxidized catalytically in the gas phase to ethylene oxide which reacts with water to form glycol and with glycol to form diglycol which also is of interest to the dynamite maker.

Glycol is a colorless liquid (bluer than water in thick layers), syrupy, sweet tasting, less viscous than glycerin, specific gravity 1.1270 at 0°, 1.12015 at 10°, and 1.11320 at 20°.[41] It shows a tendency to supercool but freezes at temperatures between −13° and −25°, and melts again at −11.5°. It boils at 197.2° at atmospheric pressure. It is very hygroscopic, miscible in all pro-

[41] C. A. Taylor and W. H. Rinkenbach, *Ind. Eng. Chem.*, **18**, 676 (1926).

portions with water, alcohol, glycerin, acetone, and acetic acid, and not miscible with benzene, chloroform, carbon disulfide, and ether.

Nitroglycol is manufactured with the same mixed acid and with the same apparatus as nitroglycerin. Somewhat more heat is produced by the nitration reaction, and, as glycol is less viscous than glycerin, it is feasible to conduct the operation at a lower temperature. The washing is done with cold water and with less agitation by compressed air, and smaller amounts of wash water are used than are used with nitroglycerin, for nitroglycol is appreciably more volatile and more soluble in water. The tendency of the partially washed product to undergo an acid-catalyzed decomposition is less in the case of nitroglycol than in the case of nitroglycerin.

Nitroglycol is a colorless liquid, only slightly more viscous than water, specific gravity ($x°/15°$) 1.5176 at 0°, 1.5033 at 10°, and 1.4890 at 20°.[42] It freezes at about $-22.3°$. Rinkenbach reports the index of refraction of nitroglycol for white light to be 1.4452 at 22.3°, and that of a commercial sample of nitroglycerin under the same conditions to be 1.4713. The same author reports the vapor pressure of nitroglycol to be 0.007 mm. of mercury at 0° and 0.0565 mm. at 22°, and points out that its vapor pressure at 22° is approximately 150 times as great as the vapor pressure, 0.00037 mm., reported by Peace and Marshall[43] for nitroglycerin at 22°. Nitroglycol produces a headache similar to that produced by nitroglycerin, but, corresponding to its greater volatility, the headache is more violent and does not last so long. Nitroglycol is non-hygroscopic. Its comportment with organic solvents is similar to that of nitroglycerin, but it is distinctly more soluble in water than that substance. Naoúm[44] reports that 1 liter of water at 15° dissolves 6.2 grams of nitroglycol, at 20° 6.8 grams of nitroglycol or 1.8 grams of nitroglycerin, and at 50° 9.2 grams of nitroglycol.

Nitroglycol has a slightly larger energy content than nitroglycerin. In the Trauzl test with 10-gram samples and water tamping, Naoúm[45] found that nitroglycol gave a net expansion

42 Rinkenbach, *Ind. Eng. Chem.*, **18**, 1195 (1926).
43 *Loc. cit.*
44 Naoúm, *op. cit.*, p. 224.
45 *Ibid.*, p. 227.

of 650 cc. and nitroglycerin one of 590 cc. Nitroglycol, like nitro-glycerin, burns with sputtering and explodes if local overheating occurs, but nitroglycol and nitroglycol explosives in general burn more quietly and show less tendency to explode from heat than the corresponding nitroglycerin preparations. Nitroglycol explodes with a sharp report if heated rapidly to 215°. It is less sensitive to mechanical shock than nitroglycerin. Naoúm [46] reports the height of drop necessary to cause explosion, with a 2-kilogram weight, as follows.

HEIGHT OF DROP, CENTIMETERS

	Nitroglycol	Nitroglycerin
Drop absorbed on filter paper	20–25	8–10
Blasting gelatin	25–30	12
Guhr dynamite	15	5

Rinkenbach [47] reports tests with a small drop machine having a weight of 500 grams, nitroglycol 110 cm., nitroglycerin 70 cm., and a commercial mixture of nitroglycerin and nitropolyglycerin 90 cm.

Nitroglycol gelatinizes collodion cotton much faster than nitro-glycerin and acts at ordinary temperatures, while nitroglycerin requires to be warmed. The greater volatility of nitroglycol does not affect its usefulness in gelatin dynamite, especially in temperate climates, but renders it unsuitable for use during the warm season of the year in ammonium nitrate explosives which contain only a few per cent of the oily nitric ester. It is too volatile for use in double-base smokeless powder, for its escape by evaporation affects the ballistic properties.

Dinitrodiglycol (Diethylene glycol dinitrate)

A study of the preparation and properties of dinitrodiglycol was reported by Rinkenbach [48] in 1927 and a further study of the nitration of diethylene glycol by Rinkenbach and Aaronson [49] in 1931. Dinitrodiglycol is a viscous, colorless, and odorless liquid, specific gravity $(x°/15°)$ 1.4092 at 0°, 1.3969 at 10°, and 1.3846 at 20°, freezing point −11.5°. It is completely miscible at ordinary temperatures with nitroglycerin, nitroglycol, ether, acetone,

[46] Op. cit., p. 225.
[47] Loc. cit.
[48] Ind. Eng. Chem., 19, 925 (1927).
[49] Ind. Eng. Chem., 23, 160 (1931).

methyl alcohol, chloroform, benzene, and glacial acetic acid. It is immiscible, or only slightly soluble, in ethyl alcohol, carbon tetrachloride, and carbon disulfide. It is slightly hygroscopic and is soluble in water to the extent of about 4.1 grams per liter of water at 24°. It can be ignited only with difficulty, and in small quantity is not readily exploded by heat. It is less sensitive than nitroglycol in the drop test. It is so insensitive to initiation that it will not propagate its own detonation under conditions where nitroglycol and nitroglycerin will do it. In 50/50 mixture however with either of these substances it detonates satisfactorily "and shows an explosive effect but little less than that of either of these compounds." It has a vapor pressure of about 0.007 mm. of mercury at 22.4°, and produces headaches similar to those produced by nitroglycerin.

Trinitrophenoxyethyl Nitrate

Another explosive which is preparable from glycol and which may perhaps be of interest for special purposes in the future is the β-2,4,6-trinitrophenoxyethyl nitrate described by Wasmer [50] in 1938. Glycol is converted into its monosodium derivative, and this is made to react with dinitrochlorobenzene at 130° for the production of β-dinitrophenoxyethyl alcohol which gives the explosive by nitration with mixed acid.

Trinitrophenoxyethyl nitrate is procured as a white powder, m.p. 104.5°, insoluble in water and readily soluble in acetone. It gelatinizes collodion nitrocotton, and is intermediate between picric acid and tetryl in its sensitivity to mechanical shock.

[50] *Mém. poudres,* **28,** 171 (1938).

Nitration of Ethylene

By passing ethylene into a mixture of concentrated nitric and sulfuric acids Kekulé [51] obtained an oil, specific gravity 1.47, which broke down when distilled with steam to give glycollic acid, oxalic acid, nitric oxide, and nitric acid. On reduction with sodium amalgam it yielded glycol and ammonia among other products. Wieland and Sakellarios [52] distilled the Kekulé oil in steam and then in vacuum, and obtained nitroglycol, b.p. 105° at 19 mm., and β-nitroethyl nitrate, b.p. 120–122° at 17 mm. These two substances are evidently formed from ethylene by the reactions indicated below.

$$\begin{array}{c} CH_2 \\ \| \\ CH_2 \end{array} + \begin{array}{c} OH \\ | \\ NO_2 \end{array} \longrightarrow \begin{array}{c} CH_2-OH \\ | \\ CH_2-NO_2 \end{array} + HNO_3 \longrightarrow H_2O + \begin{array}{c} CH_2-ONO_2 \\ | \\ CH_2-NO_2 \end{array}$$

β-Nitroethyl nitrate

$$\begin{array}{c} CH_2 \\ \| \\ CH_2 \end{array} + 3HNO_3 \longrightarrow HONO + H_2O + \begin{array}{c} CH_2-ONO_2 \\ | \\ CH_2-ONO_2 \end{array}$$

Nitroglycol

A considerable amount of nitrous acid is present in the spent acid. β-Nitroethyl nitrate is feebly acidic and dissolves in dilute alkali solutions with a yellow color. It is not sufficiently stable for use in commercial explosives. On digestion with warm water or on slow distillation with steam it undergoes a decomposition or sort of hydrolysis whereby nitrous acid and other materials are produced. Numerous patents have been issued for processes of procuring pure nitroglycol from the Kekulé oil. One hundred parts of the last-named material yield about 40 parts of nitroglycol, and the economic success of the process depends upon the recovery of valuable by-products from the β-nitroethyl nitrate which is destroyed.

Öhman [53] in Sweden has developed an ingenious electrolytic process for the production of nitric esters direct from ethylene. The discharge of the nitrate ion (NO^-) at the anode liberates the free nitrate radical (NO_3) which in part combines directly with ethylene to form nitroglycol.

$$\begin{array}{c} CH_2 \\ \| \\ CH_2 \end{array} + 2NO_3 \longrightarrow \begin{array}{c} CH_2-ONO_2 \\ | \\ CH_2-ONO_2 \end{array}$$

[51] Ber., 2, 329 (1869).
[52] Ber., 53, 201 (1920).
[53] Z. Elektrochem., 42, 862 (1936); Svensk Kemisk Tid., 50, 84 (1938).

Another portion of the free nitrate radical apparently reacts with itself and with water as indicated below, and the oxygen which becomes available enters into the reaction with the consequent formation of dinitrodiglycol.

$$
\begin{cases}
2NO_3 \longrightarrow N_2O_5 + [O] \\
N_2O_5 + H_2O \longrightarrow 2HNO_3
\end{cases}
$$

$$
\begin{array}{c}
CH_2 \\
\parallel \quad + [O] + 2NO_3 \longrightarrow \\
CH_2
\end{array}
\qquad
\begin{array}{c}
CH_2\text{—}ONO_2 \\
| \\
CH_2 \\
\diagdown \\
\quad\quad O \\
\diagup \\
CH_2 \\
| \\
CH_2\text{—}ONO_2
\end{array}
$$

A platinum gauze anode is used. It is immersed in an acetone solution of calcium nitrate which is kept continuously saturated with ethylene which is bubbled through in such manner that it sweeps over the surface of the platinum gauze. An aluminum cathode is used, in a catholyte consisting of a nitric acid solution of calcium nitrate, and the cathode compartment is filled to a higher level since the liquid moves into the anode compartment as the electrolysis progresses. After the electrolysis, the cathode liquid is fortified with nitric acid for use again. The anode liquid is neutralized with slaked lime, and distilled in vacuum for the recovery of the acetone, and the residue, after the removal of calcium nitrate, washing, and drying, consists of a mixture of nitroglycol and dinitrodiglycol and is known as *Oxinite*. Dynamites made from Oxinite differ but little from those made from nitroglycerin.

Pentryl

Pentryl, or 2,4,6-trinitrophenylnitraminoethyl nitrate, is another explosive which is derived from ethylene. It is a nitric ester, an aromatic nitro compound, and a nitroamine. The substance was described in 1925 by Moran [54] who prepared it by the action of mixed acid on 2,4-dinitrophenylethanolamine (large orange-yellow crystals from alcohol, m.p. 92°) procured by the interaction of dinitrochlorobenzene with ethanolamine. von Herz later prepared pentryl by the nitration of β-hydroxyethylaniline, a material which is more commonly called phenylethanolamine and is now available commercially in this country, and was granted

[54] U. S. Pat. 1,560,427 (1925).

British and German patents [55] for its use for certain military purposes. The genesis of pentryl from ethylene, through the intermediacy both of ethanolamine and of phenylethanolamine, is indicated below. The preparation and properties of pentryl have

been studied extensively by LeRoy V. Clark [56] at the U. S. Bureau of Mines. By the reaction of dinitrochlorobenzene in the presence of sodium hydroxide with ethanolamine in alcohol solution at 70–80° he procured dinitrophenylethanolamine in 70% yield. The alcohol solution was filtered for the removal of sodium chloride, which was found to be mixed with a certain quantity of the by-product tetranitrodiphenylethanolamine (lemon-yellow fine powder, m.p. 222°); it was then concentrated to about one-third its volume, and deposited crystals of the product on cooling. This material, dissolved in concentrated sulfuric acid and nitrated by adding the solution to nitric acid and heating, gave pentryl in yields of about 90%, minute cream-colored crystals from benzene, m.p. 128°.

Clark reports that pentryl has an absolute density of 1.82 and an apparent density of only 0.45. When compressed in a detonator shell at a pressure of 3400 pounds per square inch, it has an apparent density of 0.74. It is soluble to some extent in most of the common organic solvents, and is very readily soluble in nitroglycerin. In the drop test with a 2-kilogram weight, 0.02 gram of pentryl was exploded by a drop of 30 cm., a similar sample of

[55] Brit. Pat. 367,713 (1930); Ger. Pat. 530,701 (1931).
[56] *Ind. Eng. Chem.*, **25**, 1385 (1933).

tetryl by one of 27.5 cm., and one of picric acid by a drop of 42.5 cm., while TNT was not exploded by a drop of 100 cm. It is somewhat more sensitive to friction than tetryl, and much more sensitive than picric acid and TNT. Pentryl explodes in 3 seconds at 235°.

The results of Clark's experiments to determine the minimum amounts of primary explosive necessary to initiate the explosion of pentryl and of other high explosives are tabulated below. For

	MINIMUM INITIATING CHARGE (GRAMS) OF		
	Diazodi-nitrophenol	Mercury Fulminate	Lead Azide
Pentryl	0.095	0.150	0.025
Picric acid	0.115	0.225	0.12
TNT	0.163	0.240	0.16
Tetryl	0.075	0.165	0.03
Trinitroresorcinol	0.110	0.225	0.075
Trinitrobenzaldehyde	0.075	0.165	0.05
Tetranitroaniline	0.085	0.175	0.05
Hexanitrodiphenylamine	0.075	0.165	0.05

the purpose of these experiments a half-gram portion of the high explosive was weighed into a No. 8 detonator shell, a weighed amount of primary explosive was introduced on top of it, and both were compressed under a reenforcing capsule at a pressure of 3400 pounds per square inch. Without the reenforcing capsule diazodinitrophenol did not cause detonation, and pentryl required 0.035 gram of lead azide and more than 0.4 gram of fulminate. The results show that pentryl has about the same sensitivity to initiation as tetryl and hexanitrodiphenylamine.

In the small Trauzl test pentryl caused an expansion of 15.8 cc., while the same weight of tetryl caused one of 13.8 cc., TNT 12.2 cc., and picric acid 12.4 cc. In the small lead block compression test, in which 50 grams of the explosive was exploded by means of a detonator on top of a lead cylinder 64 mm. long, it was found that pentryl produced a shortening of the block of 18.5 mm., tetryl 16.6 mm., picric acid 16.4 mm., TNT 14.8 mm., and diazodinitrophenol 10.5 mm. Determinations of velocity of detonation made with half-meter lengths, the explosives being contained in extra light lead tubing ½ inch internal diameter and weighing 12 ounces to the foot, gave the following figures.

	Density	Velocity of Detonation (Meters per second)
Pentryl	0.80	5000
Tetryl	0.90	5400
Picric acid	0.98	4970
TNT	0.90	4450

These are not however the maximum velocities of detonation of the substances.

Hexanitrodiphenylaminoethyl Nitrate

This substance also has been studied by LeRoy V. Clark [57] who prepared it by the nitration with mixed acid of tetranitro-diphenylethanolamine, a by-product from the preparation of pentryl.

He procured the pure substance in the form of pale yellow glistening plates, m.p. 184° (corr.), precipitated from acetone solution by the addition of alcohol. Its explosive properties are not widely different from those of pentryl. Its response to initiation

[57] *Ibid.*, **26**, 554 (1934).

is about the same; it is slightly less sensitive to impact, about 7% less effective in the sand test, and about 3% more effective in the small Trauzl test. In compound detonators it is somewhat better than TNT and somewhat poorer than pentryl, tetryl, and picric acid, as indicated by the lead plate test. When heated rapidly, it ignites at 390–400°.

Trimethylene Glycol Dinitrate

Trimethylene glycol occurs in the glycerin which is produced by fermentation. There is no harm in leaving it in glycerin which is to be used for the manufacture of explosives. It may however be separated by fractional distillation. When pure it is a color-less, odorless, syrupy liquid, specific gravity $(x°/4°)$ 1.0526 at 18°. It mixes with water in all proportions and boils at atmos-pheric pressure at 211° without decomposition. At temperatures above 15° or so, it is oxidized rapidly by nitric acid or by mixed acid. It is accordingly nitrated at 0–10° under conditions similar to those which are used in the preparation of ethyl nitrate and other simple aliphatic nitric esters (except methyl nitrate).

$$
\begin{array}{ccc}
CH_2\text{---}OH & & CH_2\text{---}ONO_2 \\
| & & | \\
CH_2 & \longrightarrow & CH_2 \\
| & & | \\
CH_2\text{---}OH & & CH_2\text{---}ONO_2
\end{array}
$$

Trimethylene glycol dinitrate is a water-white liquid, very mobile, and scarcely more viscous than nitroglycol, specific gravity $(20°/4°)$ 1.393 at 20°. It boils at 108° at 10 mm. without decomposition. It is less volatile than nitroglycol and more vola-tile than nitroglycerin. It has about the same solubility relation-ships as nitroglycerin, and forms a good gelatin with collodion nitrocotton. It causes headache by contact with the skin. When heated slowly it takes fire with a puff and burns tranquilly or decomposes at about 185° and deflagrates at about 225°. It is much less sensitive to shock than nitroglycerin and is much more stable in storage. Naoúm [58] reports that a 10-gram sample in the Trauzl test with water tamping gave an expansion of 540 cc. or about 90% of the expansion produced by nitroglycerin. The cal-culated energy content of trimethylene glycol dinitrate is only

[58] *Op. cit.*, p. 235.

about 77% of that of nitroglycerin, but the relatively greater brisance results from the low viscosity of the substance which gives it a higher velocity of detonation. Naoúm also reports that a 93% trimethylene glycol dinitrate gelatin with 7% collodion cotton gave an expansion of 470 cc. or about 80% as much as a similar nitroglycerin gelatin.

Propylene Glycol Dinitrate (Methylglycol dinitrate, methyl-nitroglycol)

Propylene occurs along with ethylene in cracking gas. Its use as a raw material for the synthesis of glycerin has already been mentioned in the section on nitroglycerin. It yields propylene glycol when subjected to the same chemical processes as those which are used for the preparation of glycol from ethylene.[59] Propylene glycol shows the same tendency toward oxidation during nitration that trimethylene glycol does, but to a less extent; noticeable decomposition occurs only above 30°.

$$
\begin{array}{cccc}
CH_3 & CH_3 & CH_3 & CH_3 \\
| \quad \xrightarrow{HOCl} & | & \xrightarrow{HOH} \quad | & \xrightarrow{nitration} \quad | \\
CH & CH-OH & CH-OH & CH-ONO_2 \\
\| & | & | & | \\
CH_2 & CH_2-Cl & CH_2-OH & CH_2-ONO_2
\end{array}
$$

Propylene glycol dinitrate is a colorless liquid of characteristic aromatic odor, more volatile and less viscous than trimethylene glycol dinitrate with which it is isomeric. Its specific gravity (20°/4°) is 1.368 at 20°. It boils at 92° at 10 mm., and does not freeze at −20°. Its solubilities, gelatinizing power, and explosive properties are substantially the same as those of its isomer. Indeed, Naoúm [60] reports that it gave exactly the same expansion as trimethylene glycol dinitrate in the Trauzl lead block test, namely, 540 cc.

---

[59] Symmes, in a footnote, p. 375, in his English translation of Naoúm's book, *op. cit.*, cites U. S. patents 1,307,032, 1,307,033, 1,307,034, and 1,371,215 which describe a method for the manufacture of mixed ethylene and propylene glycols from cracking gas, satisfactory methods for the nitration of the mixture and for the stabilization of the mixed nitric esters, and explosives made from the products "which practical tests in actual use showed could not be frozen even at temperatures prevailing in winter along the Canadian border, or −10° to −30° F."

[60] *Op. cit.*, p. 237.

Butylene Glycol Dinitrate

Of the four isomeric butylene glycols, the 1,3-compound appears to be the only one which has attracted any interest as a raw material for the preparation of explosives. Its dinitrate, either alone or in admixture with nitroglycerin, has been proposed for use in non-freezing dynamites.[61] The preparation of the glycol from acetaldehyde has been suggested,[62] the acetaldehyde being condensed to aldol and the aldol reduced to glycol. Since acetaldehyde is produced commercially by the catalyzed hydration of acetylene, then butylene glycol-1,3 can be procured by synthesis from coke.

Butylene glycol shows a strong tendency to oxidize during nitration, and ought to be nitrated at a temperature of $-5°$ or lower. Butylene glycol dinitrate is a colorless liquid, intermediate in volatility between nitroglycol and nitroglycerin, possessing a specific gravity of 1.32 at 15°. It does not freeze at temperatures as low as $-20°$. It yields a good gelatin with collodion nitrocotton. It deflagrates feebly if heated suddenly. It is very insensitive to mechanical shock but detonates easily by initiation. Naoúm[63] reports that a mixture of 75% butylene glycol dinitrate and 25% kieselguhr gave about 240 cc. expansion in the Trauzl test, and that a gelatin containing 90% butylene glycol dinitrate and 10% collodion nitrocotton gave about 370 cc.

Nitroerythrite (Erythritol tetranitrate)

$$NO_2-O-CH_2-(CH-ONO_2)_2-CH_2-ONO_2$$

i-Erythrite occurs in algae and in lichens. It is a white, crystalline, sweet-tasting substance, very readily soluble in water, m.p. 120°, b.p. 330°, specific gravity 1.59. The tetranitrate is prepared

[61] U. S. Pats. 994,841 and 994,842 (1911).
[62] U. S. Pat. 1,008,333 (1911).
[63] Op. cit., p. 239.

by dissolving erythrite in strong nitric acid with cooling, and then precipitating by the addition of concentrated sulfuric acid.[64] It crystallizes from alcohol in colorless plates, m.p. 61°. Its use as an addition to smokeless powder has been suggested,[65] but it is as powerful as nitroglycerin, and has the advantage over it that it is a solid, and it would be suitable, if it were cheaper, for the same uses as nitromannite.

Nitromannite (Mannitol hexanitrate)

$$NO_2\text{—}O\text{—}CH_2\text{—}(CH\text{—}ONO_2)_4\text{—}CH_2\text{—}ONO_2$$

d-Mannitol occurs fairly widely distributed in nature, particularly in the *Fraxinus ornus*, the sap of which is *manna*. It may also be procured by the reduction of *d*-mannose either electrolytically or by means of sodium amalgam, or along with *d*-sorbite by the reduction of *d*-fructose. It may be nitrated satisfactorily with the same mixed acid as is used for the nitration of glycerin, or more conveniently, because the mass of crystals is so voluminous, by dissolving in strong nitric acid and precipitating by the addition of concentrated sulfuric acid.

Preparation of Nitromannite. Fifty grams of nitric acid (specific gravity 1.51) is cooled thoroughly in a 300-cc. Erlenmeyer pyrex flask immersed in a freezing mixture of ice and salt. Ten grams of mannite is then introduced in small portions at a time while the flask is tilted from side to side and the contents is stirred gently with a thermometer, care being taken that the temperature does not rise above 0°. After all is dissolved, 100 grams of sulfuric acid (specific gravity 1.84) is added slowly from a dropping funnel while the liquid is stirred and the temperature is maintained below 0°. The porridge-like mass is filtered on a sinter-glass filter, or on a Büchner funnel with a hardened filter paper, washed with water, then with dilute sodium bicarbonate solution, then finally again with water. The crude product is dissolved in boiling alcohol; the solution is filtered if need be, and on cooling deposits white needle crystals of nitromannite, m.p. 112-113°. A second crop of crystals may be obtained by warming the alcoholic mother liquors to boiling, adding water while still boiling until a turbidity appears, and allowing to cool. Total yield about 23 grams.

Nitromannite is readily soluble in ether and in hot alcohol, only slightly soluble in cold alcohol, and insoluble in water.

[64] Stenhouse, *Ann.*, **70**, 226 (1849); **130**, 302 (1864).
[65] Ger. Pat. 110,289 (1898); Brit. Pat. 27,397 (1898).

While its stability at ordinary temperatures is such that it can be used commercially, at slightly elevated temperatures it is distinctly less stable than nitroglycerin. Nitroglycerin will tolerate

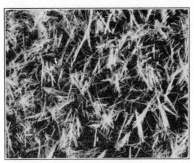

FIGURE 57. Nitromannite, Crystals from Alcohol (5×). (Courtesy Atlas Powder Company.)

heating in a covered glass vessel for several days at 75° before it begins to give off acid fumes; nitroglycol, methylglycol dinitrate, and trimethylene glycol dinitrate are more stable yet,

FIGURE 58. Nitromannite, in Grained Form for Charging Detonators (5×). (Courtesy Atlas Powder Company.)

but nitromannite decomposes after a few hours and evolves red fumes. If a small quantity is heated, it decomposes at once at about 150° with copious evolution of nitrous fumes but ordinarily does not deflagrate. With larger samples deflagration occurs at 160–170°.

Kast [66] has reported a velocity of detonation of 8260 meters per second for nitromannite compressed to a density of 1.73 in a column 12.8 mm. in diameter.

Nitromannite is about as sensitive as nitroglycerin to shock and to friction. It detonates under a 4-cm. drop of a 2-kilogram weight, and may be exploded readily on a concrete surface by a blow of a carpenter's hammer. It is not fired by the spit of a fuse, but is made to detonate by the flame of a match which causes local overheating. It is almost, but not quite, a primary explosive. It is used as the high-explosive charge in compound detonators which contain the relatively safe diazodinitrophenol as the primary explosive. A mixture of nitromannite and tetracene is a powerful and brisant primary explosive which detonates from moderate heat.

Nitrodulcite (Dulcitol hexanitrate)

Dulcite is obtained from Madagascar manna by extraction with water and recrystallizing, large monoclinic prisms, m.p. 188°, less soluble than mannite. It may also be procured by the action of sodium amalgam on aqueous solutions of lactose and of d-galactose. Nitrodulcite, isomeric with nitromannite, crystallizes from alcohol in needles which melt at 94–95°.

Nitrosorbite (Sorbitol hexanitrate)

d-Sorbite occurs in the berries of the mountain ash, but is more readily procured by the electrolytic reduction of d-glucose. It crystallizes with one molecule of water in small crystals which lose their water when heated and melt at about 110°. Nitrosorbite, isomeric with nitromannite, exists as a viscous liquid and has never been obtained in the crystalline state. It is used in nonfreezing dynamites.

Nitrated Sugar Mixtures $C_{12}H_{22}O_{11}$

The sugars are polyhydric alcohols which contain an aldehyde or a ketone group or a cyclic acetal or ketal arrangement within the molecule. They yield nitric esters which are perhaps less stable than the nitric esters of the simple polyhydric alcohols but which probably owe part of their reputation for instability to the

[66] Z. angew. Chem., **36**, 74 (1923).

fact that they are difficult to purify. The nitrosugars resemble the sugars from which they are derived in the respect that often they do not crystallize rapidly and easily. When warmed gently, they frequently soften and become sticky and resinous. In this condition they retain within their masses traces of decomposition products by which further decomposition is provoked; they cannot be washed free from acid, and in the solid or semi-solid state are impossible to stabilize. The stabilization however may be accomplished easily if the nitrosugar is in solution.

A mixture of nitrosucrose and nitroglycerin, prepared by nitrating a solution of 20 parts of cane sugar in 80 parts of glycerin, or of 25 parts in 75, has been used in this country under the name of *nitrohydrene*. It is suitable for use in non-freezing dynamites, and is cheaper than nitroglycerin to the extent that sugar is cheaper than glycerin. The nitrated product is much more viscous than nitroglycerin and forms emulsions readily. It requires repeated washings with soda solution to insure a satisfactory heat test, and then washings with concentrated salt solutions to facilitate the separation of the phases. Nitrohydrene 80/20 (from 80 parts of glycerin and 20 parts of cane sugar) consists of about 86% nitroglycerin and 14% nitrosucrose, and nitrohydrene 75/25 of about 82% nitroglycerin and 18% nitrosucrose. Naoúm [67] reports the following data. The stability of nitro-

		LEAD BLOCK EXPANSION, 10-GRAM SAMPLE IN GLASS TUBE	
	SPECIFIC GRAVITY AT 20°	Sand Tamping, cc.	Water Tamping, cc.
Nitroglycerin	1.596	550	595
Nitrohydrene 80/20	1.605	533	560
Nitrohydrene 75/25	1.612	514	535

hydrene is distinctly poorer than that of nitroglycerin and appears to depend upon the proportion of nitrosucrose which it contains, for nitrohydrene 75/25 gives a poorer heat test than nitrohydrene 80/20 which contains less nitrosucrose. Naoúm [68] points out that the wood meal, etc., which is contained in dynamite made from nitrohydrene apparently acts as a stabilizer and

[67] *Op. cit.*, p. 253.
[68] *Ibid.*, p. 255.

absorbs or reacts chemically with the first decomposition products and destroys them. He says:

> Better still, are very small additions of diphenylamine, which is admirably suited for the stabilization of smokeless powder, since it readily takes up the nitrous acid. Nitrohydrene 80/20 or 75/25, containing only 0.1 to 0.2 per cent of diphenylamine, was stored for seventy-five days at 55°C. without undergoing decomposition. The samples merely showed a coloration and became dark green, a phenomenon which also occurred but to a less extent with a check sample of nitroglycerin containing the same quantity of diphenylamine. After seventy-five days the nitroglycerin still had a slight odor of diphenylamine, but the nitrohydrene smelled slightly acid, somewhat like sour milk, but not like nitrous or nitric acid.
> Similar samples of 100 grams each of the above nitrohydrene containing 0.1 per cent diphenylamine have been stored by the author for more than eight years in diffuse daylight at room temperatures, about 20°C. So far they have remained unchanged, have no acid odor, and show no signs of decomposition. . . . From this it is evident that nitrosugar dissolved in nitroglycerin, although its stability does not reach that of the latter, is sufficiently stable for practical purposes, particularly in the presence of stabilizers.

The individual nitrosugars are stabilized similarly by diphenylamine, and certain ones of them, specifically nitromaltose, nitrolactose, and nitrosucrose, have been able by means of that substance to find a limited industrial application.

Solutions of cane sugar in glycol, and of glucose and lactose in glycerin, have been nitrated to produce mixtures of nitric esters comparable to nitrohydrene.

$C_5H_{10}O_5$

Nitroarabinose (*l*-Arabinose tetranitrate), $C_5H_6O(ONO_2)_4$

Nitroarabinose is prepared,[69] as indeed the highly nitrated sugars in general may be prepared, by adding concentrated sulfuric acid drop by drop to a solution of the corresponding sugar in concentrated nitric acid at 0°. It consists of colorless monoclinic crystals which melt at 85° and decompose at 120°. It is readily soluble in alcohol, acetone, and acetic acid, and insoluble in water and ligroin. It reduces Fehling's solution on warming. It is but little stable above 50°, and is easily exploded by shock.

[69] Will and Lenze, *Ber.,* **31,** 68 (1898).

Nitroglucose (d-Glucose pentanitrate), $C_6H_7O(ONO_2)_5$ $C_6H_{12}O_6$

d-Glucose pentanitrate [69] is a colorless viscous syrup, insoluble in water and in ligroin, readily soluble in alcohol. It becomes hard at 0°. It is unstable above 50°, and if heated slowly to a higher temperature decomposes rapidly at about 135°. It reduces Fehling's solution on warming. *Glucosan trinitrate*, $C_6H_7O_2$ $(ONO_2)_3$, is produced by the nitration of α-glucosan and by the action for several days of mixed acid on d-glucose. It is readily soluble in alcohol and insoluble in water. It has been obtained in the form of aggregates or crusts of crystals which melted not sharply at about 80° and which were probably not entirely free from glucose pentanitrate.

$C_6H_{12}O_6$

Nitromannose (d-Mannose pentanitrate), $C_6H_7O(ONO_2)_5$

d-Mannose pentanitrate,[69] transparent rhombic needles from alcohol, melts at 81–82° and decomposes at about 124°. It is soluble in alcohol and insoluble in water and reduces Fehling's solution slowly on warming. It undergoes a rapid decomposition if stored at 50°.

$C_{12}H_{22}O_{11}$

Nitromaltose (Maltose octonitrate), $C_{12}H_{14}O_3(ONO_2)_8$

Maltose octonitrate,[69, 70] glistening needles from methyl alcohol, melts with decomposition at 164–165°. If heated quickly, it puffs off at 170–180°. It decomposes slowly at 50°. If fused and allowed to solidify, it has a specific gravity of 1.62. It is readily soluble in methyl alcohol, acetone, and acetic acid, difficultly soluble in ethyl alcohol, and insoluble in water. It reduces warm Fehling's solution more rapidly than nitrosucrose.

$C_{12}H_{22}O_{11}$

Nitrolactose (Lactose octonitrate), $C_{12}H_{14}O_3(ONO_2)_8$

Lactose octonitrate,[69, 71] monoclinic needles from methyl or ethyl alcohol, melts at 145–146° with decomposition. Its specific gravity is 1.684. It is readily soluble in methyl alcohol, hot ethyl alcohol, acetone, and acetic acid, difficultly soluble in cold ethyl alcohol, and insoluble in water. It reduces Fehling's solution on warming.

[70] Pictet and Vogel, *Helv. Chim. Acta,* **10,** 588 (1927).
[71] Gé, *Ber.,* **15,** 2238 (1882).

Lactose hexanitrate, $C_{12}H_{16}O_5(ONO_2)_6$, has been found in the alcoholic mother liquors from the crystallization of the octonitrate, white, amorphous material melting not sharply at about 70°.

Crater [72] in 1934 described explosives containing nitrolactose, one consisting, say, of nitrolactose 25%, ammonium nitrate 65%, sodium nitrate 6%, and vegetable absorbent material 4%, another made by treating wood pulp with an acetone solution of nitrolactose and dinitrotoluene and containing about 78% nitrolactose, about 9% DNT, and about 13% wood pulp. For this use the nitrolactose ought to be stabilized with diphenylamine.

Nitrosucrose (Sucrose octonitrate), $C_{12}H_{14}O_3(ONO_2)_8$ $C_{12}H_{22}O_{11}$

The nitration of cane sugar [69, 73] yields sucrose octonitrate, white glistening needles, which melt at 85.5°. If heated slowly, nitrosucrose decomposes at about 135° and if heated rapidly deflagrates at about 170°. The fused and solidified material has a specific gravity of 1.67. It is readily soluble in methyl alcohol, ether, and nitrobenzene, difficultly soluble in ethyl alcohol and benzene, and insoluble in water and in petroleum ether. It reduces Fehling's solution on warming. It is relatively stable when pure. Monasterski reports that it gives a feeble puff under a 20-cm. drop of a 2-kilogram weight, a puff with one of 25 cm., and a detonation with one of 30 cm. He states that samples of 10 grams in the Trauzl test gave average net expansions of 296 cc.

Other Nitrosugars $C_5H_{10}O_5$

The nitration of *d*-xylose [69] yields *d-xylose tetranitrate*, $C_5H_6O(ONO_2)_4$, an oily substance insoluble in water, and a crystalline by-product, m.p. 141°, insoluble in water, which is evidently the *trinitrate*, $C_5H_7O_2(ONO_2)_3$. *Xylosan dinitrate*, $C_5H_6O_2(ONO_2)_2$, has been prepared by the action of mixed acid on *d*-xylose. It consists of little spherical crystal aggregates, soluble in alcohol and melting at 75–80°. $C_6H_{12}O_5$

l-Rhamnose tetranitrate,[69] $C_6H_8O(ONO_2)_4$, crystallizes in compact short rhombs which melt with decomposition at 135°. It is

[72] U. S. Pat. 1,945,344 (1934).

[73] Hoffman and Hawse, *J. Am. Chem. Soc.*, **41**, 235 (1919). Monasterski, *Z. ges. Schiess- u. Sprengstoffw.*, **28**, 349 (1933). Wyler, U. S. Pats. 2,081,161 (1938), 2,105,390 (1938), 2,165,435 (1939).

readily soluble in acetone, acetic acid, and in methyl and ethyl alcohol, and is relatively stable. It reduces Fehling's solution on warming. *l-Rhamnose trinitrate*,[74] $C_6H_9O_2(ONO_2)_3$, results from the action of mixed acid on *l*-rhamnose. It is a white amorphous material, melting below 100°, readily soluble in alcohol and insoluble in water. It explodes feebly under a hammer blow.

α-Methylglucoside tetranitrate,[69] $C_7H_{10}O_2(ONO_2)_4$, crystallizes from alcohol in quadrilateral plates which melt at 49–50° and decompose at 135°. It is more stable than the nitrate of the free sugar. It reduces Fehling's solution slowly on warming.

α-Methylmannoside tetranitrate,[69] $C_7H_{10}O_2(ONO_2)_4$, from the nitration of *d-α*-methylmannoside, crystallizes in fine asbestos-like needles which melt at 36°. It is relatively stable at 50°.

d-Galactose pentanitrate α, $C_6H_7O(ONO_2)_5$, from the nitration of *d*-galactose [69] crystallizes in bundles of transparent needles which melt at 115–116° and decompose at 126°. It is sparingly soluble in alcohol. It decomposes slowly at 50°, and reduces Fehling's solution slowly on warming. The alcoholic mother liquors from the α-form yield *d-galactose pentanitrate β*, transparent monoclinic needles which melt at 72–73° and decompose at 125°. This substance is readily soluble in alcohol, decomposes rapidly at 50°, and reduces hot Fehling's solution. *Galactosan trinitrate*, $C_6H_7O_2(ONO_2)_3$, results from the action during several days of mixed acid on *d*-galactose. It is deposited from alcohol in crusts of small crystals.

Fructosan trinitrate α, $C_6H_7O_2(ONO_2)_3$, is produced by the action of mixed acid at 0–15° on *d*-fructose or on laevulosan,[75] colorless, quickly effluorescing needles from alcohol, which melt at 139–140° and decompose at about 145°. It is readily soluble in methyl and ethyl alcohol, acetic acid, and acetone, and insoluble in water. It is relatively stable at 50°. It reduces hot Fehling's solution. The alcoholic mother liquors from the α-form yield *fructosan trinitrate β*, crusts of white crystals which melt at 48–52° and decompose at 135°. The material decomposes slowly at 50°. It reduces Fehling's solution rapidly on warming.

The action of mixed acid on *d*-sorbose at 15° yields *sorbosan trinitrate*, $C_6H_7O_2(ONO_2)_3$, a crystalline substance which melts not sharply at 40–45°.

[74] Hlasiewetz and Pfaundler, *Ann.*, 127, 362 (1863).
[75] Pictet and Reilly, *Helv. Chim. Acta*, 4, 613 (1921).

$C_7H_{14}O_7$

d-α-Glucoheptose hexanitrate, $C_7H_8O(ONO_2)_6$, from the nitration of *d-α*-glucoheptose,[69] crystallizes from alcohol in transparent needles which melt at 100°. It reduces Fehling's solution on warming. $C_{12}H_{22}O_{11}$

Trehalose octonitrate, $C_{12}H_{14}O_3(ONO_2)_8$, from the nitration of trehalose,[69] crystallizes from alcohol in birefringent pearly leaflets which melt at 124° and decompose at 136°. It reduces Fehling's solution on warming. $C_{18}H_{32}O_{16}$

Raffinose hendecanitrate, $C_{18}H_{21}O_5(ONO_2)_{11}$, from the nitration of raffinose,[69] exists in the form of amorphous aggregates which melt at 55–65° and decompose at 136°. It reduces Fehling's solution on warming. It decomposes rapidly when kept at 50°.

$(C_6H_{10}O_5)_4$ *α-Tetraamylose octonitrate*, $[C_6H_8O_3(ONO_2)_2]_4$, from α-tetraamylose,[76] crystallizes from acetic acid in fine glistening needles which decompose at 204°. It is readily soluble in ethyl acetate, amyl acetate, pyridine, and nitrobenzene, and sparingly soluble or insoluble in alcohol, ether, benzene, and water. *α-Diamylose* $(C_6H_{10}O_5)_2$ *hexanitrate*,[76] $[C_6H_7O_2(ONO_2)_3]_2$, prepared from α-diamylose or as the final product of the nitration of tetraamylose, crystallizes from acetone in plates which puff off at 206–207°. It is difficultly soluble in acetic acid, and is reported to be but little stable. The alcohol extract of the crude hexanitrate yields a certain amount of the amorphous *tetranitrate*.[76] *β-Triamylose hexanitrate*,[76] $[C_6H_8O_3(ONO_2)_2]_3$, is procured by dissolving either β-triamylose or β-hexaamylose in strong nitric acid at 0° and adding concentrated sulfuric acid drop by drop, and extracting the crude product with alcohol. It crystallizes from the alcoholic extract in aggregates of microscopic cubes, m.p. 203°. The residue which is insoluble in hot alcohol is recrystallized from acetic acid and yields crystalline crusts of *β-triamylose enneanitrate*,[76] $[C_6H_7O_2(ONO_2)_3]_3$, m.p. 198°.

Early History of Nitrated Carbohydrates

The history of modern explosives commenced with the discoveries of nitroglycerin and of nitrocellulose. At about the time that Sobrero first prepared nitroglycerin, Schönbein at Basel and Böttger at Frankfort-on-the-Main independently of each other nitrated cotton, perceived the possibilities in the product, and

[76] Leibowitz and Silmann, *Ber.*, **58**, 1889 (1925).

soon cooperated with each other to exploit its use in artillery. Pelouze had nitrated paper at an earlier time, and the question may indeed be raised whether he was not the first discoverer of nitrocellulose. Before that, Braconnot, professor of chemistry at Nancy, had prepared a nitric ester from starch. The principal events in the early history of these substances are summarized below.[77]

1833. Braconnot [78] found that starch dissolved in concentrated nitric acid and that the liquid on dilution with water gave a curdy precipitate of material which, after washing, dried out to a white, pulverulent, tasteless, and neutral mass. The product gave a brown color with a solution of iodine. It was not affected by bromine. It did not dissolve in boiling water but softened to a sticky mass. Dilute sulfuric acid did not affect it. Concentrated sulfuric acid dissolved it, and the solution gave no precipitate if it was diluted with water. The material, to which Braconnot gave the name of *xyloïdine,* dissolved in acetic acid very readily on heating, and the solution, if evaporated slowly, gave a transparent film which retained its transparency when placed in water. Applied to paper or cloth it yielded a brilliant, varnish-like coating which was impervious to water. Xyloïdine took fire very readily. It carbonized and liquefied if heated upon a piece of cardboard or heavy paper while the cardboard or paper, though exposed directly to the heat, was not appreciably damaged. Sawdust, cotton, and linen yielded products which Braconnot considered to be identical with the xyloïdine from starch.

1838. Pelouze [79] studied xyloïdine further. He found that if starch was dissolved in concentrated nitric acid and if the solution was diluted immediately with water, xyloïdine precipitated and the acid filtrate on evaporation yielded practically no residue. If the solution of starch in nitric acid was allowed to stand before being precipitated with water, then the amount of xyloïdine was less. If it was allowed to stand for 2 days, or perhaps only for some hours, the xyloïdine was entirely destroyed, a new acid was formed, no precipitate appeared when the solution was diluted,

[77] The papers which are cited in this connection have been published in English in the book by George W. MacDonald, "Historical Papers on Modern Explosives," Whittaker & Co., London and New York, 1912.

[78] *Ann. chim. phys.,* [2] **52,** 290 (1833).

[79] *Compt. rend.,* **7,** 713 (1838).

and the liquid on evaporation gave the new acid in the form of a solid, white, non-crystalline, deliquescent mass of considerably greater weight than the starch which was taken for the experiment. Neither carbon dioxide nor oxalic acid was produced during the reaction, but the new acid on long standing, or on boiling, with nitric acid was converted to oxalic acid without the formation of carbon dioxide. Pelouze considered xyloïdine to be a nitrate of starch. He observed that it was readily combustible,

FIGURE 59. Théophile-Jules Pelouze (1807-1867). (Courtesy E. Berl.) Made many important contributions to organic and inorganic chemistry— ethereal salts, the first nitrile, borneol, glyceryl tributyrate, pyroxylin, improvements in the manufacture of plate glass. He nitrated paper in 1838 and was thus probably the first to prepare nitrocellulose. Reproduced from original in Kekulé's portrait album.

that it ignited at a temperature of 180° and burned with very considerable violence leaving practically no residue. The observation, he says, led him to make certain experiments which, he believed, might have practical application in artillery. Paper, dipped into nitric acid of specific gravity 1.5 and left there long enough for the acid to penetrate into it (generally 2 or 3 minutes), removed, and washed thoroughly, gave a parchment-like material which was impervious to moisture and was extremely combustible. Pelouze had nitrocellulose in his hands, but evidently did not recognize that the material, which had not changed greatly in its physical form, was nevertheless nitrated throughout its mass, for he believed that the products which he obtained from paper and from cotton and linen fabrics owed their new properties to the xyloïdine which covered them.

1846. Schönbein announced his discovery of guncotton at a meeting of the Society of Scientific Research at Basel on May 27, 1846. In an article, probably written in 1847 but published in the *Archives des sciences physiques et naturelles* of 1846, he described some of his experiences with the material and his efforts

FIGURE 60. Christian Friedrich Schönbein (1799-1868). (Courtesy E. Berl.) Discovered guncotton, 1846. Discovered ozone, worked on hydrogen peroxide, auto-oxidation, the passivity of iron, hydrosulfites, catalysts, and prussic acid. Professor of Chemistry at Basel from 1829 until the time of his death. He published more than 300 papers on chemical subjects. Reproduced from original in Kekulé's portrait album.

to put it to practical use and discussed the controversial question of priority of discovery; he described the nitration of cane sugar but deliberately refrained from telling how he had prepared his nitrocellulose. He was led to perform the experiments by certain theoretical speculations relative to ozone which he had discovered a few years before. One volume of nitric acid (1.5) and 2 volumes of sulfuric acid (1.85) were mixed and cooled to 0°, finely powdered sugar was stirred in so as to form a paste, the stirring was continued, and after a few minutes a viscous mass separated from the acid liquid without the disengagement of gas. The pasty mass was washed with boiling water until free from acid, and was dried at a low temperature. The product was brittle at low temperatures, could be molded like jalap resin at slightly elevated ones, was semi-fluid at 100°, and at high temperatures gave off red fumes. When heated more strongly, it deflagrated suddenly and with violence. Schönbein also experimented with other organic substances, and states that in experiments carried out during December, 1845, and the first few months of 1846 he discovered, one after another, all those substances about which so much had lately been said in the French Academy. In March he sent specimens of the new compounds, among them guncotton, to several of his friends, notably, Faraday, Herschel, and Grove.

About the middle of April, 1846, Schönbein went to Württemberg where he carried out experiments with guncotton at the arsenal at Ludwigsburg in the presence of artillery officers and at Stuttgart in the presence of the king. During May, June, and July he experimented at Basel with small arms, mortars, and cannon. On July 28 he fired for the first time a cannon which was loaded with guncotton and with a projectile. Shortly afterward he used guncotton to blast rocks at Istein in the Grand Duchy of Baden and to blow up some old walls in Basel.

In the middle of August Schönbein received news from Professor Böttger of Frankfort-on-the-Main that he too had succeeded in preparing guncotton, and the names of the two men soon became associated in connection with the discovery and utilization of the material. There were, moreover, several other chemists who at about the same time, or within a few months, also worked out methods of preparing it. In a letter [80] to Schönbein dated November 18, 1846, Berzelius congratulated him on the discovery as interesting as it was important, and wrote, "Since Professor Otto of Brunswick made known a method of preparing the guncotton, this discovery has perhaps occupied a greater number of inquisitive persons than any other chemical discovery ever did. I have likewise engaged in experiments upon it."

In August Schönbein went to England where, with the help of the engineer Richard Taylor of Falmouth, he carried out experiments with guncotton in the mines of Cornwall. He also demonstrated his material successfully with small arms and with artillery at Woolwich, at Portsmouth, and before the British

[80] MacDonald, op. cit., pp. 47, 48.

Association. He did not apply for an English patent in his own name but communicated his process to John Taylor of Adelphi, Middlesex, who was granted English patent 11,407, dated October 8, 1846, for "Improvements in the Manufacture of Explosive Compounds, communicated to me from a certain foreigner residing abroad." [81] He entered into an agreement for three years

FIGURE 61. Rudolf Böttger (1806-1887). (Courtesy E. Berl.) Professor at Frankfort-on-the-Main. Discovered guncotton independently of Schönbein but somewhat later, in the same year, 1846. He also invented matches, and made important studies on the poisoning of platinum catalysts. Reproduced from original in Kekulé's portrait album.

with Messrs. John Hall & Sons of Faversham that they should have the sole right in England to manufacture guncotton by his process and in return should pay him one-third of the net profit with a minimum of £1000 down and the same each year. The first factory for the manufacture of guncotton was erected at Faversham. On July 14, 1847, within less than a year, the factory was destroyed by an explosion with the loss of twenty-one lives. After this, Messrs. John Hall & Sons refused to continue the manu-

[81] *Ibid.,* pp. 42–44.

facture. About the same time disastrous guncotton explosions occurred at Vincennes and at Le Bouchet, and these produced such an unfavorable effect that no more guncotton was manufactured in England or in France for about sixteen years.

Schönbein offered his process to the Deutscher Bund for 100,000 thalers, and a committee was formed to consider the matter, Liebig representing the state of Hesse and Baron von Lenk, who was secretary, representing Austria. The committee continued to sit until 1852 when it finally decided to take no action. At the suggestion of von Lenk, Austria then acquired the process for 30,000 gulden.

1846. The *Comptes rendus* of 1846 contains several papers on the nitration of cellulose, which papers were presented to the French Academy before the details of Schönbein's process were yet known. Among these, the papers by Dumas and Pelouze are especially interesting. Dumas [82] stated that certain details of the manufacture of guncotton had already been published in Germany. Professor Otto of Brunswick dipped the cotton for half a minute in concentrated fuming nitric acid, pressed between two pieces of glass, washed until free from acid, and afterwards dried.

> The explosive property can be considerably increased by several dippings, and I have found that a product of extreme force is obtained after an immersion of 12 hours. A point of extreme importance is the care which ought to be exercised in washing the cotton. The last traces of acid are very difficult to remove, and should any remain it will be found that, on drying, the substance smells strongly of oxides of nitrogen, and when ignited also produces a strong acid smell. The best test of a sample of guncotton is to ignite it upon a porcelain plate. Should it burn slowly, leaving a residue upon the plate, it must be considered as unsatisfactory. A good guncotton burns very violently without leaving any residue. It is also of very great importance that when the guncotton is withdrawn from the acid, it should be washed immediately in a large quantity of water. Should small quantities of water be used it will be found that the guncotton becomes very hot, and that spots of a blue or green color are produced, which are very difficult to remove, and the guncotton is very impure.

Dr. Knopp of the University of Leipzig used a mixture of equal parts of concentrated sulfuric and nitric acids, and immersed the

[82] *Compt. rend.*, 806 (1846); MacDonald, *op. cit.*, pp. 15-17.

cotton in it for several minutes at ordinary temperature. Dumas stated that satisfactory guncotton could be obtained without observing any great exactitude in the proportion of the two acids or in the duration of the immersion. Dr. Bley of Bernberg had discovered that sawdust, treated in the same way as cotton, yielded an explosive which, he believed, might replace gunpowder in firearms and in blasting.

1846.   Pelouze [83] made clear distinction between xyloïdine and guncotton. "I shall call *pyroxyline* or *pyroxyle* the product of the action of monohydrated nitric acid on cotton, paper, and ligneous substances, when this action has taken place without having caused the solution of the cellulose." Braconnot in 1833 had prepared xyloïdine from starch; Pelouze had prepared pyroxylin in 1838. He pointed out that xyloïdine dissolves readily in strong nitric acid and, in the course of a day, is destroyed by it and converted to a deliquescent acid. Pyroxylin does not dissolve in concentrated nitric acid. Xyloïdine is very inflammable and explodes when struck, but it leaves a considerable residue of carbon when heated in a retort and may be analyzed like an ordinary organic substance by heating with copper oxide. Pyroxylin explodes when heated to 175° or 180° and cannot be distilled destructively. Pelouze found that 100 parts of starch, dissolved in nitric acid and precipitated immediately, yielded at most 128 to 130 parts of xyloïdine. One hundred parts of cotton or paper, after a few minutes' or after several days' immersion in concentrated nitric acid, yielded 168 to 170 parts of washed and dried pyroxylin. The acid mother liquors, both from the nitration of the starch and from the nitration of the cotton, contained not more than mere traces of organic matter.

1846.   Schönbein's process soon became known through the publication of the English patent to John Taylor (cited above). He carried out the nitration by means of a mixture of 1 volume of strong nitric acid (1.45 to 1.5) and 3 volumes of strong sulfuric acid (1.85). The cotton was immersed in this acid at 50–60°F. for 1 hour, and was then washed in a stream of running water until free from acid. It was pressed to remove as much water as possible, dipped in a very dilute solution of potassium carbonate (1 ounce to the gallon), and again pressed as dry as possible.

[83] *Ibid.*, 809, 892 (1846); MacDonald, *op. cit.*, pp. 17–20.

It was then rinsed with a very dilute solution of potassium nitrate (1 ounce to the gallon). The patent states that "the use of this solution appears to add strength to the compound, but the use of this solution and also potassium carbonate are not essential and may be dispensed with." The product is pressed, opened out, and dried at 150°F., and when dried it is fit for use. The patent also covers the possibility of using instead of cotton "other matters of vegetable origin and the possibility of carrying out the nitration with nitric acid alone or with mixed acids of inferior strength."

1846. Teschemacher[84] studied the preparation of guncotton and demonstrated that no sulfuric acid is consumed by the reaction.

1847. Gladstone[85] by exercising special precautions was able to carry out combustion analyses of xyloïdine and of pyroxylin prepared according to the directions of Schönbein. Nitrogen was determined by the differential method. The pyroxylin was found to contain 12.75% nitrogen and was thought to correspond to a pentanitrate while the xyloïdine corresponded more nearly to a trinitrate.

1847. Crum[86] nitrated cotton until he could introduce no further nitrogen into the molecule, and analyzed the product for nitric acid by the method which is used in the nitrometer. His result calculated as nitrogen gives a figure of 13.69%. It is interesting to note that Crum's cotton was "bleached by boiling in caustic soda and put in a solution of bleaching powder; then caustic soda again, and afterwards weak nitric acid. It was well washed and beaten in a bag with water after each operation. . . . The cotton, dried and carded after bleaching, was exposed in parcels of 10 grains each for several hours to the heat of a steam bath, and each parcel was immersed, while hot, into a 1 oz. measure of the following mixture: Sulphuric acid (1.84) 1 measure, and 3 measures of pale lemon-colored nitric acid (1.517). After one hour it was washed in successive portions of water until no trace of acid remained, and was then dried in the open air"—or, for analysis, was dried completely in a vacuum desiccator over sulfuric acid.

[84] *Mem. of the Chem. Soc.*, 253 (1846); MacDonald, *op. cit.*, pp. 28–31.
[85] *Ibid.*, 412 (1847); MacDonald, *op. cit.*, pp. 31–41.
[86] *Proc. Phil. Soc. Glasgow*, 163 (1847); MacDonald, *op. cit.*, pp. 21–27.

1852. The Austrian government acquired the use of Schönbein's process (as mentioned above) and the Emperor of Austria
appointed a committee to investigate the use of guncotton for
military purposes. This committee, of which von Lenk was the
leading spirit, continued to function with some interruptions until
1865. In 1853 a factory was erected at Hirtenberg for the manufacture of guncotton by the method of von Lenk which involved
a more elaborate purification than Schönbein's original process.
The product was washed for 3 weeks, then boiled with dilute
potassium carbonate solution for 15 minutes, washed again for
several days, impregnated with water glass, and finally dried.
Von Lenk constructed 12-pounder guns which were shot with
guncotton cartridges, but they were much damaged by the firing.
About 1860 he tried bronze guns, which were less likely to burst
than iron ones, and with propelling charges of guncotton fired
from them shells which were filled with bursting charges of guncotton. The shells often burst within the barrel, for the acceleration produced by the propelling charge of guncotton was much
too sudden and shocking. They could be shot out without exploding when a propelling charge of black gunpowder was used. On
July 20, 1863, the magazine at Hirtenberg exploded, and the
Austrian government thereupon decided to abandon the use of
guncotton as a propellent explosive. Von Lenk was permitted to
communicate his process to other nations. In 1862 and 1863, under
the name of Révy, he took out English patents to protect his
method of purification.[87] In 1863 he visited England and described
his process to a committee of the British Association. In the same
year Messrs. Prentice and Co. commenced the manufacture of
guncotton at Stowmarket by von Lenk's process, but an explosion soon occurred at their establishment. In 1865 a guncotton
magazine at Steinfelder Heath, near Vienna, exploded, and on
October 11 of that year the manufacture of guncotton in Austria
was officially forbidden.

1862. Tonkin's English patent [88] deserves our notice because
it mentions the pulping of guncotton—and it was the pulping of
guncotton, introduced later by Abel, which remedied in large
measure the difficulties of stability which had given guncotton
a bad repute and brought it back again to the favorable con-

[87] Brit. Pats. 1090 (1862), 2720 (1863).

[88] Brit. Pat. 320 (1862); MacDonald, op. cit., p. 44.

sideration of the users of explosives. The patent describes the
nitration of the cotton with mixed acid, the washing with running water, the pressing, and the dipping in a very dilute solution
of potassium carbonate. "The fibre is then taken in the wet state
and converted into pulp in the same manner as is practiced by
paper-makers, by putting the fibre into a cylinder, having knives
revolving rapidly, working close to fixed knives." The patent
makes no claim to the pulping of guncotton, but only claims the
use of pulped guncotton in an explosive consisting of sodium
nitrate 65%, charcoal 16%, sulfur 16%, and guncotton pulp 3%.

1865. Abel's patent [89] for "Improvements in the Preparation
and Treatment of Guncotton" claims the pulping and the pressing of it into sheets, discs, cylinders, and other forms and was
probably designed to cover the process of getting it into a state
where it would burn less violently in the gun. The compressed
blocks were an improvement over the yarn of von Lenk, but they
were still much too fast; they damaged the guns and were not
ballistically uniform in performance. The blocks of compressed
guncotton, however, have continued to find use in blasting. And
the outstanding advantage of Abel's pulping was that it converted the guncotton into a state where the impurities were more
easily washed out of it, and resulted thereby in a great improvement in stability.

1866–1867. Abel's "Researches on Guncotton" [90] demonstrated
that guncotton, after proper purification, is far more stable than
it had been thought to be. Moisture does not harm it, or exposure
to sunlight, and it decomposes only slowly at elevated temperatures; the principal cause of its decomposition is acid, and this is
removed by the pulping. Abel wrote:

> In reducing the material to a very fine state of division by
> means of the ordinary beating and pulping machines, the
> capillary power of the fibre is nearly destroyed, and the gun-
> cotton is, for a considerable period, very violently agitated
> in a large volume of water. It would be very difficult to
> devise a more perfect cleansing process than that to which
> the guncotton is submitted; and the natural result of its
> application is that the material thus additionally purified
> acquires considerably increased powers of resisting the de-

[89] Brit. Pat. 1102 (1865); MacDonald, *op. cit.*, pp. 45-46.
[90] *Loc. cit.*

structive effects of heat. Samples of the pulped guncotton, even in the most porous conditions, have been found to resist change perfectly upon long-continued exposure to temperatures which developed marked symptoms of decomposition in the guncotton purified only as usual. The pulping process applied to guncotton affords, therefore, important additional means of purifying the material, the value of which may be further enhanced by employing a slightly alkaline water in the pulping machine. The slightest change sustained by guncotton is attended by the development of free acid, which, if it accumulates in the material, even to a very trifling extent, greatly promotes decomposition.

Numerous experimental data have been collected with respect to the establishment and acceleration of decomposition in guncotton by free acid whilst exposed to light or elevated temperature. This acid is present either in the imperfectly purified material or has been developed by decomposition of guncotton or its organic impurities. Samples of guncotton which, by exposure to elevated temperatures or for considerable periods to strong daylight, had sustained changes resulting in a considerable development of acid, have afterwards been thoroughly purified by washing. When exposed to light for months, and in some instances for two or three years (up to the present time), they have undergone no further change, while corresponding samples confined in close vessels without being purified, have continued, in some instances, to undergo decomposition, and the original substance has been completely transformed into the products repeatedly spoken of.

Abel found that the guncotton regularly produced at Waltham Abbey contained a small amount of material soluble in ether-alcohol, an average amount of 1.62% in the guncotton which was made by treating cotton with 18 times its weight of mixed acid, and an average of 2.13% in the guncotton which was made by the use of 10 parts of acid. "The employment of the higher proportion of acid furnished results more nearly approaching perfection than those obtained when the guncotton was left in contact with a smaller proportion of the acid mixture. As far as can be judged at present, however, from the general properties of the products, the difference observed when the larger or the smaller proportion of acid is used, is not of sufficient importance to render necessary the consumption of the larger quantity of acid in the manufacture." Abel was able to carry out satisfactory combustion analyses, with the following average results:

Material soluble in ether-alcohol, C 30.50%; H 2.91%; N 11.85%; Material insoluble in ether-alcohol, C 24.15%; H 2.46%; N 13.83%.

He concluded that the different analytical results which had been procured with different samples of guncotton resulted from the samples containing different amounts of the ether-alcohol soluble material, and judged that completely nitrated guncotton is the trinitrate of cellulose, $[C_6H_7O_2(ONO_2)_3]_n$, as had been first suggested by Crum. This substance contains theoretically 14.14% nitrogen.

1868. E. A. Brown, assistant to Abel, discovered [91] that dry compressed guncotton could be made to detonate very violently by the explosion of a fulminate detonator such as Nobel had already used for exploding nitroglycerin. Shortly afterwards he made the further important discovery that wet guncotton could be exploded by the explosion of a small quantity of dry guncotton (the principle of the booster). This made it possible to use large blocks of wet guncotton in naval mines with comparative safety.

Nitrocellulose (NC)

Cellulose occurs everywhere in the vegetable kingdom; it is wood fiber and cell wall, the structural material of all plants. Cotton fiber is practically pure cellulose, but cellulose of equal purity, satisfactory in all respects for the manufacture of explosives and smokeless powder, may be produced from wood. Cellulose and starch both yield glucose on hydrolysis, and the molecules of both these substances are made up of anhydroglucose units linked together.

[91] Brit. Pat. 3115 (1868).

The two substances differ in the configuration of the number 1 carbon atom. In cellulose this atom has the β-configuration; 2000 or 3000 anhydroglucose units are linked together in long, straight, threadlike masses which are essentially one dimensional. In starch the number 1 carbon atom has the α-configuration which leads to spiral arrangements essentially three dimensional, and the molecule contains not more than 25 or 30 anhydroglucose units.

Cellulose contains 3 hydroxyl groups per anhydroglucose unit, and yields a trinitrate on complete nitration (14.14% N). An absolutely complete nitration is difficult to secure, but a product containing 13.75% nitrogen may be produced commercially. If the conditions of nitration, concentration of acid, temperature, and duration of the reaction, are less severe, less nitrogen is introduced, and products ranging all the way from a few per cent of nitrogen upward, and differing widely in solubilities and viscosities, may be secured. In the cellulose nitrates which contain less than enough nitrogen to correspond to the trinitrate, the nitrate groups are believed to be distributed at random among the three possible positions, and no definite structural formulas can be assigned to the materials. Nor is it to be supposed that a sample which may correspond in empirical composition to cellulose mononitrate or dinitrate really represents a single chemical individual.

Collodion is a nitrocellulose which is soluble in ether-alcohol and contains, according to the use for which it is destined, from 8%, more or less, of nitrogen to 12% or thereabouts. The name of *pyroxylin* is now generally applied to collodion of low nitrogen content intended for use in pharmacy, in the making of lacquers or of photographic film, or intended in general for industrial uses outside of the explosives industry. In 1847 Maynard discovered that nitrocellulose existed which was soluble in a mixture of ether and alcohol although it would not dissolve in either of these solvents taken singly.[92] The discovery soon led to the invention of collodion photography by Archer in 1851. Chardonnet's first patent [93] for artificial silk was granted in 1884. *Celluloid*, made by dissolving collodion nitrocellulose in camphor with the use of

[92] After the material is dissolved, the solution may be diluted either with alcohol or with ether without precipitating.

[93] French Pat. 165,345 (1884).

heat and pressure, was patented by J. W. and I. S. Hyatt [94] in 1870. Worden [95] states that collodion for the manufacture of celluloid is made by nitrating tissue paper with a mixed acid which contains nitric acid 35.4%, sulfuric acid 44.7%, and water 19.9%. Twenty-two pounds of acid are used per pound of paper. The nitration is carried out at 55° for 30 minutes, and the product contains 11.0–11.2% nitrogen. Ether-alcohol solutions of collodion, to which camphor and castor oil have been added in order that they may yield tough and flexible films on evaporation, are used in pharmacy for the application of medicaments to the skin in cases where prolonged action is desired. Two per cent of salicylic acid, for example, in such a mixture makes a "corn remover." Collodion for use with nitroglycerin to make blasting gelatin is generally of higher nitrogen content. Here the desideratum is that the jelly should be stiff, and the higher nitrogen content tends in that direction, but the collodion dissolves in the nitroglycerin more slowly, and the product becomes stiffer on prolonged storage, and less sensitive, and may cause misfires. The nitrogen content of collodion for use in the manufacture of blasting explosives is generally between 11.5 and 12.0%. The official definition in England of collodion for this purpose gives an upper limit of 12.3% nitrogen.

Two kinds of nitrocellulose were used in France at the time of the first World War, *coton-poudre No. 1* (CP₁), insoluble in ether-alcohol and containing about 13% nitrogen, and *coton-poudre No. 2* (CP₂), soluble in ether-alcohol and containing about 12% nitrogen.[96] CP_1 thus contained a little less nitrogen than the material which we are accustomed to call guncotton, and CP_2 contained a little more than the material which we are accustomed to call collodion. CP_1 and CP_2 were not respectively wholly insoluble and wholly soluble in ether-alcohol; their compositions were approximate, and CP_2 always contained a certain amount of material soluble in alcohol alone. A mixture of CP_1 and CP_2 colloided with ether-alcohol was used for making *pou-*

[94] U. S. Pat. 105,338 (1870).

[95] *J. Soc. Chem. Ind.*, **29**, 540 (1910).

[96] The French are accustomed to report their analyses of nitrocellulose, not as per cent nitrogen, but as cubic centimeters of NO (produced in the nitrometer and measured under standard conditions) per gram of sample. Per cent nitrogen times 15.96 equals number of cubic centimeters of NO per gram of nitrocellulose.

dre B. Either CP_1 with nitroglycerin and an acetone solvent or both with nitroglycerin and an ether-alcohol solvent were used for making ballistite, and both of them with nitroglycerin and with non-volatile solvents were used in attenuated ballistite. CP_2 was also used in France for the manufacture of blasting gelatin.

Mendeleev studied the nitration of cellulose during the years 1891 to 1895 in an effort to prepare a nitrocellulose which should have the largest content of nitrogen (and hence the greatest explosive power) compatible with complete solubility in ether-alcohol. He produced *pyrocellulose* containing 12.60% nitrogen. Russia adopted a military smokeless powder made from pyrocellulose by colloiding with ether-alcohol, and the United States in 1898 was using a similar powder in the Spanish-American War.

The word *guncotton* has about the same meaning in English and in American usage, namely, nitrocellulose containing 13% or more of nitrogen, usually 13.2–13.4%, insoluble in ether-alcohol and soluble in acetone and in ethyl acetate. One American manufacturer prefers to call guncotton *high-grade nitrocellulose.*

Preparation of Pyrocellulose. Equal volumes of sulfuric acid (1.84) and nitric acid (1.42) are mixed by pouring the sulfuric acid with stirring into the nitric acid, and the mixture is allowed to cool to room temperature. Five grams of absorbent cotton, previously dried at 100° for 2 hours, is thrust quickly into 150 cc. of this mixed acid and allowed to remain there for 30 minutes while it is stirred occasionally with a glass rod. The cotton is removed, freed as much as possible from acid by pressing against the side of the vessel, and introduced quickly into a large beaker of cold water where it is stirred about in such manner as to accomplish the prompt dilution of the acid with which it is saturated. The product is washed thoroughly in running water, and boiled for an hour with distilled water in a large beaker, then boiled three times with fresh portions of distilled water for a half hour each time. If the water from the last boiling shows the slightest trace of acidity to litmus paper, the pyrocellulose ought to be rinsed and boiled once more with distilled water. Finally, the excess of water is wrung out, and the pyrocellulose is dried in a paper tray for 48 hours at room temperature.

Pyrocellulose is made commercially from purified cotton *linters* or *hull shavings* or wood cellulose, most commonly by the mechanical dipper process. The thoroughly dry cellulose is introduced into the mixed acid contained in an iron or stainless steel nitrator which is equipped with two paddles revolving vertically in opposite directions and designed to thrust the cotton quickly under the surface of the acid. For 32 pounds of cellulose a charge of about 1500 pounds of mixed acid is used. This contains approximately 21% nitric acid, 63% sulfuric acid, and 16% water. It may contain also a small amount, say 0.5%, of nitrous acid, NO_2 or N_2O_4, which, however, is calculated as being equivalent to a like amount of water and is not reckoned as any part of the *nitrating total* of actual nitric and sulfuric acids. The sulfuric acid content of the nitrating acid is kept as constant as possible in practice; the nitric acid content may vary somewhat, less than 1%, however, for slightly more nitric acid is necessary in warm weather to offset the tendency toward denitration which exists at that time. At the start the acid has a temperature of about 30°, the introduction of the cellulose requires about 4 minutes, and the nitration is continued for 20 minutes longer while the mixture is stirred mechanically with the paddles and the temperature is kept between 30° and 34°. When the nitration is complete, a valve in the bottom of the nitrator is opened and the slurry is allowed to run into a centrifuge on the floor below. Here the crude nitrocellulose is separated quickly from the spent acid which is fortified for use again or, in part, goes to the acid recovery plant. Wringer fires are by no means uncommon, especially on damp days, for the air which is sucked through the acid-soaked material in the centrifuge gives up its moisture to the strong acid and dilutes it with the development of considerable heat. The nitrated product is forked through an orifice in the bottom of the wringer and falls into an immersion basin below, where it is *drowned* by being mixed rapidly with a swiftly moving stream of water. Thence it proceeds on its way down the *guncotton line* where it is *stabilized* or purified and then prepared for shipment or for use.

The crude nitrocellulose contains certain amounts of cellulose sulfate, of nitrate of oxycellulose, and possibly of some cellulose nitrate which is less stable than the ordinary, all of which are capable of being hydrolyzed by long-continued boiling with slightly acidified water. Guncotton requires a longer stabilizing boil than pyrocellulose. After the boiling the acid is washed off and removed from the nitrocellulose, yielding a product which is now stabilized because it contains neither free acid nor compo-

nent materials which are prone to decompose with the formation
of acid.

The *preliminary boiling* or *sour boiling* is carried out in large
wooden tubs heated by means of steam. At the beginning the
nitrocellulose is boiled with water which contains 0.25% to 0.50%

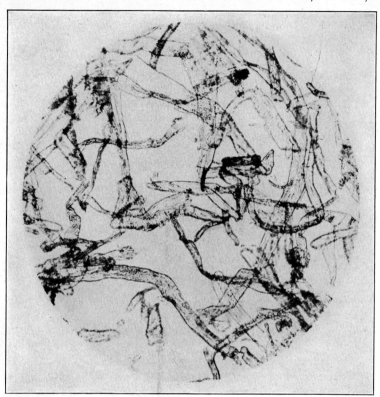

FIGURE 62. Nitrocellulose Fibers before Beating (132×). (Courtesy Western
Cartridge Company.)

of acidity calculated as sulfuric acid. The first boil lasts usually
for 16 hours during which time the acidity of the solution increases. The increase is due largely to actual sulfuric acid. After
16 hours the steam is shut off, the solution is decanted from the
nitrocellulose, the tub is filled with fresh water, and the material
is boiled again for 8 hours. The boiling is repeated until each
tubful has been boiled for 40 hours with at least 4 changes of
water.

The hollow fibers still contain an acid solution within them. In order that this acid may be washed out, they are *pulped* or broken up into short lengths by means of apparatus like that which is used in the manufacture of paper. A Jordan mill cuts the fibers off rather sharply, leaving square ends, but a beater tears

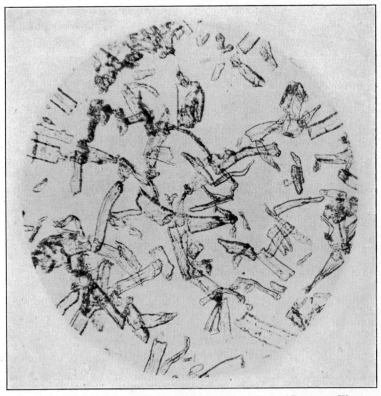

FIGURE 63. Nitrocellulose Fibers after Beating (132×). (Courtesy Western Cartridge Company.)

them, leaving ends which appear rough and shredded under the microscope and which result on the whole in the better opening up of the tubular fibers. The two machines are usually used in series. A weak solution of sodium carbonate is added during the pulping to neutralize the acid which is liberated. The pulping is continued until the desired fineness has been attained as shown by laboratory test.

The pulped fibers still retain acid adsorbed or occluded on their surface. This is removed by *poaching* the nitrocellulose, by boiling it again, first for 4 hours with fresh water with or without the addition of dilute sodium carbonate solution,[97] then for 2 hours with water without addition of soda, then twice with water for 1 hour each time. The material is then washed at least 8 times by thorough agitation with cold water, and by decantation each time of at least 40% of the liquid. After the washing, the material undergoes *screening*, where it passes through apertures 0.022 inch in width, *wringing*, whereby its moisture content is reduced to 26–28%, and finally *packing* for shipment or for storage in containers which are hermetically sealed.

Guncotton is made in substantially the same way as pyrocellulose except that a stronger mixed acid containing approximately 24% nitric acid, 67% sulfuric acid, and 9% water is used. Long-fiber high-grade guncotton is usually manufactured by the pot process and with the use of mixed acid which is nearly anhydrous. Iron pots are generally used. For the nitration of 4 pounds of dry cotton, 140 pounds of acid is introduced into the pot and the cotton is immersed in it, pressed down, and allowed to digest for 20 or 30 minutes. The contents of several pots are centrifuged at once, and the product is stabilized in the same way as pyrocellulose except that it is not pulped.

There can be no doubt that, in the standard method of stabilizing nitrocellulose, there are, among the results which the poaching accomplishes, at least some which would have been accomplished much earlier during the boiling if the material at that time had been pulped. This seems especially evident with respect to the hydrolysis of easily hydrolyzed material adjacent to the inner wall of the tubular fibers. Olsen,[98] discussing the standard method, has written, "The preliminary boiling tub treatment reduced the acidity of the fibers and of the interstitial material, but the pulping process, by macerating these fibers, has set free an additional amount of acid. It is, therefore, necessary to repurify the pyrocotton by boiling." He discovered that a marked reduction in time and in cost could be secured by carrying out the pulping operation prior to the hydrolyzing boils. If the pulping is done at

[97] Not more than 10 gallons of sodium carbonate solution (1 pound per gallon) for every 2000 pounds of nitrocellulose (dry weight).

[98] U. S. Pat. 1,798,270 (1931).

the outset, "less than half of the 16 hours sour boiling usually
employed will suffice for obtaining the desired degree of purity
when followed by alternating boils in fresh water and washes
with cold fresh water, again less than half of the amount of boiling being sufficient." With less than 20 hours total time of
purification, he obtained results as good as are ordinarily procured by the 52 hours of the standard method.

FIGURE 64. Boiling Tubs for Purification of Nitrocellulose.

Olsen's quick stabilization process [99] is the result of further
thinking along this same line and represents an ingenious application of a simple principle of colloid chemistry. After the nitrocellulose has been thoroughly pulped, and after the easily decomposed cellulose sulfate, etc., have been hydrolyzed, there remains
only the necessity for removing the acid which clings to the fiber.
The acid, however, is adsorbed on the nitrocellulose, or bound to
it, in such manner that it is not easily washed away by water or
even by dilute soda solution; many boilings and washings are
necessary to remove it. Olsen has found that the acid is removed
rapidly and completely if the nitrocellulose is digested or washed
with a solution of some substance which is adsorbed by nitro-

[99] U. S. Pat. 1,893,677 (1933).

cellulose with greater avidity than the acid is adsorbed, that is, with a solution of some substance which has, as he says, a greater *adhesion tension* for nitrocellulose than the acid has. Such substances are aniline red, Bismarck brown, methyl orange,

FIGURE 65. Fred Olsen. Has done important work on cellulose and has made many improvements in detonating explosives, high explosives, and smokeless powder; in particular, has invented processes for the quick stabilization of nitrocellulose and for the production of ball-grain powder. Chief of Chemical Research, Aetna Explosives Company, 1917-1919; Chemical Adviser, Picatinny Arsenal, 1919-1928; Technical Director, Western Cartridge Company, 1929—.

m-phenylenediamine, urea, substituted ureas such as diethyldiphenylurea, and diphenylamine. A 0.5% solution of urea in water may be used. A half-hour washing with a 0.5% solution of diphenylamine in alcohol was more effective in producing stability than 20 hours of boiling with water. A solution of 0.1 gram of Bismarck brown in 300 cc. of water gave better stabilization of 30 grams of nitrocellulose in 1 hour than 10 boilings of 1 hour each with separate 300-cc. portions of water.

Nitrocellulose, like all other nitric esters with the possible exception of PETN, is intrinsically unstable, even at ordinary temperatures. Yet the decomposition of a thoroughly purified sample is remarkably slow. Koehler and Marqueyrol [100] have made a careful study of the decomposition of nitrocellulose at various temperatures in the vacuum of a mercury pump. They found that it evolved gas at the rate of about 0.7 cc. per gram per day at 100°, 0.01 cc. per gram per day at 75°, and 0.0001 cc. per gram per day at 40°.

A sample of CP_1 was freed from carbonate by digestion with carbonated water and subsequent washing; it was dried thoroughly, and 35.152 grams of the material (analyzing 211.2 cc. NO per gram) was heated in vacuum at 75°. The results are summarized in the following table, where all gas volumes have been reduced to 0° and 760 mm. The residual gas, insoluble both

DURATION OF HEATING AT 75°	TOTAL VOLUME, CUBIC CENTI- METERS	CUBIC CENTI- METERS PER GRAM PER DAY	COMPOSITION OF GAS, %		
			NO	CO_2	Residue
1st period (5 days)	2.25	0.0128	62.5	16.7	20.8
2nd period (56 days)	17.29	0.0088	63.2	19.5	17.3
3rd period (56 days)	18.25	0.00927	60.8	21.5	17.6
4th period (56 days)	18.34	0.0080	65.5	18.0	16.5
5th period (56 days)	18.19	0.0079	60.0	20.7	19.6
6th period (56 days)	18.3	0.0084	61.2	20.4	18.3

in ferrous sulfate and in caustic soda solution, was analyzed and was found to consist approximately of 46% carbon monoxide, 18% nitrous oxide, 35% nitrogen, and a trace of hydrocarbons. After 309 days of heating at 75°, the temperature of the oven was reduced, and the same sample of nitrocellulose was heated in vacuum at 40° for 221 days. During this time it evolved a total of 0.697 cc. of gas or 0.0001154 cc. per gram per day. The same sample was then heated in vacuum at 100°, as follows.

[100] *Mém. poudres,* **18**, 101, 106 (1921).

DURATION OF HEATING AT 100°	TOTAL VOLUME, CUBIC CENTIMETERS	CUBIC CENTIMETERS PER GRAM PER DAY	COMPOSITION OF GAS, %		
			NO	CO₂	Residue
1st period (30 hrs.)	29.09	0.662	51.9	24.1	24.0
2nd period (8.5 hrs.)	8.57	0.689 ⎫	68.1	17.6	14.3
3rd period (9 hrs.)	8.09	0.614 ⎭			

The residual gas, neither NO nor CO_2, was found to contain about 64% of carbon monoxide, the remainder being nitrous oxide and nitrogen with a trace of hydrocarbons. The nitrocellulose left at the end of the experiment weighed 34.716 grams corresponding to a loss of 1.24% of the weight of the original material. It gave on analysis 209.9 cc. NO per gram corresponding to a denitration per gram of 2.2 cc.

The gases from the decomposition of nitrocellulose in vacuum contain nothing which attacks nitrocellulose. If the decomposition occurs in air, the nitric oxide which is first produced combines with oxygen to form nitrogen dioxide, and the red fumes, which are acidic in the presence of moisture, attack the nitrocellulose and promote its further decomposition. The decomposition then, if it occurs in the presence of air or oxygen, is self-catalyzed. The amount of nitric oxide which is produced if the decomposition occurs in the absence of air, or the amount of nitrogen dioxide which is produced in the first instance if the decomposition occurs in the presence of air, is a function solely of the mass of the sample. The extent to which the red fumes attack the nitrocellulose depends, on the other hand, upon the concentration of the gases and upon the area of the surface of the sample which is accessible to their attack. The greater the density of loading of the sample, the greater will be the concentration of the red fumes. For the same density of loading, the finer the state of subdivision of the sample, the greater will be the surface. Pellets of compressed nitrocellulose, heated in the air, decompose more rapidly than the same nitrocellulose in a fluffier condition. The pellets give a poorer heat test (see below) but obviously consist of material which has the same stability. Likewise, nitrocellulose which has been dissolved in ether-alcohol and precipitated by the addition of water, decomposes in the air more rapidly than the original, bulkier material. Straight nitrocellulose powder always gives a better heat test than the nitrocellulose from which it was made. If small grains and large grains of smokeless powder are made from the same nitrocellulose, the large grains will give the better heat test.

In this country the most common heat tests which are made regularly upon nitrocellulose and smokeless powder are the 65.5° KI starch test and the 134.5° methyl violet test. In the former of these, five several portions of the material under test, differing in their moisture content from nearly dry to thoroughly dry, are heated in test tubes in a bath warmed by the vapors of boiling methyl alcohol. Within each tube, a strip of potassium iodide starch paper, spotted with a 50% aqueous solution of glycerin, hangs from a hook of platinum wire a short distance above the sample, the hook itself being supported from a glass rod through a cork stopper. The tubes are examined constantly, and the time needed for the first appearance of any color on the test paper in any one of the tubes is reported.

In the 134.5° methyl violet test, heavy glass test tubes about a foot long are used. They are closed loosely at their upper ends with perforated or notched cork stoppers, and are heated for almost their whole length in a bath which is warmed by the vapors of boiling xylene. Two tubes are used. The samples occupy the lower 2 inches of the tubes, strips of methyl violet paper are inserted and pushed down until their lower ends are about 1 inch above the samples, the tubes are heated and examined every 5 minutes, and the times are noted which are necessary for the test papers to be turned completely to a salmon-pink color, for the first appearance of red fumes, and for explosion. The explosion usually manifests itself by the audible popping of the cork from the tube, but causes no other damage. A test similar to this one, but operated at 120°, using blue litmus paper and reporting the time necessary for the paper to be reddened completely, is sometimes used.

In the Bergmann-Junk test the number of cubic centimeters of nitrogen dioxide produced by heating a 5-gram sample for 5 hours at 132° is reported. The determination was originally made by absorbing the gas in ferrous sulfate solution, liberating the nitric oxide by warming, and measuring its volume. A method based upon the absorption of the gas in caustic soda solution and the titration of its acidity is now often used instead.

There are many other variations of the heat test.[101] They are sometimes called *stability tests*, but most of them, it will be noted, involve the self-catalyzed decomposition of the sample in an atmosphere of air or of red fumes. They indicate the comparative stability only of materials which are physically alike. True indications of the stability of nitric esters are to be secured only by studying the decomposition of the substances in vacuum. For this purpose the 120° vacuum stability test is most generally preferred.

Ash in nitrocellulose is determined by gelatinizing the sample with acetone which contains 5% of castor oil, setting fire to the colloid, allowing it to burn tranquilly, and igniting the charred residue to constancy of weight. It is sometimes determined as sulfate by dissolving the sample in pure concentrated sulfuric acid and igniting to constant weight.

Nitrogen in nitrocellulose is determined by means of the *nitrometer*, an instrument of great usefulness to the chemist who is working with nitric esters or with nitroamines.

Determination of Nitrogen

Nitric acid and organic and inorganic nitrates, and in general all substances which contain free nitric acid or yield nitric acid when they are treated with concentrated sulfuric acid, are analyzed by means of the nitrometer. The method depends upon the measurement of the volume of the nitric oxide which is produced when concentrated sulfuric acid acts upon the sample in the presence of mercury. It is satisfactory also for the determination of nitro group nitrogen in certain nitroamines, in nitroguanidine and in tetryl but not in methylnitramine. It is not satisfactory in the presence of mononitro aromatic compounds or of other substances which are nitrated readily by a solution of nitric acid in concentrated sulfuric acid.

[101] U. S. War Department Technical Manual TM 9–2900 and the U. S. Bureau of Mines *Bulletins* on the analysis of explosives describe the standard heat tests in detail. "Explosives, Matches, and Fireworks" by Joseph Reilly, New York, D. Van Nostrand Company, Inc., 1938, pp. 71–83, describes about 40 different heat tests.

Cold concentrated sulfuric acid does not attack mercury. Cold nitric acid acts upon mercury to form mercurous nitrate with the evolution of nitric oxide. If concentrated sulfuric acid is present, mercurous nitrate cannot form, and the nitric acid is converted by the mercury quantitatively into nitric oxide. The method appears to have been used for the first time by Walter Crum [102] who applied it at an early date to the analysis of guncotton.

FIGURES 66 and 67. Georg Lunge and His Nitrometer. Obverse and reverse of commemorative bronze plaquette by Hans Frei in celebration of Lunge's seventieth birthday.

He introduced the sample of guncotton into a eudiometer filled with mercury and inverted in that liquid, and carried out the reaction and measured the gas volume in the same eudiometer. Since he was unable to separate the guncotton from the air entangled with it, the measured gas volume was too large. The true volume of nitric oxide was determined by admitting a solution of ferrous sulfate to the eudiometer and noting the volume of gas which was absorbed.

The Lunge nitrometer is so designed that the nitrate or nitric ester is dissolved first in concentrated sulfuric acid and the solution, without entrained gas, is afterwards admitted to the re-

[102] *Loc. cit.*

action vessel. In the usual form of the instrument as used in Europe, the gas from the reaction is measured in cubic centimeters at atmospheric pressure, the barometer and the thermometer are read, and the weight of the nitrogen in the nitric oxide and the percentage of nitrogen in the sample are calculated.

In the extremely ingenious DuPont nitrometer, a 1-gram sample is used for the analysis, and the gas is collected in a measuring tube which has been graduated to read, at a certain temperature and pressure, the correct percentage of nitrogen in the 1-gram sample. By means of a compensating bulb and leveling device, the gas in the measuring tube is brought to the volume which it would occupy if it were confined at the temperature and pressure at which the graduations are correct, and the percentage of nitrogen is then read off directly. The DuPont nitrometer [103] was invented by Francis I. DuPont about 1896. It quickly came into general use in the United States, and represents the form of the nitrometer which is preferred and generally used in this country. Lunge in 1901 claimed that it differs in no significant respect from the "gasvolumeter" or "five-part nitrometer" [104] which he had described in 1890.

Calibration and Use of the DuPont Nitrometer. The five essential parts of the DuPont nitrometer are illustrated in Figure 68. The graduations on the measuring bulb correspond to dry nitric oxide measured at 20° and 760 mm., which nitric oxide contains the indicated number of centigrams of nitrogen. Thus, the point marked 10 indicates the volume which would be occupied under the standard conditions of temperature and pressure by the quantity of dry nitric oxide which contains 0.10 gram of nitrogen, that is, by the nitric oxide produced in the nitrometer reaction from a 1-gram sample of nitrate containing 10% nitrogen. The point marked 12 corresponds to 12/10 of this volume, that marked 14 to 14/10, and so on. And the tube reads correctly the per cent of nitrogen in a 1-gram sample provided the gas is measured at 20° and 760 mm.

In setting up the instrument, dry air is introduced into the compensating bulb and the outlet at the upper end of the bulb is sealed. Dry air is introduced into the measuring bulb, the outlet is connected to a sulfuric acid manometer, and the mercury reservoir and the compensating bulb are raised or lowered until the portions of air confined

[103] Pitman, *J. Soc. Chem. Ind.*, **19**, 982 (1900).
[104] *Ibid.*, **9**, 547 (1890); **20**, 100 (1901).

in both bulbs are at atmospheric pressure. The stopcock is closed, the volume in the measuring bulb is read, thermometer and barometer are noted, the volume which the air in the measuring bulb would occupy at 20° and 760 mm. is calculated, and the mercury reservoir and the bulbs are adjusted until the air in the measuring bulb occupies this calculated volume and until the air in the compensating bulb is at exactly the same pressure as that in the measuring bulb. A glass tube

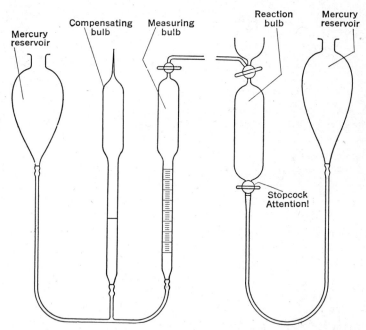

Figure 68. Du Pont Nitrometer.

bent twice at right angles and containing some water is used for leveling the mercury in the two bulbs. The position of the mercury in the compensating bulb is now marked by means of a strip of paper glued to the glass. Whenever in the future the gas in the compensating bulb is again confined in this same volume, and whenever the nitric oxide in the measuring bulb is confined at the same pressure as the gas in the compensating bulb, then the nitric oxide will occupy the volume which it would occupy if confined at 20° and 760 mm., and, if a 1-gram sample was taken for the analysis, the reading will indicate correctly the nitrogen content. If a sample larger or smaller than 1 gram was taken, then the reading is to be corrected accordingly.

At the beginning of an analysis, the reaction bulb and the measuring bulb and the capillary tubes at the tops of the bulbs are completely filled with mercury. A sample of about 1 gram of nitrocellulose is weighed in a small weighing bottle, dried for an hour and a half at 100°, cooled in a desiccator, and weighed accurately. A little 95% sulfuric acid is poured onto the nitrocellulose and the whole is washed into the reaction bulb. The weighing bottle is rinsed out with several small portions of sulfuric acid, the same acid is used for rinsing the cup and is finally introduced into the reaction bulb, until altogether about 20 cc. of acid has been used, care being taken that no air is introduced. The mercury reservoir is lowered to give a reduced pressure in the reaction bulb and the bulb is shaken gently, *the stopcock at its bottom being open,* until the generation of gas has practically ceased. The bulb is then raised until the level of the mercury drops nearly to its lower shoulder, the stopcock is closed, and the bulb is shaken vigorously for 3 minutes. The cock is opened and the apparatus is allowed to stand for several minutes. The mercury level is then adjusted as before, the cock is closed, and the shaking is repeated for another 3 minutes. Finally the gas is transferred to the measuring bulb and allowed to stand for about 20 minutes. The measuring bulb and the compensating bulb are then adjusted in such fashion that the mercury in both stands at the same level and that the mercury in the compensating bulb stands at the point indicated by the paper strip. The volume in the measuring bulb is then read. After each determination the reaction bulb is rinsed out twice with concentrated sulfuric acid.

In practice it is convenient to standardize the nitrometer from time to time by means of a sample of pure potassium nitrate (13.85% N) or of nitrocellulose of known nitrogen content.

The nitrometer is dangerous to one who does not understand it fully. The closing at the wrong time of the stopcock at the bottom of the reaction bulb may result in the explosion of that vessel and the throwing about of glass and of acid.

Nitrostarch

Nitrostarch [105] is manufactured and used in the United States, but has not found favor in other countries. In all the early attempts to manufacture nitrostarch, the starch was dissolved in strong nitric acid and the nitric ester was precipitated by mixing the solution with sulfuric acid or with the spent acid from some

[105] The article by Urbanski and Häckel in *Z. ges. Schiess- u. Sprengstoffw.,* **30, 98** (1935), is accompanied by an extensive bibliography.

other nitration, as from the nitration of glycerin. The product resembled the xyloïdine of Braconnot, showed a very poor stability, and could not be stored or handled safely in the dry condition. The pulverulent, dusty form of the dry material probably also contributed to the disrepute into which it fell in Europe. In this country starch is nitrated with mixed acid in which it does not dissolve, and the product retains the appearance of ordinary starch, as guncotton retains the appearance of cotton.

Cassava or tapioca starch was preferred at first, for it was claimed that it contained less fat than corn starch and that the

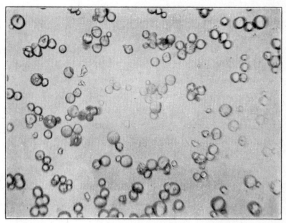

FIGURE 69. Nitrostarch Granules (about 30×). (Courtesy Trojan Powder Company.)

granules, being smaller than those of corn and potato starch, permitted a more uniform nitration and a more efficient purification. Since 1917 corn starch has been used in this country. The starch is first freed from fats and from pectic acid by washing with dilute caustic soda or ammonia solution and then with water, and it is dried until it contains less than 0.5% of moisture. In one process which produced a nitrostarch containing 12.75% nitrogen, a mixed acid containing 38% of nitric acid and 62% of sulfuric acid was used, 800 pounds of the acid in a single nitrator for 200 pounds of starch. The initial temperature of the acid was 32°, the mixture was agitated by a mechanical stirrer having a downward pitch, and the temperature during the nitration was kept between 38° and 40°. At the end of the nitration the contents of the nitrator was drowned in a small tub of water. The product was purified entirely by cold-water washings, without boiling. Ammonia was used to neutralize the acidity during the preliminary washing, and it is probable that this use of ammonia determined the stability of the product, perhaps because ammonia was preferentially adsorbed, instead of acid, by the material of the nitrostarch granules. The product was dried at 35–40°.

Nitrostarch gives no color with iodine. It is insoluble in water and does not gelatinize to form a paste as starch does when it is boiled with water. It is not notably hygroscopic, but may take up 1 or 2% of moisture from a damp atmosphere. It is soluble in acetone. The varieties of nitrostarch which are soluble in ether-alcohol contain about the same amounts of nitrogen as the varieties of nitrocellulose which dissolve in that mixed solvent. Nitrostarch does not form a good film or tough colloid as nitrocellulose does.

During the first World War a *Trojan explosive* which contained nitrostarch was used in trench mortar shells and in hand and rifle grenades.[106] Its composition was as follows.

	Not Less Than	Not More Than
Nitrostarch	23.0%	27.0%
Ammonium nitrate	31.0	35.0
Sodium nitrate	36.0	40.0
Charcoal	1.5	2.5
Heavy hydrocarbons	0.5	1.5
Anti-acid	0.5	1.5
Diphenylamine	0.2	0.4
Moisture	....	1.2

All the *dope materials* were first ground to the desired fineness and dried, and then turned over in a large mixing barrel while the dry nitrostarch was added. Trench mortar shells were loaded by *stemming*, but the explosive was *jarred* into the grenades through small funnel-shaped openings. Another nitrostarch explosive, which was used only in grenades, was called *Grenite* and consisted almost entirely of nitrostarch (about 97%) with small amounts (about 1.5% each) of petroleum oil and of gum arabic. It was made by spraying the dry materials with a solution of the

[106] U. S. War Department Technical Manual TM 9–2900, p. 109.

binder while the mixture was stirred in a rotary mixer. The resulting granules were dried and screened, and yielded a free-running explosive which could be loaded easily by machine.

Three United States patents [107] granted in 1916 to Bronstein and Waller describe several nitrostarch blasting explosives, of which the following table reports typical examples. In actual use,

	I	II	III	IV	V	VI
Nitrostarch	30.0%	39.0%	30.0%	40.0%	40.0%	40.0%
Ammonium nitrate TNT						
mixture	15.0	20.0	...	...	...	20.0
Sodium nitrate	46.8	37.25	58.0	37.7	34.7	17.7
Barium nitrate	...	...	...	20.0	20.0	20.0
Carbonaceous material	3.0	...	5.0	...	...	...
Paraffin oil	0.7	0.75	0.5	0.8	0.8	0.8
Sulfur	3.0	2.0	5.0	...	3.0	...
Calcium carbonate	1.5	1.0	1.5	1.5	1.5	1.5

these explosives would also contain a small amount of some stabilizer, say 0.2% of diphenylamine or of urea.

Utilization of Formaldehyde

At the time of the first World War the methyl alcohol which was needed for the preparation of tetryl was procured from the distillation of wood. It was expensive and limited in amount. Formaldehyde was produced then, as it is now, by the oxidation of methyl alcohol, and a demand for it was a demand upon the wood-distillation industry. Formaldehyde was the raw material from which methylamine was produced commercially, and the resulting methylamine could be used for the preparation of tetryl by the alternative method from dinitrochlorobenzene. It was also the raw material from which certain useful explosives could be prepared, but its high price and its origin in the wood-distillation industry deprived the explosives in question of all but an academic interest. With the commercial production of synthetic methyl alcohol, the same explosives are now procurable from a raw material which is available in an amount limited only by the will of the manufacturers to produce it.

Carbon monoxide and hydrogen, heated under pressure in the presence of a suitable catalyst, combine to form methyl alcohol. A mixture of zinc oxide and chromium oxide has been used as a

[107] U. S. Pats. 1,188,244, 1,188,245, 1,188,246 (1916).

catalyst for the purpose. Carbon monoxide and hydrogen (equimolecular amounts of each) are produced as *water gas* when steam is passed over hot coke.

$$C + H_2O \longrightarrow CO + H_2$$

Additional hydrogen, from the action of iron on steam or from the electrolysis of water, is added to the water gas to provide the mixture which is needed for the synthesis of methyl alcohol.

$$CO + 2H_2 \longrightarrow CH_3-OH$$

It is evident that carbon dioxide may be used instead of the monoxide if a correspondingly larger amount of hydrogen is also used.

$$CO_2 + 3H_2 \longrightarrow CH_3-OH + H_2O$$

Methyl alcohol in fact is made in this manner from the carbon dioxide which results from certain industrial fermentations. When methyl alcohol vapor is mixed with air and passed over an initially heated catalyst of metallic copper or silver gauze, oxidation occurs, sufficient heat is evolved to maintain the catalyst at a bright red, and formaldehyde is formed.

$$2CH_3-OH + O_2 \longrightarrow 2H_2O + 2 \; \begin{matrix} H \\ \\ H \end{matrix}\!\!>\!\!C\!\!=\!\!O$$

Of the several explosives which are preparable from formaldehyde, two are the most powerful and brisant of the solid high explosives which are suitable for military use. One of these, *cyclotrimethylenetrinitramine* or *cyclonite*, is a nitroamine and is discussed in the chapter which is devoted to those substances. The other, *pentaerythrite tetranitrate* or PETN, is a nitric ester. Both may be prepared from coke and air.

Formaldehyde enters readily into combination with substances which add to its unsaturated carbonyl group. If a substance containing an active hydrogen adds to formaldehyde or condenses with it, the active hydrogen attaching itself to the oxygen of the formaldehyde and the rest of the molecule attaching itself to the carbon, the result is that the position originally occupied by the active hydrogen is now occupied by a $-CH_2-OH$ or methylol group. Hydrogens which are active in condensation reactions are those which are α- to a carbonyl, a nitro, or a cyano group, etc., that is, they are attached to a carbon atom to which a carbonyl, a nitro, or a cyano group is also attached and are in general the hydrogen atoms which are involved in the phenomena of tautomerism. The condensation of formaldehyde with acetaldehyde, with nitromethane, with cyclopentanone, and with cyclohexanone thus leads to polyhydric primary alcohols the nitric esters of which are useful explosives.

Pentaerythrite Tetranitrate (PETN, penta, niperyth, penthrit)

Four equivalents of formaldehyde in warm aqueous solution in the presence of calcium hydroxide react with one equivalent of acetaldehyde to form pentaerythrite. Three of the four react with the three α-hydrogens of the acetaldehyde, the fourth acts as a reducing agent, converts the —CHO group to —CH$_2$—OH, and is itself oxidized to formic acid.

The name, pentaerythrite, indicates that the substance contains five carbon atoms and (like erythrite) four hydroxyl groups. In commercial practice [108] the reaction is carried out at 65–70°. After 2 hours at this temperature, the calcium is precipitated by means of sulfuric acid, the mixture is filtered, and the filtrate is concentrated and crystallized by evaporation in vacuum. Penta-

[108] For the laboratory preparation see *Org. Syntheses*, **4**, 53 (1912), John Wiley & Sons, New York. Also Tollens and Wigand, *Ann.*, **265**, 316 (1891); Rave and Tollens, *ibid.*, **276**, 58 (1893); Stettbacher, *Z. ges. Schiess- u. Sprengstoffw.*, **11**, 182 (1916).

erythrite crystallizes from water in white tetragonal crystals, m.p. 253°. One part requires 18 parts of water at 15° for its solution.

PETN may be prepared, according to Naoúm,[109] by adding 100 grams of finely powdered pentaerythrite to 400 cc. of nitric acid (1.52) while the temperature is maintained between 25° and 30° by efficient cooling. Toward the end of the nitration a certain amount of the tetranitrate crystallizes out. The separation of the product is completed by the gradual addition of 400 cc. of concentrated sulfuric acid (1.84) while the stirring and cooling are continued. The mixture is not drowned, but the crude PETN (85–90% of the theory) is filtered off directly, and washed first with 50% sulfuric acid and then with water. It still contains some occluded acid and is purified, according to Naoúm, by dissolving in hot acetone to which a little ammonium carbonate is added, and filtering the hot solution into twice its volume of 90% alcohol by which the PETN is precipitated in fine needles.

Pentaerythrite may also be nitrated satisfactorily, and probably in better yield, without the use of sulfuric acid and with the use of nitric acid from which the nitrous acid has been removed.

Preparation of Pentaerythrite Tetranitrate. Four hundred cc. of strong *white* nitric acid—prepared by adding a little urea to fuming nitric acid, warming, and blowing dry air through it until it is completely decolorized—is cooled in a 600-cc. beaker in a freezing mixture of ice and salt. One hundred grams of pentaerythrite, ground to pass a 50-mesh sieve, is added to the acid a little at a time with efficient stirring while the temperature is kept below 5°. After all has been added, the stirring and the cooling are continued for 15 minutes longer. The mixture is then drowned in about 3 liters of cracked ice and water. The crude product, amounting to about 221 grams or 95% of the theory, is filtered off, washed free from acid, digested for an hour with a liter of hot 0.5% sodium carbonate solution, again filtered off and washed, dried, and finally recrystallized from acetone. A good commercial sample of PETN melts at 138.0–138.5°. The pure material melts at 140.5–141.0°, short prismatic needles, insoluble in water, difficultly soluble in alcohol and ether.

Pentaerythrite tetranitrate is the most stable and the least reactive of the explosive nitric esters. It shows no trace of decomposition if stored for a very long time at 100°. While nitrocellulose

[109] *Op. cit.,* p. 244.

is destroyed within a few minutes by boiling with a 2.5% solution of caustic soda, PETN requires several hours for its complete decomposition. Ammonium sulfide solution attacks PETN slowly at 50°, and a boiling solution of ferrous chloride decomposes it fairly rapidly. It does not reduce Fehling's solution even on boiling, and differs in this respect from erythrite tetranitrate.

PETN does not take fire from the spit of a fuse. If a small quantity is submitted to the action of a flame, it melts and takes fire and burns quietly with a slightly luminous flame without smoke. Above 100° it begins to show appreciable volatility, and at 140–145°, or at temperatures slightly above its melting point, it shows red fumes within half an hour. It inflames spontaneously at about 210°. It is relatively insensitive to friction but makes a loud crackling when rubbed in a rough porcelain mortar. It may be exploded readily by pounding with a carpenter's hammer on a concrete floor. In the drop test it is detonated by a 20-cm. drop of a 2-kilogram weight, sometimes by a drop of 10 or 15 cm.

Naoúm [110] reports that 10 grams of PETN in the Trauzl test with sand tamping gave a net expansion of about 500 cc., with water tamping one of 560 cc. The same investigator [111] found a velocity of detonation of 5330 meters per second for the material, only slightly compressed, at a density of loading of 0.85 in an iron pipe 25 mm. in internal diameter. For PETN compressed to a density of 1.62 Kast [112] found a velocity of detonation of 8000 meters per second.

PETN is extraordinarily sensitive to initiation. It is detonated by 0.01 gram of lead azide, whereas tetryl requires 0.025 gram of lead azide for its certain detonation. This sensitivity and its great brisance combine to make PETN exceptionally serviceable in compound detonators.

Under high pressure powdered PETN agglomerates to a mass which has the appearance of porcelain, but which, when broken up into grains, is a very powerful smokeless powder functioning satisfactorily with the primers which are commonly used in small arms ammunition. The powder is hot and unduly erosive, but cooler powders have been prepared by incorporating and compressing PETN in binary or in ternary mixtures with TNT,

[110] Ibid., p. 246.
[111] Ibid., p. 247.
[112] Z. angew. Chem., 36, 74 (1923).

nitroguanidine, and guanidine picrate. A mixture of PETN with guanidine picrate is less sensitive to heat and to shock than ordinary colloided smokeless powder, and is stable at all temperatures which are likely to be encountered. PETN does not colloid with nitrocellulose. It dissolves readily in warm trinitrotoluene, and mixtures may be prepared which contain 65% or more of PETN. The richer mixtures may be used as propellent powders. The less-rich mixtures are brisant and powerful high explosives comparable in their behavior and effects to TNB.

Stettbacher [113] in 1931 described several dynamite-like explosives which contained both PETN and nitroglycerin. He called them by the general name of *Penthrinit,* and described simple penthrinit, *gelatin penthrinit,* and *ammonpenthrinit.* Naoúm [114] later in the same year reported comparative tests of ammonpenthrinit and gelatin dynamite, as follows.

	AMMONPENTHRINIT	GELATIN DYNAMITE
Composition		
PETN	37%	....
Nitroglycerin	10%	63%
Collodion nitrocotton	....	2%
Dinitrotoluene	5%	....
Wood meal	....	5%
Ammonium nitrate	48%	30%
Trauzl test (average)	430 cc.	465 cc.
Velocity of detonation (average)	6600 meters per sec.	7025 meters per sec.
At density of loading	1.36	1.47

A Swiss patent of 1932 to Stettbacher [115] covers the conversion of PETN into a plastic mass by means of 10–30% of a fluid nitric ester such as nitroglycerin or nitroglycol. It states that a mixture of 80% PETN and 20% nitroglycerin is a plastic mass, density 1.65, which does not separate into its components and which is suitable for loading shells and detonators. For the latter purpose it is initiated with 0.04 gram of lead azide.

Dipentaerythrite Hexanitrate (Dipenta)

The formation of a certain amount of dipentaerythrite is unavoidable during the preparation of pentaerythrite. It is nitrated

113 *Z. ges. Schiess- u. Sprengstoffw.,* **26,** 8, 39 (1931).
114 *Ibid.,* **26,** 42 (1931).
115 Swiss Pat. 137,476 (1932).

along with the latter substance, and, unless a special purification is made, remains in the PETN where its presence is undesirable because of its lower stability.

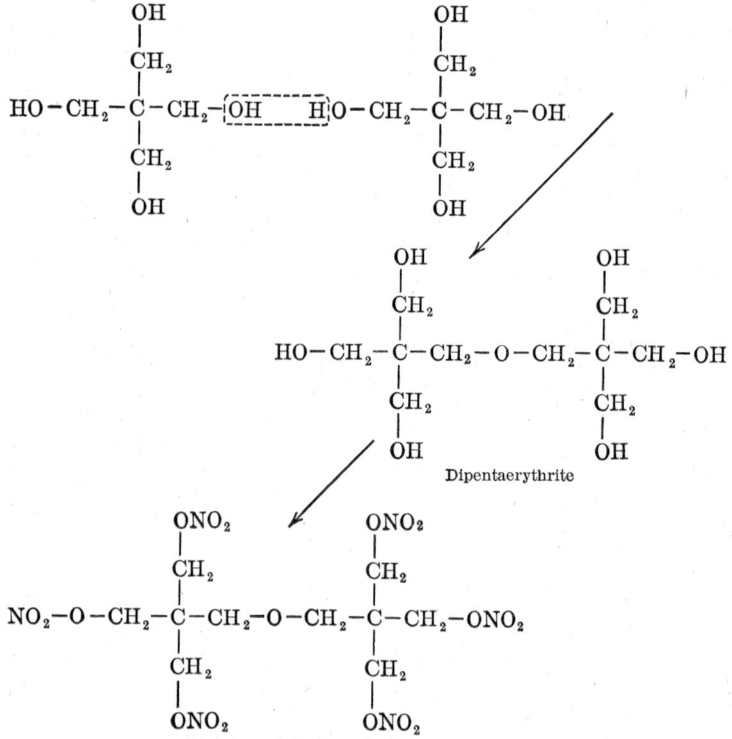

$$
\begin{array}{ccc}
OH & & OH \\
| & & | \\
CH_2 & & CH_2 \\
| & & | \\
HO-CH_2-C-CH_2-\boxed{OH \quad H}O-CH_2-C-CH_2-OH \\
| & & | \\
CH_2 & & CH_2 \\
| & & | \\
OH & & OH
\end{array}
$$

$$
\begin{array}{ccc}
OH & & OH \\
| & & | \\
CH_2 & & CH_2 \\
| & & | \\
HO-CH_2-C-CH_2-O-CH_2-C-CH_2-OH \\
| & & | \\
CH_2 & & CH_2 \\
| & & | \\
OH & & OH
\end{array}
$$

Dipentaerythrite

$$
\begin{array}{ccc}
ONO_2 & & ONO_2 \\
| & & | \\
CH_2 & & CH_2 \\
| & & | \\
NO_2-O-CH_2-C-CH_2-O-CH_2-C-CH_2-ONO_2 \\
| & & | \\
CH_2 & & CH_2 \\
| & & | \\
ONO_2 & & ONO_2
\end{array}
$$

Dipentaerythrite hexanitrate

Dipentaerythrite hexanitrate [116] is procured in the pure state by the fractional crystallization from moist acetone of the crude PETN which precipitates when the nitration mixture is drowned in water, white crystals, m.p. 72°. The crystals have a specific gravity of 1.630 at 15°, after being fused and solidified 1.613 at 15°. The substance is less sensitive to friction, less sensitive to the mechanical shock of the drop test, and less sensitive to temperature than PETN, but it is less stable and decomposes much more rapidly at 100°.

Brün [117] reports measurements by the Dautriche method of the

[116] Friederich and Brün, *Ber.*, **63**, 2861 (1930); Brün, *Z. ges. Schiess- u. Sprengstoffw.*, **27**, 71, 125, 156 (1932).

[117] *Ibid.*, **27**, 126 (1932).

velocities of detonation of several explosives loaded in copper
tubes 10 mm. in diameter and compressed under a pressure of

Explosive	Density	Velocity of Detonation, Meters per Second
Dipentaerythrite hexanitrate	1.589	7370
	1.589	7450
Pentaerythrite tetranitrate	1.712	8340
	1.712	8340
Tetryl	1.682	7530
	1.682	7440
Trinitrotoluene	1.615	7000
	1.615	7000

2500 kilograms per square centimeter. He also reports that a
10-gram sample of dipentaerythrite hexanitrate in the Trauzl
test gave a net expansion of 283 cc. (average of 2), and PETN
under the same conditions gave a net expansion of 378 cc. (average of 3).

Trimethylolnitromethane Trinitrate (Nitroisobutanetriol trinitrate, nitroisobutylglycerin trinitrate, nib-glycerin trinitrate)[118]

This explosive was first described in 1912 by Hofwimmer[119]
who prepared it by the condensation of three molecules of formaldehyde with one of nitromethane in the presence of potassium
bicarbonate, and by the subsequent nitration of the product.

[118] The first two of these names are scientifically correct. The third is not
correct but is used widely. The trihydric alcohol from which the nitric
ester is derived is not an isobutylglycerin. In the abbreviated form of this
name, the syllable, nib, stands for nitro-iso-butyl and is to be pronounced,
not spelled out like TNT and PETN.

[119] *Z. ges. Schiess- u. Sprengstoffw.,* **7**, 43 (1912). Brit. Pat. 6447 (1924).
Stettbacher, *Nitrocellulose,* **5**, 159, 181, 203 (1935).

At a time when the only practicable methods for the preparation of nitromethane were the interaction of methyl iodide with silver nitrite and the Kolbe reaction from chloracetic acid, the explosive was far too expensive to merit consideration. The present cheap and large scale production of nitromethane by the vapor-phase nitration of methane and of ethane has altered the situation profoundly. Trimethylolnitromethane trinitrate is an explosive which can now be produced from coke, air, and natural gas. Nitromethane too has other interest for the manufacturer of explosives. It may be used as a component of liquid explosives, and it yields on reduction methylamine which is needed for the preparation of tetryl.

The crude trimethylolnitromethane from the condensation commonly contains a small amount of mono- and dimethylolnitromethane from reactions involving one and two molecules of formaldehyde respectively. It is recrystallized from water to a melting point of 150°, and is then nitrated. Stettbacher reports that the pure substance after many recrystallizations melts at 164–165°. The nitration is carried out either with the same mixed acid as is used for the nitration of glycerin (40% nitric acid, 60% sulfuric acid) or with very strong nitric acid, specific gravity 1.52. If the trihydric alcohol has been purified before nitration, there is but little tendency for the nitrate to form emulsions during the washing, and the operation is carried out in the same way as with nitroglycerin. In the laboratory preparation, the nitric ester is taken up in ether, neutralized with ammonium carbonate, dried with anhydrous sodium sulfate, and freed from solvent in a vacuum desiccator.

The explosive is procured as a yellow oil, more viscous than nitroglycerin, density 1.68 at ordinary temperature. It has but little tendency to crystallize at low temperatures. A freezing point of −35° has been reported. It is very readily soluble in ether and in acetone, readily soluble in alcohol, in benzene, and in chloroform, and insoluble in ligroin. It is less soluble in water and less volatile than nitroglycerin. Because it is less volatile, it is slower to cause headaches, and for the same reason the headaches are slower to go away. It is distinctly inferior to nitroglycerin as a gelatinizing agent for collodion nitrocotton. The nitro group attached directly to an aliphatic carbon atom appears to have an unfavorable effect on stability, for trimethylolnitromethane trinitrate gives a poorer potassium iodide 65.5° heat test than nitroglycerin. Naoúm [120] reports the data which are tabulated below.

	TRIMETHYLOL-NITROMETHANE TRINITRATE	NITRO-GLYCERIN
Trauzl test: 75% kieselguhr dynamite	325 cc.	305 cc.
93% blasting gelatin	580 cc.	600 cc.
Drop test, 2-kilogram weight	6 cm.	2 cm.

Nitropentanone and Related Substances

Cyclopentanone and cyclohexanone contain four active hydrogen atoms and condense with formaldehyde to form substances which contain four —CH_2—OH groups. The latter may be converted directly into explosive tetranitrates or they may be reduced, the carbonyl groups yielding secondary alcohol groups, and the products then may be nitrated to pentanitrates.

Tetramethylolcyclopentanone tetranitrate

Tetramethylolcyclopentanol pentanitrate

The explosives derived in this way from cyclopentanone and cyclohexanone were patented in 1929 by Friederich and Flick.[121] They

[120] *Op. cit.*, p. 241.
[121] Ger. Pat. 509,118 (1929).

are less sensitive to mechanical shock than PETN, and three out of four of them have conveniently low melting points which permit them to be loaded by pouring. *Tetramethylolcyclopentanone tetranitrate,* called *nitropentanone* for short, melts at 74°. *Tetramethylolcyclopentanol pentanitrate* is called *nitropentanol* and melts at 92°. *Tetramethylolcyclohexanone tetranitrate,* m.p. 66°, is called *nitrohexanone,* and *tetramethylolcyclohexanol pentanitrate,* m.p. 122.5°, *nitrohexanol.* They are less brisant than PETN. Wöhler and Roth [122] have measured their velocities of detonation at various densities of loading, as follows.

Explosive	Density of Loading	Velocity of Detonation, Meters per Second
Nitropentanone	1.59	7940
	1.44	7170
	1.30	6020
	1.13	4630
Nitropentanol	1.57	7360
	1.51	7050
	1.29	6100
	1.11	5940
	1.01	5800
	0.91	5100
	0.75	5060
Nitrohexanone	1.51	7740
	1.42	7000
	1.25	5710
Nitrohexanol	1.44	7670
	1.28	6800
	1.00	5820
	0.81	5470

[122] *Z. ges. Schiess- u. Sprengstoffw.,* **29,** 332–333 (1934).

CHAPTER VI

SMOKELESS POWDER

An account of smokeless powder is, in its main outlines, an account of the various means which have been used to regulate the temperature and the rate of the burning of nitrocellulose. After the degree of nitration of the nitrocellulose, other factors which influence the character of the powder are the state of aggregation of the nitrocellulose, whether colloided or in shreds, the size and shape of the powder grains, and the nature of the materials other than nitrocellulose which enter into its composition.

Bulk Powder

The first successful smokeless powder appears to have been made by Captain Schultze of the Prussian Artillery in 1864. At first he seems only to have impregnated little grains of wood with potassium nitrate, but afterwards he purified the wood by washing, boiling, and bleaching, then nitrated it, purified the nitrated product by a method similar to that which had been used by von Lenk, and finally impregnated the grains with potassium nitrate alone or with a mixture of that salt and barium nitrate.[1] The physical structure of the wood and the fact that it contained material which was not cellulose both tended to make the nitrated product burn more slowly than guncotton. The added nitrates further reduced the rate of burning, but Schultze's powder was still too rapid for use in rifles. It found immediate favor for use in shot guns. It was manufactured in Austria by a firm which in 1870 and 1871 took out patents covering the partial gelatinization of the powder by treatment with a mixture of ether and alcohol. The improved powder was manufactured between 1872 and 1875 under the name of *Collodin*, but the Austrian gov-

---

[1] Brit. Pat. 900 (1864).

ernment stopped its manufacture on the grounds that it infringed the government's gunpowder monopoly. A company was formed in England in 1868 to exploit Schultze's invention, a factory was established at Eyeworth in the New Forest in 1869, and the

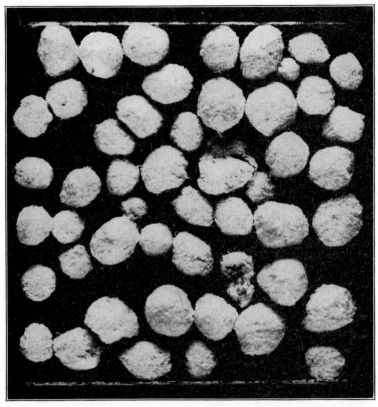

FIGURE 70. Shreddy Grains of Bulk Powder (25×). (Courtesy Western Cartridge Company.)

methods of manufacture were later improved by Griffiths and achieved great success. In 1883 Schultze entered into a partnership in Germany and started a factory at Hetzbach in Hesse-Darmstadt.

The next successful smokeless powder was invented [2] at the works of the Explosives Company at Stowmarket in England. It

[2] Brit. Pat. 619 (1882) to Walter F. Reid and D. Johnson.

was called E. C. powder (Explosives Company), and consisted of nitrocotton mixed with potassium and barium nitrates with the addition of coloring matter and small amounts of other organic material. It was made into grains which were hardened by being partially gelatinized with ether-alcohol. A separate company was organized to develop the invention, and the manufacture was started at Green Street Green, near Dartford, in Kent.

Schultze powder and E. C. powder are known as *bulk sporting* powders, either because they are loaded by bulk or because, for the same bulk, they have about the same power as black powder. Bulk powders burn quickly. They are used in shot guns, in hand grenades, in blank cartridges, and occasionally in the igniter charges which set fire to the dense colloided propellent powder which is used in artillery.

Bulk powders are made in considerable variety, but they consist always of nitrocellulose fibers which are stuck together but are not completely colloided. Some contain little else but nitrocellulose; others contain, in addition to potassium and barium nitrates, camphor, vaseline, paraffin, lampblack, starch, dextrine, potassium dichromate or other oxidizing or deterrent salts, and diphenylamine for stabilization, and are colored in a variety of brilliant hues by means of coal-tar dyes. In the United States bulk powders are manufactured by one or the other of two processes, either one of which, however, may be modified considerably; the materials are incorporated under wooden wheels, grained, and partially gelatinized, or the grains are formed in a still where a water suspension of pulped nitrocellulose is stirred and heated with a second liquid, a solvent for nitrocellulose which is volatile and immiscible with water.

Three typical bulk powders are made up according to the approximate formulas tabulated below. The nitrogen content of

Nitrocellulose	84.0	87.0	89.0
% N in nitrocellulose	13.15	12.90	12.90
Potassium nitrate	7.5	6.0	6.0
Barium nitrate	7.5	2.0	3.0
Starch	....	....	1.0
Paraffin oil	....	4.0	....
Diphenylamine	1.0	1.0	1.0

the nitrocellulose is an average secured by mixing pyrocellulose and guncotton. A batch usually amounts to 200 pounds, 100 pounds of water is added and about 90 grams of rosaniline or some other, generally bright-colored, water-soluble dyestuff, and the charge is incorporated by milling for about 45 minutes in a wheel mill which is built like a black-powder mill but is smaller and has light wooden wheels. The charge is then run through a mechanical rubber, which consists of wooden blocks rubbing with a reciprocating motion on a perforated zinc plate; the larger lumps are broken up and the material is put into proper condition for granulating. For this purpose about 50 pounds is placed in a copper pan or "sweetie barrel" which is revolving in a vat of hot water and is heated by that means. The pan rotates fairly rapidly, say at about 15 r.p.m., and carries the powder up along its sloping side to a point where it is scraped off by suitably arranged wooden scrapers and falls back again. It thus receives a rolling motion which has the effect of granulating the powder into spherical grains. The operation requires about 40 minutes, and its completion is indicated by the failure of the powder to carry up on the pan because of the loss of moisture.

After it has been granulated, the powder is given a preliminary screening with a 12-mesh sieve. The material which is retained on the sieve is returned to the wheel mill. That which passes through is hardened. It is put into a horizontal revolving cylinder and a mixed solvent, consisting of about 1 part of acetone and 6 parts of alcohol, is added in the proportion of 1 gallon of solvent to 15 pounds of powder. Acetone dissolves nitrocellulose, alcohol does not; the mixed solvent swells and softens the fibers and makes them stick together. The cylinder is rotated, while hot air is blown through, until the solvent has been volatilized. During this process the temperature is allowed to rise as high as 50° or 55°. The product, which consists of grains now more or less completely agglutinated, is given a final screening. In a typical case, the portion passed by a 12-mesh sieve and retained by a 50-mesh sieve is taken; it is given a final drying and is ready for use.

In a typical example of the still process for the manufacture of bulk sporting powder, 500 pounds of pulped nitrocellulose (12.60% N) is placed in a vertical cast-iron still along with 700 gallons of water containing 2% of potassium nitrate and 6% of barium nitrate dissolved in it. The material is mixed thoroughly

FIGURE 71. Sweetie Barrel. (Courtesy Western Cartridge Company.) The moist and mixed ingredients of bulk powder, tumbled in this apparatus, take on the form of grains. Similar equipment is used for sugar-coating pills and for applying a deterrent coating or a graphite glaze to grains of colloided smokeless powder.

and agitated actively by mechanical stirrers while 145 gallons of mixed solvent (2 parts butyl acetate, 3 parts benzene) containing about 3 pounds of diphenylamine dissolved in it is pumped in. The stirring is violent enough to break the solvent phase up into many small droplets, and around each droplet a globular cluster of nitrocellulose shreds builds up. The mixture is stirred continuously and distilled in vacuum at a temperature of about 30°. The distillate is collected in a separating device in such manner that the solvent is drawn off while the water is returned to the still. At the end of the process the contents of the still consists of water with potassium and barium nitrates in solution along with granules of the wet but otherwise finished powder. The individual grains of the powder are broken apart by a very violent stirring, filtered off in a centrifuge, and dried. The finished powder contains about 1 or 1.5% of potassium nitrate and about 3.5% of barium nitrate.

Early History of Colloided Powders

1884. The first smokeless powder which was satisfactory for use in rifled guns was the dense, colloided *poudre B*,[3] invented by the French physicist, Paul Vieille, and adopted immediately for the use of the French army and navy. It was made by treating a mixture of soluble and insoluble nitrocotton with ether-alcohol, kneading to form a stiff jelly, rolling into thin sheets, cutting into squares and drying, or, in later practice, extruding through a die in the form of a strip, cutting to length, and drying. The results of the first proof firing of this powder, made with a 65-mm. cannon, were communicated to the Minister of Armaments on December 23, 1884.

> It was then established that the new processes would permit the ballistic effect of black powder to be secured with the same pressure and with the charge reduced to about a third, and that the power of the arms could be increased notably, with a slight reduction of the charge, while still keeping to the ordinary pressures. The standard powder for the model 1886 rifle was determined in the early months of the year 1885. . . . The standard powder made possible an increase of velocity of 100 meters per second for the same pressures.

[3] *Poudre blanche,* white powder in contradistinction to *poudre N, poudre noire,* black powder.

. . . This substitution has had the foreseen consequence of suppressing the smoke from the shooting.[4]

The author of the note in the *Mémorial des poudres* in which the above-quoted public announcement was made concerning the new powder was so impressed by the importance of the invention that he concludes the note by saying:

> It results from this that the adaptation to firearms of any other explosive known at the present time would be able to bring to the armament only a perfectioning of detail, and that a new progress, comparable to that which has been realized recently, cannot be made except by the discovery of explosives of a type entirely different from those which chemistry today puts at our disposition.

French powder for the military rifle consists of small square flakes lightly glazed with graphite. The glazing serves to retard slightly the rate of burning of the surface layer, and, more important, it serves to make the powder electrically conducting and to prevent the accumulation of a static charge during the blending of small lots of the powder into a single, ballistically uniform large lot. For guns the powder consists of unglazed strips. The squares and strips, ignited over their entire surfaces, burn for lengths of time which depend upon their thicknesses, and they retain, during the burning, surfaces which change but little in area until at the end the grains are completely consumed.

1888. The second successful dense smokeless powder was the *ballistite* which was invented by Alfred Nobel.[5] This was a stiff gelatinous mixture of nitroglycerin and soluble nitrocellulose in proportions varying between 1 to 2 and 2 to 1, prepared with the use of a solvent which was later removed and recovered. Nobel appears to have been led to the invention by thinking about celluloid, for the patent specification states that the substitution of almost all the camphor in celluloid by nitroglycerin yields a material which is suitable for use as a propellant. In the method of manufacture first proposed, camphor was dissolved in nitroglycerin, benzene was added, and then dry, pulped, soluble nitrocellulose; the mixture was kneaded, the benzene was allowed to evaporate, and the material was rolled between warm rollers

[4] *Mém. poudres,* **3,** 11–12 (1890).
[5] Brit. Pat. 1471 (1888).

to make it completely homogeneous. It was rolled into thin sheets which were cut with a knife or scissors into the desired shape and size. The use of nitrostarch instead of part of the nitrocellulose, and the addition of pulverized chlorate or picrate in various proportions, were also mentioned in the patent.

FIGURE 72. Paul Vieille (1854-1934). Inventor of *poudre B,* the first progressive-burning smokeless powder, 1884. Author of classic researches on erosion. Secretary and later, as successor to Berthelot, President of the French Powder and Explosives Commission.

1889. Nobel soon discovered [6] that the use of soluble nitrocellulose made it possible to manufacture ballistite without using camphor or any other solvent. The nitroglycerin and soluble nitrocellulose were brought together under water. As soon as the nitroglycerin had been absorbed by the nitrocellulose, the mass was heated to 80° to complete the gelatinization, and was then rolled and cut up in the usual way. In an alternative process the gelatinization was hastened by using more nitroglycerin than was

[6] Brit. Pat. 9361 (1889).

desired in the powder, and the excess was removed by means of 75% methyl alcohol by which it was extracted while the nitrocellulose was unaffected by that solvent.

1889. Lundholm and Sayers [7] devised a better process of incorporating the materials. The nitroglycerin and the soluble nitrocellulose were brought together under hot water and stirred by means of compressed air. The nitroglycerin presently gelatinized, or dissolved in, the nitrocellulose. The doughlike mass was removed, and passed between rollers heated to 50° or 60° whereby the water was pressed out. The sheet was folded over and passed through the rolls again, and the process was repeated until a uniform colloid resulted. It was rolled to the desired thickness and cut into squares which were generally glazed with graphite and finally blended.

1889. At about the time that Vieille was developing *poudre B*, the British government appointed a committee to investigate and report upon a smokeless powder for the use of the British service. Samples of ballistite and other smokeless powders were procured, the patent specifications relative to them were studied, and the decision was reached to use a powder which differed from Nobel's ballistite in being made from insoluble nitrocellulose containing more nitrogen than the soluble material which he used. The guncotton and nitroglycerin were incorporated together by means of acetone, mineral jelly (vaseline) was added, the colloid was pressed through dies into the form of cords of circular or oval cross section, and the acetone was evaporated off. The product was called *cordite*. The experimental work in connection with its development was done mostly in Abel's laboratory, and mostly by Kellner who later succeeded Abel as War Department chemist. Patents [8] in the names of Abel and Dewar, members of the committee, were taken out on behalf of the government in 1889, and later in the same year the manufacture of cordite was commenced at the royal gunpowder factory at Waltham Abbey.

The mineral jelly was added to cordite originally with the idea that it would lubricate the barrel of the gun, but it seems to have no such effect. Actually it is consumed during the combustion. Because of it the powder gases contain a larger number of mols

[7] Brit. Pat. 10,376 (1889).
[8] Brit. Pats. 5614, 11,664 (1889).

at a lower temperature, and produce, with less erosion, substantially the same ballistic effect as the same weight of powder made up without mineral jelly. The original cordite Mk. I. contained guncotton 37%, nitroglycerin 58%, and mineral jelly 5%. This produced such serious erosion of the guns in the British South African war that the composition was modified; the relative amount of nitroglycerin was reduced for the purpose of making it cooler. Cordite M. D. (modified) consists of guncotton 65%, nitroglycerin 30%, and mineral jelly 5%.

Mineral jelly in cordite has a distinct stabilizing action. The material is known to take up nitric oxide in the nitrometer and to cause a falsely low nitrogen analysis if it is present in the material which is being analyzed.[9]

Any distinction between cordite and ballistite which is based upon the methods by which the materials are manufactured is now no longer valid. Certain cordites are made without the use of a volatile solvent. Ballistites are made from soluble and from insoluble nitrocellulose, with and without the use of acetone, ethyl acetate, or other volatile solvent. Cordite is the name of the propellant which is used by the British armed forces. Ballistite, generally in flakes, sometimes in cords and in single-perforated tubes, is the preferred military powder of Italy, Germany, and the Scandinavian countries.

1891. Charles E. Munroe commenced investigations of smokeless powder at the Naval Torpedo Station, Newport, Rhode Island, about 1886, and about 1891 invented *indurite*. This was made from guncotton, freed from lower nitrates by washing with methyl alcohol, and colloided with nitrobenzene. The colloid was rolled to the desired thickness and cut into squares or strips which were hardened or indurated by the action of hot water or steam. Most of the nitrobenzene was distilled out by this treatment, and the colloid was left as a very hard and tough mass. Indurite was manufactured which gave satisfactory tests in guns ranging in caliber from the one-pounder to the six inch.[10]

1895–1897. After Munroe's resignation from the Torpedo Station, Lieutenant John B. Bernadou, U. S. Navy, took up the

---

[9] *U. S. Bur. Mines Bull.* 96, "The Analysis of Permissible Explosives," by C. G. Storm, Washington, 1916, p. 44.

[10] Ballistic tests are reported in Munroe's interesting article on "The Development of Smokeless Powder," *J. Am. Chem. Soc.,* 18, 819–846 (1896).

work on smokeless powder and in 1895 patented a powder consisting of a mixture of guncotton, collodion cotton, and potassium nitrate, colloided with acetone, and in 1897 an improved powder made from nitrocellulose alone colloided with ether-alcohol. The nitrocellulose first used contained approximately 12.45% nitrogen, but this was later replaced by pyrocellulose, 12.60% nitrogen. The powder was made in multiperforated cylindrical grains, and was substantially the same as was used by the United States in the first World War. Patents covering various improvements in the manufacture of pyrocellulose powder were taken out in the names of Lieutenant Bernadou and Captain Converse, U. S. Navy, and were licensed or sold to private interests, the United States government retaining the right to manufacture under these patents powder for its own use.

1900–1907.   About 1900 the Navy Department built the Naval Powder Factory at Indian Head, Maryland. The plant was capable of producing several thousand pounds of smokeless powder per day, and was enlarged during the course of a few years to a capacity of about 10,000 pounds daily. About 1907 the Ordnance Department, U. S. Army, built at Picatinny Arsenal, Dover, New Jersey, a powder plant with a capacity of several thousand pounds per day.

Classification of Colloided Nitrocellulose Powders

American pyrocellulose powder and French *poudre B* are *straight nitrocellulose* or *single-base* powders. They are made by the use of a volatile solvent, generally ether-alcohol, which solvent is removed wholly or in large part during the process of manufacture. They are the simplest of colloided powders, the pyrocellulose powder being really the simpler of the two, for it is made from one single kind of nitrocellulose. Modified forms of these powders are made by incorporating into the colloid nonvolatile solvents (i.e. solvents which remain in the finished powder) which may be either explosive or non-explosive or by distributing throughout the colloid as a separate phase materials, either explosive or non-explosive, which affect the rate or the temperature of the burning or the strength of the powder. Aromatic nitro compounds, such as DNT, TNX oil, etc., dissolve nitrocellulose or are dissolved by it, and thus constitute themselves non-volatile solvents, but they are also explosives in their own right, and a nitrocellulose powder which contains one of them might, it would seem, be designated with propriety as a *double-base powder*. This, however, is not in accordance with prevailing usage. The name of double-base powder is reserved for such powders as ballistite and cordite which contain nitrocellulose and nitroglycerin (or perhaps some substitute for nitro-, glycerin such as nitroglycol). Double-base powders are made both with and without volatile solvent, and are also capable of being modified in all of the ways in which a single base powder may be modified. We have, therefore, colloided powder of various kinds, as follows.

I. Nitrocellulose powder without nitroglycerin
   a. with volatile solvent,
   b. with non-explosive non-volatile solvent,
   c. with explosive non-volatile solvent,
   d. with non-explosive non-volatile non-solvent,
   e. with explosive non-volatile non-solvent.
II. Nitrocellulose powder with nitroglycerin
   a. with volatile solvent,
   b. with non-explosive non-volatile solvent,
   c. with explosive non-volatile solvent,
   d. with non-explosive non-volatile non-solvent,
   e. with explosive non-volatile non-solvent.
III. Coated and laminated powders the grains of which are non-homogeneous combinations of the powders above classified.

This classification is offered, not in any belief that it clarifies a matter which is otherwise difficult to understand, but because it directs attention to the various possibilities and displays their relationships to one another. Some of the possibilities correspond to powders which are or have been used in this country or in Europe, and which are sufficiently described for our present purpose if they are mentioned specifically. Others will be discussed at greater length in the sections, below, which are concerned with the absorption of moisture, with gelatinizing agents, and with flashless charges and flashless powder. All the possibilities are actually exploited, though not always separately.

Cordite MD, it may be noted, is a double base powder made with volatile solvent and containing a non-volatile, non-explosive non-solvent, namely mineral jelly, and is classified in class II *a d*, while a flashless ballistite of class II *b c* is made by incorporating centralite and DNX oil with nitroglycerin and nitrocellulose, and one of class II *b e* by mixing centralite and nitroguanidine with nitroglycerin and nitrocellulose. The nitroguanidine does not dissolve in the colloid but is distributed through it in a state of fine subdivision. Ten or 15 parts of nitroguanidine incorporated with 90 or 85 parts of pyrocellulose colloided with ether-alcohol gives a mixture which may be extruded through dies and yields a powder (I *a e*) which is flashless. PETN is another substance, insoluble in nitrocellulose colloids, which in the state of a fine powder may be incorporated in single-base or in double-base mixtures to yield powders (I *a e* and II *a e*) which are hotter and more powerful than otherwise.

Manufacture of Single-Base Powder

The operations in the manufacture of smokeless powder from pyrocellulose, briefly, are as follows.

1. *Dehydrating.* The pulped pyrocellulose contains about 25% moisture when it arrives at the smokeless powder plant. Most of this is squeezed out by pressing with a moderate pressure, say 250 pounds per square inch, for a few moments. The pressure is then released, alcohol in an amount at least equal to the dry weight of the pyrocellulose is forced into the mass by means of a pump, and the pressure is increased to about 3500 pounds per square inch. The process is managed in such fashion that the resulting cylindrical block consists of pyrocellulose moistened with exactly the amount of alcohol which is needed for the formation of the colloid. The requisite amount of ether is added later. The solvent consists altogether of 1 part by weight of alcohol and 2 parts of ether, 105 pounds of the mixed solvent for every 100 pounds of pyrocellulose if the colloid is to be made into 0.30-caliber powder, 100 parts if into powder of which the web thickness is approximately 0.025 inch, and 85 parts for powder having a web thickness of 0.185 inch. The block is received in a cannister of vulcanized fiber and is covered over in order that loss of solvent by evaporation may be reduced to a minimum. From this point on, in fact, the material is kept and is moved from one operation to another in covered cannisters at all times except when it is being worked.

FIGURE 73. Smokeless Powder Manufacture. (Courtesy E. I. du Pont de Nemours and Company, Inc.) Dehydrating Press. The nitrocellulose comes from the dehydrating press in the form of a cylindrical block, impregnated with alcohol, ready for the mixer where ether is added and where it is colloided.

FIGURE 74. Smokeless Powder Manufacture. (Courtesy E. I. du Pont de Nemours and Company, Inc.) Smokeless Powder Mixer—open to show the crumbly, partially colloided material. In use, the apparatus is closed tightly to prevent the loss of volatile solvent.

2. *Mixing or incorporating.* The compressed block from the dehydrating press is broken up by hand against the blades of the mixing machine. This is similar to the bread-mixing machines which are used in large commercial bakeries, and consists of a water-cooled steel box in which two shafts carrying curved blades rotate in opposite directions and effectively knead the material. The ether is added rapidly and mixed in as fast as possible. Diphenylamine sufficient to constitute 0.9–1.1% of the weight of the finished powder is previously dissolved in the ether, and is thus distributed uniformly throughout the colloid. The incorporated material has an appearance similar to that of a mass of brown sugar which has been churned; it is soft enough to be deformed between the fingers, and, when squeezed, welds together in the form of a film or colloid.

3. *Pressing.* The loose and not yet completely colloided material is pressed into a compact cylindrical mass by means of a pressure of about 3500 pounds per square inch in the *preliminary blocking press.* The *preliminary block* is then placed in the *macaroni press* where it is pressed or strained through 1 12-mesh steel plate, 2 sheets of 24-mesh and 1 sheet of 36-mesh steel wire screen, and through the perforations in a heavy plate of brass from which it emerges in wormlike pieces resembling macaroni. A pressure of 3000 to 3500 pounds per square inch is commonly used. The material drops directly into the cylinder of the *final blocking press*, where it is squeezed into a compact cylindrical block of the right size to fit the graining press. A pressure of about 3500 pounds per square inch is maintained for 1 or 2 minutes, and completes the colloiding of the pyrocellulose. The *final block* is dense, tough, elastic, light brown or amber colored, and translucent.

4. *Graining and cutting.* The colloid is forced by an hydraulic press through dies by which it is formed into single-perforated or into multiperforated tubes. For the formation of a single-perforated tube, the plastic mass is forced in the die into the space which surrounds a centrally fixed steel wire; it is then squeezed past the wire through a circular hole and emerges in the form of a tube. For the formation of a multiperforated tube, 7 such wires are accurately spaced within the die. A pressure of 2500 to 3800 pounds per square inch is used. For small arms powder the head of the press may contain as many as 36 dies, for large-

FIGURE 75. Smokeless Powder Manufacture. (Courtesy E. I. du Pont de Nemours and Company, Inc.) Blocking Press.

caliber powder, such as that for the 16-inch gun, it usually contains only one. The cord or rope of powder as it comes from the press is passed over pulleys or through troughs to a rotary cutter where it is cut into short cylinders about 2.1 to 2.5 times as long as their diameters or it is coiled up in a fiber cannister in which it is taken to another room for cutting. In France the colloid is

FIGURE 76. Smokeless Powder Manufacture. (Courtesy E. I. du Pont de Nemours and Company, Inc.) Finishing Press. The colloid is extruded in the form of a perforated cylinder which is later cut into pieces or grains.

pressed through slots from which it emerges in the form of ribbons which are cut into strips of a length convenient for loading into the gun for which the powder is intended.

5. *Solvent recovery.* The *green powder* contains a large amount of ether and alcohol which presents a twofold problem: (1) the recovery of as much of the valuable volatile solvent as is economically feasible, and (2) the removal of the solvent to such an extent that the finished powder will not be disposed either to give off or to take up much volatile matter or moisture under changing atmospheric conditions. For the recovery of the solvent, the pow-

der is put into a closed system and warm air at 55–65° is circulated through it; the air takes up the alcohol and ether from the powder and deposits much of it again when it is passed through a condenser. It is then heated and again passed through the powder. In some European plants the air, after refrigeration, is passed upward through an absorption tower down which cresol or other suitable liquid is trickling. This removes the ether which was not condensed out by the cooling, and the ether is recovered from it by distillation. The whole process of solvent recovery requires careful control, for the colloid on drying tends to form a skin on its surface (the way a pot of glue does when drying) and the skin tends to prevent the escape of volatile matter from the interior of the powder grain.

6. *Water-drying.* Powder is now most commonly dried by the rapid water-drying process whereby the formation of a skin upon its surface is prevented and certain other advantages are gained. Water at 65° is circulated throughout the powder. The water causes the production of microscopic cracks and pores through which the alcohol and ether escape more freely. These substances leave the powder to dissolve in the water, and then the ether in particular evaporates out from the water. When the volatile solvent content of the powder is sufficiently reduced, the powder grains are taken out and the water with which they are superficially covered is removed in a dry-house or in a continuous dryer at 55–65°. The finished powder contains 3.0 to 7.5% of volatile solvent in the interior of the grain, the amount depending upon the thickness of the web, and 0.9 to 1.4% of *external moisture*, mostly water actually resident in the cracks or pores of the surface. The amount of moisture which the powder thus holds upon its surface is an important factor in maintaining its ballistic stability under varying atmospheric conditions. The amount ought to be such that there is no great tendency for the moisture to evaporate off in dry weather, and such also that there is no great tendency for the powder to take up moisture in damp weather. The importance of surface moisture is so considerable that the French powder makers, long before there was any thought of using warm water to dry the powder, were accustomed to submit it to a *trempage* or tempering by immersion in water for several days. Later, periods of air-drying were alternated

with periods of *trempage* in warm water at temperatures sometimes as high as 80°.

Powder for small arms is generally *glazed* with graphite, by
which treatment its attitude toward the loss and absorption of
moisture is improved, and by which also it is made electrically
conducting so that it can be *blended* without danger from static

FIGURE 77. Smokeless Powder Blending Tower. The powder is blended
by being made to flow through troughs and bins. Lots as large as 50,000
pounds of rifle powder and 125,000 pounds of cannon powder have been
blended in this tower.

electricity and loaded satisfactorily by a volumetric method. The
powder is blended in order that large lots can be made up which
will be ballistically uniform, and hence that the proof firing, the
operations of loading, and the calculations of the artilleryman
may all be either simplified in kind or reduced in amount. Powder
in short cylindrical grains, such as is used in the United States,
is particularly easy to blend, but the blending of strips, or of
long tubes or cords, is obviously difficult or impracticable. The
finished powder is stored and shipped in airtight boxes which
contain 110–150 pounds.

Stabilizers

The spontaneous decomposition of nitrocellulose in the air produces nitrous and nitric acids which promote a further decomposition. If these products however are removed continuously, the uncatalyzed decomposition is extremely slow, and smokeless pow-

FIGURE 78. Bernhart Troxler. (Greystone Studios, Inc.) Introduced many innovations into the manufacture of smokeless powder and improved the design of equipment in such manner as to increase production while reducing the hazard—the steam-air-dry process for double-base powder, methods of coating, apparatus for solvent recovery, water drying, and air drying of single-base powder without transferring the powder during the three operations. His whole professional life has been devoted to smokeless powder, with the Laflin and Rand Powder Company until 1913, and afterwards with the Hercules Powder Company from the time when that company was organized and built its first smokeless powder line.

der may be stabilized by the addition to it of a substance which reacts with these acids and removes them, provided neither the substance itself nor the products of its reaction with the acids attacks the nitrocellulose.

Vieille suggested the use of amyl alcohol as a stabilizer, and powder containing this material was used in France until 1911

when, in consequence of the disastrous explosion of the battleship
Jena in 1907 and of the battleship *Liberté* in 1911, both ascribed
to the spontaneous inflammation of the powder, and in consequence of the researches of Marqueyrol, its use was discontinued
entirely. Indeed no powder containing amyl alcohol was manufactured in France after October, 1910. Freshly manufactured
poudre BAm smelled of amyl alcohol; the alcohol was converted
by the products of the decomposition into the nitrous and nitric
esters, and these soon broke down to produce red fumes anew and
evil-smelling valerianic acid. The presence of the latter in the
powder was easily detected, and was taken as evidence that the
powder had become unstable. The Italians early used aniline as
a stabilizer for their military ballistite. This forms nitro derivatives of aniline and of phenol, but it attacks nitrocellulose and
is now no longer used. As early as 1909, diphenylamine was being
used in the United States, in France, and in Germany, and, at
the present time, it is the most widely used stabilizer in smokeless powder. The *centralites* (see below) also have a stabilizing
action in smokeless powder but are used primarily as non-volatile
solvents and deterrent coatings.

Calcium carbonate, either powdered limestone or precipitated
chalk, is used as an anti-acid in dynamite where it serves as a
satisfactory stabilizer. Urea is used in dynamite and in celluloid.
It reacts with nitrous acid to produce nitrogen and carbon dioxide, and is unsuitable for use in smokeless powder because the
gas bubbles destroy the homogeneity of the colloid and affect the
rate of burning. The small gas bubbles however commend it for
use in celluloid, for they produce an appearance of whiteness and
counteract the yellowing of age.

In addition to the ability of certain substances to combine with
the products of the decomposition of nitrocellulose, it is possible
that the same or other substances may have a positive or a nega-
tive catalytic effect and may hasten or retard the decomposition
by their presence. But it has not yet been made clear what types
of chemical substance hasten the decomposition or why they do
so. Nitrogen dioxide hastens it. Pyridine hastens it, and a powder
containing 2 or 3% of pyridine will inflame spontaneously if
heated for half an hour at 110°. Powders containing tetryl are
very unstable, while those containing 10% of trinitronaphthalene
(which does not react with the products of decomposition) are as

stable as those containing 2% of diphenylamine (which does react).

In a series of researches extending over a period of 15 years Marqueyrol [11] has determined the effect of various substances, particularly naphthalene, mononitronaphthalene, diphenylbenzamide, carbazol, diphenylamine, and diphenylnitrosamine, upon the stability of smokeless powder at 110°, 75°, 60°, and 40°. Samples of *poudre BF* [12] were made up containing different amounts of each stabilizer, and were subjected to dry heat in open vessels and in vessels closed with cork stoppers. Samples were removed from time to time and the nitrogen content of their nitrocellulose was determined. A sample of the powder was taken up in a solvent, and precipitated in a granular state; the precipitate was washed with cold chloroform until a fresh portion of chloroform was no longer colored by 18 hours contact with it, and was dried, and analyzed by the nitrometer. It was necessary to isolate the pure nitrocellulose and to separate it from the stabilizer, for the reason that otherwise the stabilizer would be nitrated in the nitrometer and a low result for nitrogen would be secured. A selected portion of Marqueyrol's results, from experiments carried out by heating in open vessels, are shown in the tables on

Days of heating at 40°....	0	387	843	1174	2991	3945	4016
Analysis:							
no stabilizer	201.8	....	199.5	*147.8*	....	....	....
2% amyl alcohol	202.2	....	198.7	200.6	199.2	....	172.9
8% " "	201.4	....	199.2	200.8	198.9	....	198.2
1% diphenylamine	201.3	....	199.5	201.0	200.9	....	201.0
2% "	199.5	....	198.2	199.2	199.4	....	200.2
5% "	200.1	201.2	....	....	....	197.6	....
10% "	200.1	199.0	198.2	....	....	....	....

Days of heating at 60°	0	146	295	347	1059	2267	3935
Analysis:							
no stabilizer	201.8	*146.5*	....	....	....	....	....
2% amyl alcohol	202.2	197.4	....	*147.2*	....	....	....
8% " "	201.4	197.3	....	198.3	159.5	....	....
1% diphenylamine	201.3	197.6	....	200.0	....	....	....
2% "	199.5	196.1	....	198.3	....	....	....
5% "	200.1	....	196.0	....	....	....	185.7
10% "	200.1	....	192.3	....	....	....	173.0

[11] *Mém. poudres*, **23**, 158 (1928).
[12] F = *fusil*, rifle.

Days of heating at 75°....	0	86	231	312	516	652	667
Analysis:							
2% amyl alcohol	203.1	*191.4*	....	....	....	....	....
1% diphenylamine	201.3	196.0	....	198.0	190.9	....	....
2% "	199.5	194.7	....	198.1	....	192.1	....
5% "	200.1	....	192.8	....	....	....	186.2
10% "	200.1	....	184.2	....	....	....	175.9

Days of heating at 75°....	0	55	146	312	419	493	749
Analysis:							
1% diphenylnitrosamine	200.4	197.9	198.4	199.2	197.5	198.2	194.0
2% "	200.0	201.5	198.3	198.5	197.6	171.5	....
10% "	201.5	195.3	194.1	193.0	190.6	187.3	184.3

Days of heating at 75°....	0	60	85	108	197	377	633
Analysis:							
2% amyl alcohol	200.9	198.9	*196.9*	....	....	....	....
1.25% carbazol	200.6	199.4	....	199.1	*182.8*	....	....
10% "	200.3	198.7	....	197.7	198.2	193.0	190.2

Days of heating at 75°....	0	31	50	62	87	227	556
Analysis:							
1.5% diphenylbenzamide	200.2	199.3	*186.1*	....	....	....	....
10% "	200.2	198.1	....	....	200.3	....	....
1.5% mononitronaphthalene	202.4	199.8	....	....	....	....	....
10% mononitronaphthalene	202.0	198.1	....	*193.0*	....	....	....
1.5% naphthalene	202.3	200.2	194.8	....	....	....	....
10% "	201.8	199.2	....	....	....	199.1	200.2

pages 309–310, where the numbers representing *analyses* indicate the nitrogen contents as usually reported in France, namely, cubic centimeters of nitric oxide per gram of nitrocellulose. When the numbers are printed in italics, the samples which were taken for analysis were actively giving off red nitrous fumes.

Diphenylnitrosamine, which is always present in powders made from diphenylamine, is decomposed at 110°, and that temperature therefore is not a suitable one for a study of the stability of smokeless powder. At 75° diphenylnitrosamine attacks nitrocellulose less rapidly than diphenylamine itself, but this is not true at lower temperatures (40° and 60°) at which there is no appreciable difference between the two substances. Carbazol at 110° is an excellent stabilizer but at 60° and 75° is so poor as to deserve no further consideration. Ten per cent of diphenylamine gives unstable smokeless powder. Powder containing 40% of diphenylamine inflames spontaneously when heated in an open vessel at 110° for an hour and a half. Diphenylamine attacks nitrocellulose, but it does not attack it as rapidly as do the products themselves of the decomposition of nitrocellulose in air; and 1 or 2% of the substance, or even less, in smokeless powder is as good a stabilizer as has yet been found.

Transformations of Diphenylamine During Aging of Powder

Desmaroux,[13] Marqueyrol and Muraour,[14] and Marqueyrol and Loriette [15] have studied the diphenylamine derivatives which give a dark color to old powder, and have concluded that they are produced by impurities in the ether which is used in the manufacture or by the oxidizing action of the air during drying and storage. Their presence is not evidence that the powder has decomposed, but indicates that a certain amount of the diphenylamine has been consumed and that correspondingly less of it remains available for use as a stabilizer.

The transformations of diphenylamine [16] in consequence of its reaction with the products of the decomposition of nitrocellulose are indicated by the following formulas. None of these substances imparts any very deep color to the powder.

[13] Mém. poudres, 21, 238 (1924).
[14] Ibid., 21, 259, 272 (1924).
[15] Ibid., 21, 277 (1924).
[16] Davis and Ashdown, Ind. Eng. Chem., 17, 674 (1925).

The diphenylamine is converted first into diphenylnitrosamine which is as good a stabilizer as diphenylamine itself. Since both of these substances may be detected by simple tests upon an alcoholic extract of a sample of the powder, the fitness of the powder for continued storage and use may be easily demonstrated. A strip of filter paper on which the alcoholic extract has been allowed to evaporate is colored blue by a drop of ammonium persulfate solution if unchanged diphenylamine is present. Likewise the extract, if it contains diphenylamine, is colored blue by the addition of a few drops of a saturated aqueous solution of ammonium persulfate. Since the alcoholic extract is often colored, the test is best carried out by comparing the colors of two equal portions of the extract, one with and one without the addition of ammonium persulfate. Diphenylnitrosamine gives no color with ammonium persulfate. One-tenth of a milligram of diphenylnitrosamine imparts an intense blue color to a few cubic centimeters of cold concentrated sulfuric acid. It gives no color with a cold 1% alcoholic solution of α-naphthylamine, but an orange color if the solution is heated.[17] None of the other diphenylamine derivatives which occur in smokeless powder give these tests.

Diphenylnitrosamine rearranges under the influence of mineral acids to form p-nitrosodiphenylamine. The latter substance is evidently formed in smokeless powder and is oxidized and nitrated by the products of the decomposition to form 2,4'- and 4,4'-dinitrodiphenylamine. Davis and Ashdown[16] have isolated both of these substances from old powder, and have also prepared[17] them by the nitration of diphenylnitrosamine in glacial acetic acid solution. Both substances on further nitration yield 2,4,4'-trinitrodiphenylamine, which represents the last stage in the nitration of diphenylamine by the products of the decomposition of smokeless powder. This material has been isolated from a sample of U. S. pyrocellulose powder which was kept at 65° in a glass-stoppered bottle for 240 days after the first appearance of red fumes. The several nitro derivatives of diphenylamine may be distinguished by color reactions with alcoholic solutions of ammonia, sodium hydroxide, and sodium cyanide, and some insight into the past history of the powder may be gained from tests on the alcohol extract with these reagents, but their pres-

---

[17] Davis and Ashdown, *J. Am. Chem. Soc.*, **46**, 1051 (1924).

ence is evidence of instability, and no powder in which the diphenylnitrosamine is exhausted is suitable for further storage and use.

Absorption of Moisture [18]

Nitrocellulose itself is hygroscopic, but its tendency to take up moisture is modified greatly by other substances with which it is incorporated. Colloided with nitroglycerin in the absence of solvent, it yields a product which shows no tendency to take up moisture from a damp atmosphere. Colloided with ether-alcohol, as in the case of the *poudre B* and the straight pyrocellulose powders which were used in the first World War, it yields a powder which is hygroscopic both because of the hygroscopicity of the nitrocellulose itself and because of the hygroscopicity of the alcohol and ether which it contains. In water-dried powder the alcohol and ether of the surface layer have been largely removed or replaced with water, the hygroscopicity of the surface layer is reduced, and the interior of the grain is prevented to a considerable extent from attracting to itself the moisture which it would otherwise attract. In certain coated and *progressive burning* powders, the surface layers are made up of material of greatly reduced hygroscopicity and the interiors are rendered inaccessible to atmospheric influences.

The tendency of straight nitrocellulose powder to take up moisture and the effect of the absorbed moisture in reducing the ballistic power of the powder are shown by the table below.

Period of exposure, hrs.	0	24	48	72	96
Total volatiles, %	3.26	3.55	3.71	3.84	3.93
External moisture, %	1.02	1.15	1.40	1.47	1.57
Residual solvent, %	2.24	2.40	2.31	2.37	2.35
Velocity, ft. per sec.	1706.6	1699.0	1685.4	1680.4	1669.0
Pressure, lb. per sq. in.	31,100	31,236	30,671	29,636	28,935

A sample of water-dried powder was exposed to an atmosphere practically saturated with water vapor. Portions were removed each day; one part was fired in the gun, and another part was analyzed for *total volatile* matter (TV) and for volatile matter driven off by an hour's heating at 100° (*external moisture*, EM).

[18] Cf. Davis, *Army Ordnance*, **2**, 9 (1921).

The amount of total volatile matter increased regularly during the period of exposure, as did also the amount of volatile matter resident at or near the surface of the powder grains. The amount of volatile matter in the interior of the powder grains (*residual solvent*, RS) did not alter materially during the experiment.

Total volatiles in powder is determined by dissolving the sample in a solvent, precipitating in a porous and granular condition, evaporating off the volatile matter, and drying the residue to constant weight. External moisture is the amount of volatile matter which is driven off by some convenient method of desiccation. The difference between the two is residual solvent, $TV - EM = RS$, and is supposed to correspond to volatile matter resident within the interior of the grain and not accessible to desiccating influences. Various methods of determining external moisture have been in use among the nations which use straight nitrocellulose powder and in the same nation among the manufacturers who produce it. At the time of the first World War, for example, external moisture was determined in Russia by heating the sample at 100° for 6 hours, in France by heating at 60° for 4 hours, and in the United States by heating at 60° in a vacuum for 6 hours. These several methods, naturally, all give different results for external moisture and consequently different results for residual solvent.

There appears really to be no method by which true external moisture may be determined, that is, no method by which only the surface moisture is removed in such fashion that the residual solvent in the powder is found to be the same both before and after the powder has been allowed to take up moisture. Samples of powder were taken and residual solvent was determined by the several methods indicated in the next table. The samples were exposed 2 weeks to an atmosphere practically saturated with water vapor, and residual solvent was again determined as before. The surprising result was secured in every case, as indicated, that the amount of residual solvent was less after the powder had been exposed to the moist atmosphere than it was before it had been exposed. Yet the powder had taken up large quantities of moisture during the exposure. It is clear that the exposure to the moist atmosphere had made the volatile matter of the interior of the grains more accessible to desiccating influences. Evidently the moisture had opened up the interior of the grains, presumably by precipitating the nitrocellulose and producing minute cracks and pores in the colloid. Verification of this explanation is found in the effect of alcohol on colloided pyrocellulose powder. The powder took up alcohol from an atmosphere saturated with alcohol vapor, but alcohol does not precipitate the colloid, it produces no cracks or pores, and in every case residual solvent was found to be greater after the powder had been exposed to alcohol vapor than it had been before such exposure. The following table shows data for typical samples of powder before and after exposures of 2 weeks to atmospheres saturated respectively with water and with alcohol.

Method of Determining External Moisture and Residual Solvent	Exposure to Water Residual solvent			Exposure to Alcohol Residual solvent		
	Before	After	Difference	Before	After	Difference
1 hr. at 100° in open oven..	3.12	2.82	−0.30	2.41	4.57	+2.16
6 hrs. at 100° in open oven..	2.81	2.36	−0.45	2.22	3.92	+1.70
6 hrs. at 55° in vacuum.....	2.91	2.54	−0.37	2.27	4.10	+1.83
55° to constant weight in open oven..............	3.00	2.72	−0.28	2.58	4.25	+1.67
Over sulfuric acid to constant weight...........	2.95	2.39	−0.56	2.32	4.10	+1.78

Samples of pyrocellulose powder, varying in size from 0.30 caliber single-perforated to large multiperforated grains for the 10-inch gun, were exposed to a moist atmosphere until they no longer gained any weight. They were then desiccated by the rather vigorous method of heating for 6 hours at 100°. All the samples lost more weight than they had gained. As the exposures to moisture and subsequent desiccations were repeated, the differences between the weights gained by taking up moisture and the weights lost by drying became less and less until finally the powders on desiccation lost, within the precision of the experiments, exactly the amounts of volatile matter which they had taken up. At this point it was judged that all residual solvent had been driven out of the powder and that further treatment would produce no additional cracks and pores in the grains. The gain or loss (either one, for the two were equal) calculated as per cent of the weight of the desiccated sample gave the apparent hygroscopicities listed below. Since all the powders were made from the

CALIBER	APPARENT HYGROSCOPICITY, %
0.30	3.00
75 mm.	2.75
4.7 inches	2.42
6 inches	2.41
10 inches	2.11

same material, namely, straight pyrocellulose, the differences in the apparent hygroscopicity are presumed to be caused by the drying treatment not being vigorous enough to drive out all the moisture from the interior of the grains of greater web thickness. The drying, however, was so vigorous that the powders became unstable after a few more repetitions of it. The losses on desiccation became greater because of decomposition, and the gains on exposure to moisture became greater because of the hygroscopicity of the decomposition products.

Although hygroscopicity determined in this way is apparent and not absolute, it supplies nevertheless an important means of estimating the effects both of process of manufacture and of composition upon the attitude of the powder toward moisture. Thus, samples of pyrocellulose powder for the 4.7-inch gun, all of them being from the same batch and pressed through the same die, one air-dried, one water-dried, one dried under benzene at 60°, and one under ligroin at 60°, showed apparent hygroscopicities of 2.69%, 2.64%, 2.54%, and 2.61%, which are the same within the experimental error. Milky grains [19] of 75-mm. powder showed an apparent hygroscopicity of 2.79%, compared with 2.75% for the normal amber-colored grains. The experiment with this powder was continued until considerable decomposition was evident; the successive gains and losses were as follows, calculated as per cent of the original weight of the sample.

[19] Grains which had a milky appearance because of the precipitation of the colloid during the water-dry treatment. This result follows if the grains contain more than 7 or 7.5% of ether-alcohol when they are submitted to water-drying.

Gain, %	Loss, %
2.315	3.030
2.439	2.623
2.259	2.337
2.279	2.319
2.179	2.577
2.448	2.554
2.325	2.630
2.385	3.022

Experiments with 75-mm. powders, made from pyrocellulose with the use of ether-alcohol and with various other substances incorporated in the colloids, gave the following results for hygroscopicity. Hydrocellulose does not dissolve in the nitrocellulose

Pyrocellulose with

5% hydrocellulose	....	2.79%
10% crystalline DNX	....	2.09%
10% DNX oil	....	1.99%
10% crystalline DNT	....	1.93%
15% " "	....	1.41%
20% " "	....	1.23%
25% " "	....	1.06%

colloid, and does not affect its hygroscopicity. The aromatic nitro compounds dissolve, and they have a marked effect in reducing the absorption of moisture. They are explosive non-volatile solvents and contribute to the energy of the powder.

Other non-volatile solvents which are not explosive are discussed below in the section on gelatinizing agents. These tend to reduce the potential of the powder, but their action in this respect is counteracted in practice by using guncotton in place of part or all the nitrocellulose. The guncotton is colloided by the gelatinizing agent, either in the presence or in the absence of a volatile solvent, and the resulting powder is non-hygroscopic and as strong or stronger than straight pyrocellulose powder.

Control of Rate of Burning

Cordite is *degressive* burning, for its burning surface decreases as the burning advances. Powder in strips, in flakes, and in single-perforated tubes has a burning surface which is very nearly constant if the size of the strips or flakes, or the length of the tubes, is large relative to their thickness. Multiperforated grains are *progressive* burning, for their burning surface actually increases as the burning advances, and, other things in the gun being equal, they produce gas at a rate which accelerates more rapidly and, in consequence, gives a greater velocity to the projectile.

A progressive burning strip ballistite was used to some extent by the French in major caliber guns during the first World War. It consisted of a central thick strip or slab of ballistite, 50%

FIGURE 79. Progressive Burning Colloided Smokeless Powder. 12-Inch powder at different stages of its burning. A grain of 12-inch powder, such as appears at the left, was loaded into a 75-mm. gun along with the usual charge of 75-mm. powder (of the same form as the 12-inch grain but of less web thickness). When the gun was fired, a layer of colloid having a thickness equal to one-half the web of the 75-mm. powder was burned off from every grain in the gun. This consumed the 75-mm. powder completely. The 12-inch grain was extinguished when thrown from the muzzle of the gun; it was picked up from the ground—and is the second grain in the above picture. The next grain was shot twice from a 75-mm. gun, the last grain three times. After three shootings, the perforations are so large that a fourth shooting would cause them to meet one another, and the grain to fall apart, leaving slivers.

nitroglycerin and 50% soluble nitrocellulose, made without volatile solvent, and sandwiched between two thin strips of powder made, without volatile solvent, from 50% soluble nitrocellulose and 50% crystalline dinitrotoluene. The two compositions were rolled to the desired thicknesses separately between warm rolls, and were then combined into the laminated product by pressing between warm rolls. The outer layers burned relatively slowly with a temperature of about 1500°; the inner slab burned rapidly with a temperature of about 3000°.

Progressive burning *coated powders*, usually flakes or single-perforated short cylinders, are made by treating the grains with a gelatinizing agent, or non-volatile, non-explosive solvent for nitrocellulose, dissolved in a volatile liquid, generally benzene or acetone, tumbling them together in a sweetie barrel or similar device, and evaporating off the volatile liquid by warming while the tumbling is continued. The material which is applied as a coating is known in this country as a *deterrent*, in England as a

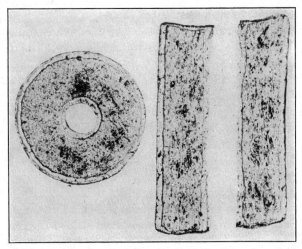

FIGURE 80. Cross Section and Longitudinal Section of a Grain of .50 Caliber Extruded Smokeless Powder, Deterrent Coated (25✕). (Courtesy Western Cartridge Company.)

moderant. At the time of the first World War *sym*-dimethyldiphenylurea was already used widely as a deterrent in rifle powder intended for use in shooting matches and in military propellants designed to produce especially high velocities. The substance was called *centralite* because its use had been developed in Germany at the Central War Laboratory at Spandau. The ethyl analog, diethyldiphenylurea, at first known as *ethyl centralite*, is usually called Centralite No. 1 and has generally superseded the methyl compound (or Centralite No. 2) for use in smokeless powder. Although many other substances have been tried and have been patented, this remains the most widely used of any. *Butyl centralite* is a better gelatinizing agent for nitrocellulose than either the methyl or the ethyl compound, and is likely to find more extensive use in the future.

Gelatinizing Agents

Gelatinizing agents, of which the centralites are examples, are often incorporated in colloided straight nitrocellulose and double-base powders where they cause the materials to burn more slowly, where they serve as flash reducing agents, and where they reduce the tendency of the powders to take up moisture. They reduce the amount of volatile solvent which is needed in the manufacture of nitrocellulose powders, and facilitate the manufacture of double-base powders without any volatile solvent at all. The centralites happen also to be effective stabilizers, but this is not a general property of gelatinizing agents.

Marqueyrol and Florentin [20] have published a list of patents for gelatinizing agents, esters, amides, urea derivatives, halogen compounds, ketones, and alcohols, and have reported their study of many of them with respect to their effectiveness on the CP_1 and CP_2, insoluble and soluble nitrocellulose respectively, which were standard in the French service. To a weighed quantity of the dry nitrocellulose a dilute solution of the gelatinizing agent in 95% alcohol was added in portions of 1 cc. at a time, the alcohol was then evaporated at a temperature of 35–40°, more of the alcohol solution was added, and the evaporation was repeated until gelatinization was complete. The results with the best gelatinizing agents are shown in the table below, where the numbers

	CP_1 (INSOLUBLE)	CP_2 (SOLUBLE)
Ethyl sebacate	320	65
Dimethylphenyl-o-tolylurea	260	65
Dimethyldiphenylurea	...	80
Ethyl succinate	400	90
Ethyl phthalate	360	95

represent the amounts by weight of the several substances which were needed for the complete gelatinization of 100 parts of the nitrocellulose. Ninety parts of ethyl citrate or of benzyl benzoate almost completely gelatinized 100 parts of CP_2, 90 of ethyl malonate incompletely, 90 of ethyl oxalate or of ethyl stearate more incompletely, and 90 of ethyl acetoacetate or of ethyl ricinoleate

[20] Mém. poudres, 18, 150, 163 (1921).

but very little. Four hundred parts of triphenyl phosphate almost completely gelatinized 100 parts of CP_1, and 400 of ethyl malonate or of ethyl oxalate produced only incomplete gelatinization.

Marqueyrol and Florentin point out that the lower members of the series of esters, the acetates, butyrates, valerates, etc., are good solvents for nitrocellulose—ethyl and amyl acetate have long been used for the purpose—but the higher members, the stearates and oleates, gelatinize nitrocellulose but very little. To the esters of the dibasic acids the opposite rule appears to apply; the higher members are better than the lower. Acetone is a well-known solvent both for soluble and for "insoluble" nitrocellulose, but acetophenone gelatinizes even soluble nitrocellulose only feebly.

Experiments by the present writer [21] with a variety of other gelatinizing agents have shown that the amounts necessary to produce complete gelatinization of pyrocellulose are different if different solvents are used for applying them. In general they are more effective in benzene than in alcohol, and more in alcohol than in ligroin. Half-gram samples of dry pyrocellulose were treated in 30-cc. beakers with known quantities of the gelatinizing agents dissolved in convenient volumes (15–30 cc.) of alcohol, benzene, or ligroin. The volatile liquids were evaporated off slowly at 60°, the residues were warmed at 60° for 10 minutes longer (during which time a considerable improvement in the gelatinization was generally observed), and were then examined to determine their condition. If complete gelatinization had not occurred, other experiments were carried out with fresh samples. The results, summarized in the table on page 322, are accurate to the nearest 10%. They support several conclusions. *Sym*-dialkyl ureas are excellent gelatinizing agents for nitrocellulose, and the property remains if additional aliphatic or aromatic groups are introduced into the molecule. The heavier the alkyl groups, the greater appears to be the gelatinizing power. Of the aromatic substituted ureas, those in which there are less than three aromatic groups appear to be without action. Among the alkyl esters of sebacic and phthalic acids, those which contain the heavier alkyl groups are generally the better gelatinizing agents. The alkyl esters of aliphatic and of aromatic substituted

[21] Davis, *Ind. Eng. Chem.,* **14**, 1140 (1922).

Parts by Weight Necessary for the Complete Gelatinization of 100 Parts of Pyrocellulose

	In Alcohol	In Benzene	In Ligroin
Methylurea	No action with 100 parts		
Ethyleneurea	No action with 100 parts		
Sym-dimethylurea	60	70	...
Sym-diethylurea	50	50	...
Unsym-dimethylurea	No action with 100 parts		
Tetramethylurea	80	...	...
Benzylurea	No action with 100 parts		
Sym-diphenylurea	No action with 100 parts		
Sym-di-*p*-tolylurea	No action with 100 parts		
Unsym-diphenylurea	No action with 100 parts		
Triphenylurea	...	35	...
α,α-diphenyl-*p*-tolylurea	...	40	...
Tetraphenylurea	No action with 160 parts	30	...
Ethyltriphenylurea	80	...	...
Sym-dimethyldiphenylurea	70	25	...
Sym-diethyldiphenylurea	70	30	...
Sym-di-*n*-butyldiphenylurea	60	20	...
Unsym-dimethyldiphenylurea	60	...	...
Carbamic acid ethyl ester	140	80	...
Methylcarbamic acid ethyl ester	90	60	...
Ethylcarbamic acid ethyl ester	90	60	...
Phenylcarbamic acid ethyl ester	20	90	...
Phenylcarbamic acid phenyl ester	No action with 200 parts		
Phenylcarbamic acid benzyl ester	No action with 100 parts		
Diphenylcarbamic acid phenyl ester	80	70	...
Methyl sebacate	80	70	105
Ethyl sebacate	80	50	90
Iso-amyl sebacate	70	95	90
Methyl phthalate	95	70	115
Ethyl phthalate	95	50	100
Iso-amyl phthalate	95	50	80
DNX oil	120	130	330
Trinitrotoluene	...	300	...

carbamic acids are excellent gelatinizing agents, but the aromatic esters appear to be without action unless the total number of aromatic groups is equal to three.

Flashless Charges and Flashless Powder

The discharge of a machine gun shooting ordinary charges of smokeless powder produces bright flashes from the muzzle which at night disclose the position of the gun to the enemy. When a large gun is fired, there is a large and dazzlingly bright muzzle flash, from a 12-inch gun for example a white-hot flame 150 feet or more in length. The light from such a flame reflects from the heavens at night and is visible for a distance of as much as 30 miles, much farther than the sound from the gun may be heard. The enemy by the use of appropriate light-ranging apparatus may determine the position of the flash, and may undertake to bombard and destroy the battery from a great distance.

Smokeless powder, burning in the chamber of the gun at the expense of its own combined oxygen, produces gas which contains hydrogen, carbon monoxide, carbon dioxide, etc., and this gas, being both hot and combustible, takes fire when it emerges from the muzzle and comes into contact with the fresh oxygen supply of the outer air. One part of the brilliancy of the flash is the result of the emergent gas being already preheated, often to a temperature at which it would be visible anyway, generally to a point far above the temperature of its inflammation in air. In thinking about this latter temperature, it is necessary to take account of the fact that, other things being equal, a small cloud of gas from a small gun loses its temperature more quickly and becomes completely mixed with the air more rapidly than a large cloud of gas from a large gun. The gas emerging from a small gun would need to be hotter in the first place if it is to inflame than gas of the same composition emerging from a large gun. It is for this reason perhaps that it is easier to secure flashless discharges with guns of small caliber (not over 6 inch) than with those of major caliber.

There are four ways, distinguishably different in principle, by which flashlessness has been secured, namely,

(1) by the addition to the charge of certain salts, particularly potassium chloride or potassium hydrogen tartarate, or by the use of powdered tin or of some other substance which, dispersed throughout the gas from the powder, acts as an anti-oxidant and prevents its inflammation; [22]

(2) by incorporating carbonaceous material in the smokeless powder, by which means the composition of the gas is altered and

[22] Cf. Demougin, *Mém. poudres,* **25,** 130 (1932–33); Fauveau and Le Paire, *ibid.,* **25,** 142 (1932–33); Prettre, *ibid.,* **25,** 160, 169 (1932–33).

the number of mols of gas is actually increased while the temperature is lowered;

(3) by incorporating in the powder a *cool explosive*, such as ammonium nitrate, guanidine nitrate, or nitroguanidine, which explodes or burns with the production of gas notably cooler than the gas from the combustion of ordinary smokeless powder; and

(4) by contriving the ignition of the powder, the acceleration of its burning rate, and the design of the gun itself, any or all these factors, in such fashion that the projectile takes up energy from the powder gas more quickly and more effectively than is ordinarily the case, and thereby lowers the temperature of the gas to a point where the flash is extinguished.

The first of these methods is applicable to all calibers; the second and the third are successful only with calibers of less than 6 inches; the fourth has not yet been sufficiently studied and exploited. It is true, however, that an improved igniter, with the same gun and with the same powder, may determine the difference between a flash and a flashless discharge.

The use of salts to produce flashlessness appears to derive from an early observation of Dautriché that a small amount of black powder, added to the smokeless powder charge of small-arms ammunition, makes the discharge flashless. During the first World War the French regularly loaded a part of their machine gun ammunition with a propellant consisting of 9 parts of smokeless powder and 1 of black powder.

The Germans in their cannon used *anti-flash bags* or *Vorlage*, loaded at the base of the projectiles, between the projectiles and the propelling charges. These consisted of two perforated discs of artificial silk or cotton cloth sewed together in the form of doughnut-shaped bags. The bags were filled with coarsely pulverized potassium chloride. The artillerymen were not informed of the nature of the contents of the bags but were advised against using any whose contents had hardened to a solid cake, and were instructed in their tactical use as follows.

> In firing with *Vorlage*, there is produced a red fire [a red glow] at the muzzle and in front of the piece. The smoke is colored red [by the glow]. This light however gives no reflection in the heavens. In fact it is visible and appreciable at a distance only if the piece is placed in such a way that

the enemy can see its muzzle. In the daytime, *Vorlage* must be used only when the weather is so dark that the flashes of the shots without them are more visible than the clouds of smoke which they produce. The opaqueness of the background against which the battery stands out or the obscurity of the setting which surrounds it are also at times of a kind to justify the use of *Vorlage* in the daytime.

The anti-flash bags reduced the range by 4.5 to 8%.

Fauveau and Le Paire [23] studied the anti-flash effect of potassium chloride and of other salts and concluded that the lowering of the temperature of the gas which undoubtedly results from their volatilization and dissociation is insufficient to account for the extinction of the flash. Prettre [24] found that the chlorides of sodium and of lithium, and other alkali metal salts which are volatile, had the same effect as potassium chloride. He found that small amounts of potassium chloride, volatilized in mixtures of carbon monoxide and air, had a powerful anti-oxidant action and a correspondingly large effect in raising the temperature of inflammation of the gas. Some of his results are shown in the table below. He found that potassium chloride was without effect

MILLIGRAMS OF KCl PER LITER OF GASEOUS MIXTURE	TEMPERATURE (°C.) OF INFLAMMATION OF AIR CONTAINING		
	24.8% CO	44.1% CO	67.3% CO
0.0	656	657	680
0.4	...	750	800
0.5	730	...	820
0.7	...	810	900
1.0	790	850	1020
1.3	810	...	...
2.0	890	950	...
2.5	...	1000	...
3.0	970	...	...
3.5	1010	...	...

upon the temperature of inflammation of mixtures of hydrogen and air.

The French have used anti-flash bags (*sachets antilueurs*) filled with the crude potassium hydrogen tartarate (about 70%

[23] *Loc. cit.*
[24] *Loc. cit.*

pure) or *argols* which is a by-product of the wine industry. The flat, circular, cotton bags containing the argols were assembled along with the smokeless powder and black powder igniter in silk cartridge bags to make up the complete charge. Since the anti-flash material tended to reduce the ballistic effect of the charge, it was necessary when firing flashless rounds to add an *appoint* or additional quantity of smokeless powder. Thus, for ordinary firing of the 155-mm. gun, the charge consisted of 10 kilograms of *poudre BM7* along with an igniter system containing a total of 115 grams of black powder. For a flashless round, 3 *sachets* containing 500 grams of argols each were used and an additional 305 grams of smokeless powder to restore the ballistics to normal.

Another method of securing flashlessness was by the use of pellets (*pastilles*) of a compressed intimate mixture of 4 parts of potassium nitrate and 1 part of crystalline DNT. Pellets for use in the 155-mm. gun weighed 1 gram each, and were about 2 mm. thick and 15 mm. in diameter. Two or three hundred of these were sewed up in a silk bag which was loaded into the gun along with the bag containing the powder. The pellets burned with the same velocity as *poudre B*, and had but very little effect upon the ballistics. They of course produced a certain amount of smoke and the discharge gave a red glow from the muzzle of the gun.

Oxanilide functions well as an anti-flash agent if it is distributed throughout the powder charge, but not if it is loaded into the gun in separate bags like the materials which have just been mentioned. It is made into a thick paste with glue solution, the paste is extruded in the form of little worms or pellets, and these are dried. Pellets to the amount of 15% of the powder charge produce flashlessness in the 6-inch gun, but the charge is more difficult to light than ordinarily and requires a special igniter.

Oxanilide and many other carbonaceous materials, incorporated in the grains of colloided powder, yield powders which are flashless in guns of the smaller calibers and, in many cases, are as powerful, weight for weight, as powders which contain none of the inert, or at least non-explosive, ingredients. If nitrocellulose burning in the gun produces 1 mol of carbon dioxide and a certain amount of other gaseous products, then nitrocellulose plus 1 mol of carbon under the same conditions will produce 2 mols of carbon monoxide along with substantially the same amount of the other gaseous products. There will be more gas and cooler gas. A colloided powder made from pyrocellulose 85 parts and hydrocellulose 15 parts is flashless in the 75-mm. gun, and gives practically the same ballistic results as a hotter and more expensive powder made from straight nitrocellulose. The strength of the powder may be increased without affecting its flashlessness by substituting part of the pyrocellulose by guncotton of a higher nitrogen content.

Among the materials which have been incorporated into colloided powder for the purpose of reducing or extinguishing the flash are (1) substances, such as starch, hydrocellulose, and anthracene, which are insoluble in the colloid and are non-explosive. They, of course, must exist in a state of fine subdivision to be suitable for this use. Other anti-flash agents are (2) solid or liquid non-explosive substances, such as diethyldiphenylurea and dibutyl phthalate, which are solvents for nitrocellulose and dissolve in the colloid. They reduce the hygroscopicity of the powder and they reduce the amount of volatile solvent which is needed for the manufacture. Still others are (3) the explosive solid and liquid aromatic nitro compounds which are solvents for nitrocellulose and are effective in reducing both the flash and the hygroscopicity. All or any of the substances in these three classes may be used either in a straight nitrocellulose or in a nitrocellulose-nitroglycerin powder. Several flashless powders have been described in the section on the "Classification of Smokeless Powders." Many varieties have been covered by numerous patents. We cite only a single example,[25] for a smokeless, flashless, non-hygroscopic propellent powder made from about 76–79% nitrocellulose (of at least 13% nitrogen content), about 21–24% dinitrotoluene, and about 0.8–1.2% diphenylamine. During the first World War the French and the Italians used a *superattenuated* ballistite, made without volatile solvent, and containing enough aromatic dinitro compound (in place of part of the nitroglycerin) to make it flashless. In a typical case the powder was made from 30 parts CP_1, 30 CP_2, 15 DNT, and 25 nitroglycerin.

[25] U. S. Pat. 2,228,309 (1941), Ellsworth S. Goodyear.

Ball-Grain Powder

The process for the manufacture of ball-grain powder which Olsen and his co-workers have devised [26] combines nicely with Olsen's process for the quick stabilization of nitrocellulose to form a sequence of operations by which a finished powder may be produced more rapidly and more safely than by the usual process. It supplies a convenient means of making up a powder which contains non-volatile solvents throughout the mass of the grains or deterrent or accelerant coatings upon their surface.

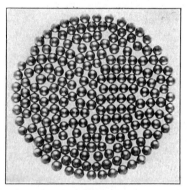

FIGURE 81. Ball Grains (Smokeless Powder) (3×). (Courtesy Western Cartridge Company.)

Nitrocellulose, pulped and given a preliminary or sour boiling, may be used directly without poaching. Deteriorated smokeless powder, containing nitro derivatives of diphenylamine and acidic decomposition products, may be reduced to a coarse powder under water in a hammer mill, and may then be used. Whichever is used, the first necessity is to stabilize it by complete removal of the acid. For this purpose, the material in the presence of water (which may contain a little chalk in suspension or urea in solution) is introduced into a still where it is dissolved with agitation in ethyl acetate to form a heavy syrup or lacquer, and is treated with some substance which is adsorbed by nitrocellulose more readily than acid is adsorbed. It is a curious fact that nitrocellulose is dissolved or dispersed by ethyl acetate much more readily

[26] U. S. Pat. 2,027,114 (1936), Olsen, Tibbitts, and Kerone; also U. S. Pats. 2,111,075 (1938), 2,175,212 (1939), 2,206,916 (1940).

in the presence of water than when water is absent. Diphenylamine is dissolved in the ethyl acetate before the latter is added
to the water and nitrocellulose in the still. At the same time,
centralite or DNT or any other substance which it may be desired
to incorporate in the powder is also dissolved and added. The
water phase and the lacquer are then stirred for 30 minutes by
which operation the nitrocellulose is stabilized.[27] Starch or gum
arabic solution to secure the requisite colloidal behavior is then
introduced into the still, the still is closed, the temperature is
raised so that the lacquer becomes less viscous, and the mixture

FIGURE 82. Cross Section of Ball Grain, Double Base, Deterrent Coated
(112×). (Courtesy Western Cartridge Company.)

under pressure is agitated vigorously until the lacquer is broken
up into small globules of the correct size. The pressure is then
reduced, and the ethyl acetate is distilled off and recovered. If
the distillation is carried out too rapidly, the grains are shaped
like kernels of popcorn. If it is carried out at such a rate that the
volatile solvent is evaporated from the surface of the globules no
faster than it moves from the interior to the surface, if the distillation is slow at first and more rapid afterwards, then smooth
ball grains are formed, dense and of homogeneous structure.

[27] Diphenylamine in the presence of water thus has an action beyond
that which it has when it is added to the nitrocellulose gel (in the absence
of a separate water phase) during the manufacture of smokeless powder
by the usual process. Being preferentially adsorbed by the nitrocellulose, it
drives any acid which may be present out of the nitrocellulose and into
the water. After that it fulfils its usual function in the powder.

After the material has cooled, the powder grains are transferred
in a slurry to another still and are treated with an emulsion of
nitroglycerin dissolved in toluene, or of some other coating agent
dissolved in a solvent in which nitrocellulose itself is insoluble,
and the volatile solvent is distilled off, leaving the nitroglycerin
or other material deposited on the surface of the grains. As much
nitroglycerin as 15% of the weight of the powder may be applied
in this way. A coating of centralite may, if desired, be put on top
of it. The grains are sieved under water and are then dried for
use in shotguns. If the powder is to be used in rifles, it is passed
in a slurry between warm steel rollers by which all the grains are
reduced to the same least dimension or web thickness. Previous
to the drying, all the operations in the manufacture of ball-grain
powder are carried out under water, and are safe. After the drying, the operations involve the same hazards, by no means in-
surmountable, as are involved in the ordinary process. The grains
are glazed with graphite and blended.

CHAPTER VII

DYNAMITE AND OTHER HIGH EXPLOSIVES

Invention of Dynamite

Dynamite and the fulminate blasting cap both resulted from Alfred Nobel's effort to make nitroglycerin more safe and more convenient to use.[1] Having discovered that nitroglycerin is exploded by the explosion of a small firecracker-like device filled with black powder, he tried the effect of mixing the two materials, and in 1863 was granted a patent [2] which covered the use of a liquid explosive, such as nitroglycerin or methyl or ethyl nitrate, in mixture with gunpowder in order to increase the effectiveness of the latter. The amount of the liquid was limited by the requirement that the mixtures should be dry and granular in character. The explosives were supposed to be actuated by fire, like black powder, but the liquid tended to slow down the rate of burning, and they were not notably successful. The same patent also covered the possibility of substituting a part of the saltpeter by nitroglycerin. Because this substance is insoluble in water and non-hygroscopic, it acts as a protective covering for the salt and makes the use of sodium nitrate possible in these mixtures.

Nobel's next patent,[3] granted in 1864, related to improvements in the manufacture of nitroglycerin and to the exploding of it by heating or by means of a detonating charge. He continued his experiments and in 1867 was granted a patent [4] for an explosive prepared by mixing nitroglycerin with a suitable non-explosive, porous absorbent such as charcoal or siliceous earth. The resulting material was much less sensitive to shock than nitroglycerin. It was known as *dynamite*, and was manufactured and sold also

---

[1] For an account of Nobel and his inventions see de Mosenthal, *Jour. Soc. Chem. Ind.*, 443 (1899).

[2] Brit. Pat. 2359 (1863).

[3] Brit. Pat. 1813 (1864).

[4] Brit. Pat. 1345 (1867).

under the name of Nobel's Safety Powder. The absorbent which was finally chosen as being most satisfactory was diatomaceous earth or kieselguhr (guhr or fuller's earth). Nobel believed that dynamite could be exploded by a spark or by fire if it was confined closely, but preferred to explode it under all conditions by means of a special exploder or cap containing a strong charge of

FIGURE 83. Alfred Nobel (1833-1896). First manufactured and used nitroglycerin commercially, 1863; invented dynamite and the fulminate blasting cap, 1867; straight dynamite, 1869; blasting gelatin and gelatin dynamite, 1875; and ballistite, 1888. He left the major part of his large fortune for the endowment of prizes, now known as the Nobel Prizes, for notable achievements in physics, in chemistry, in physiology and medicine, in literature, and in the promotion of peace.

mercury fulminate, crimped tightly to the end of the fuse in order that it might detonate more strongly. He stated that the form of the cap might be varied greatly but that its action depended upon the sudden development of an intense pressure or shock.

Dynamite with an inactive base (guhr dynamite) is not manufactured commercially in this country. Small quantities are used for experimental purposes where a standard of comparison is needed in studies on the strength of various explosives.

The next important event in the development of these explosives was Nobel's invention of *dynamite with an active base*,[5] an explosive in which the nitroglycerin was absorbed by a mixture of materials which were themselves not explosive separately, such as potassium, sodium, or ammonium nitrate mixed with wood meal, charcoal, rosin, sugar, or starch. The nitroglycerin formed a thin coating upon the particles of the solid materials, and caused them to explode if a fulminate cap was used. The patent suggested a mixture of barium nitrate 70 parts, rosin or charcoal 10, and nitroglycerin 20, with or without the addition of sulfur, as an example of the invention. Nitroglycerin alone was evidently not enough to prevent the deliquescence of sodium and ammonium nitrate in these mixtures, for a later patent[6] of Nobel claimed the addition of small amounts of paraffin, ozokerite, stearine, naphthalene, or of any similar substance which is solid at ordinary temperatures and is of a fatty nature, as a coating for the particles to prevent the absorption of moisture by the explosive and the resulting danger from the exudation of nitroglycerin.

Dynamite with an active base is manufactured and used extensively in this country and in Canada and Mexico. It is known as *straight dynamite*, or simply as dynamite, presumably because its entire substance contributes to the energy of its explosion. The standard 40% straight dynamite which is used in comparative tests at the U. S. Bureau of Mines contains[7] nitroglycerin 40%, sodium nitrate 44%, calcium carbonate (anti-acid) 1%, and wood pulp 15%. Since the time when this standard was adopted, the usage of the term "straight" has altered somewhat in consequence of changes in American manufacturing practice, with the result that this standard material is now better designated as 40% straight nitroglycerin (straight) dynamite. This name distinguishes it from 40% l. f. or 40% low-freezing (straight) dynamite which contains, instead of straight nitroglycerin, a mixture of nitric esters produced by nitrating a mix-

---

[5] Brit. Pat. 442 (1869).

[6] Brit. Pat. 1570 (1873).

[7] C. A. Taylor and W. H. Rinkenbach, "Explosives, Their Materials, Constitution, and Analysis," *U. S. Bur. Mines Bull.* 219, Washington, 1923, p. 133.

ture of glycerin and glycol or of glycerin and sugar. Practically all active-base dynamites now manufactured in the United States, whether straight or ammonia or gelatin, are of this l. f. variety. American straight dynamites contain from 20 to 60% of mixed nitric esters absorbed on wood pulp and mixed with enough sodium or potassium nitrate to maintain the oxygen balance and to take care of the oxidation of part or occasionally of all the wood pulp.

Judson powder is a special, low-grade dynamite in which 5 to 15% of nitroglycerin is used as a coating on a granular *dope* made by mixing ground coal with sodium nitrate and sulfur, warming the materials together until the sulfur is melted, forming into grains which harden on cooling and are screened for size. It is intermediate in power between black powder and ordinary dynamite and is used principally for moving earth and soft rock in railroad work.

Nobel's inventions of *blasting gelatin* and *gelatin dynamite* are both covered by the same patent.[8] Seven or 8% of collodion cotton dissolved in nitroglycerin converted it to a stiff jelly which was suitable for use as a powerful high explosive. Solvents, such as acetone, ether-alcohol, and nitrobenzene, facilitated the incorporation of the two substances in the cold, but Nobel reported that collodion cotton dissolved readily in nitroglycerin without additional solvent if the nitroglycerin was warmed gently on the water bath. A cheaper explosive of less power could be made by mixing the gelatinized nitroglycerin with black powder or with mixtures composed of an oxidizing agent, such as a nitrate or chlorate, and a combustible material, such as coal dust, sulfur, sawdust, sugar, starch, or rosin. A typical gelatin dynamite consists of nitroglycerin 62.5%, collodion cotton 2.5%, saltpeter 27.0%, and wood meal 8%. A softer jelly is used for making gelatin dynamite than is suitable for use by itself as a blasting gelatin, and somewhat less collodion is used in proportion to the amount of nitroglycerin.

All straight nitroglycerin explosives can be frozen. Straight dynamite when frozen becomes less sensitive to shock and to initiation, but blasting gelatin becomes slightly more sensitive.

[8] Brit. Pat. 4179 (1875).

When the explosives are afterwards thawed, the nitroglycerin shows a tendency to exude.

Invention of Ammonium Nitrate Explosives

In 1867 two Swedish chemists, C. J. Ohlsson and J. H. Norrbin, patented an explosive, called *ammoniakkrut*, which consisted of ammonium nitrate either alone or in mixture with charcoal, sawdust, naphthalene, picric acid, nitroglycerin, or nitrobenzene. Theoretical calculations had shown that large quantities of heat and gas were given off by the explosions of these mixtures. The proportions of the materials were selected in such manner that all the carbon should be converted to carbon dioxide and all the hydrogen to water. Some of these explosives were difficult to ignite and to initiate, but the trouble was remedied by including some nitroglycerin in their compositions and by firing them with fulminate detonators. They were used to some extent in Sweden. Nobel purchased the invention from his fellow-countrymen early in the 1870's, and soon afterwards took out another patent [9] in connection with it, but still found that the hygroscopicity of the ammonium nitrate created real difficulty. He was not able to deal satisfactorily with the trouble until after the invention of gelatin dynamite. In present manufacturing practice in this country the tendency of the ammonium nitrate to take up water is counteracted by coating the particles with water-repelling substances, oils, or metallic soaps.

In 1879 Nobel took out a Swedish patent for *extra-dynamite* (ammon-gelatin-dynamit), one example of which was a fortified gelatin dynamite consisting of nitroglycerin 71%, collodion 4%, charcoal 2%, and ammonium nitrate 23%. Another contained much less nitroglycerin, namely, 25%, along with collodion 1%, charcoal 12%, and ammonium nitrate 62%, and was crumbly and plastic between the fingers rather than clearly gelatinous.

In these explosives, and in the ammonium nitrate *permissible* explosives which contain still less nitroglycerin, it is supposed that the nitroglycerin or the nitroglycerin jelly, which coats the particles of ammonium nitrate, carries the explosive impulse originating in the detonator, that this causes the ammonium nitrate to decompose explosively to produce nitrogen and water

[9] The above-cited Brit. Pat. 1570 (1873).

and oxygen, the last named of which enters into a further explosive reaction with the charcoal or other combustible material. Other explosive liquids or solids, such as liquid or solid DNT, TNT, or TNX, nitroglycol, nitrostarch, or nitrocellulose, may be used to sensitize the ammonium nitrate and to make the mixture more easily detonated by a blasting cap. Non-explosive combustible materials, such as rosin, coal, sulfur, cereal meal, and paraffin, also work as sensitizers for ammonium nitrate, and a different hypothesis is required to explain their action.

Guhr Dynamite

Guhr dynamite is used rather widely in Europe. It is not hygroscopic. Liquid water however, brought into contact with it, is absorbed by the kieselguhr and displaces the nitroglycerin which separates in the form of an oily liquid. The nitroglycerin thus set free in a wet bore hole might easily seep away into a fissure in the rock where it would later be exploded accidentally by a drill or by the blow of a pick. Water does not cause the separation of nitroglycerin from blasting gelatin or gelatin dynamite. It tends to dissolve the soluble salts which are present in straight dynamite and to liberate in the liquid state any nitroglycerin with which they may be coated.

Guhr dynamite, made from 1 part of kieselguhr and 3 parts of nitroglycerin, is not exploded by a blow of wood upon wood, but is exploded by a blow of iron or other metal upon iron. In the drop test it is exploded by the fall of a 1-kilogram weight through 12 to 15 cm., or by the fall of a 2-kilogram weight through 7 cm. The frozen material is less sensitive: a drop of more than 1 meter of the kilogram weight or of at least 20 cm. of the 2-kilogram weight is necessary to explode it. Frozen or unfrozen it is exploded in a paper cartridge by the impact of a bullet from a military rifle. A small sample will burn quietly in the open, but will explode if it is lighted within a confined space. A cartridge explodes if heated on a metal plate.

The velocity of detonation of guhr dynamite varies with the density of loading and with the diameter of the charge, but does not reach values equal to the maxima under best conditions for nitroglycerin and blasting gelatin. Velocities of 6650 to 6800 meters per second, at a density of loading of 1.50 (the highest which is practical) have been reported. Naoúm,[10] working with charges in an iron pipe 34 mm. in internal diameter and at a density of loading of 1.30, found for nitroglycerin guhr dynamite a velocity of detonation of 5650 meters per second, and, under the same conditions, for nitroglycol guhr dynamite one of 6000 meters per second.

Figure 84. Determination of the Velocity of Detonation of Dynamite by the Dautriche Method. (Courtesy Hercules Powder Company.) Compare Figure 9, page 17.

Dynamites, like guhr dynamite and straight dynamite, which contain nitroglycerin in the subdivided but liquid state communicate explosion from cartridge to cartridge more readily, and in general are more easy to initiate, than blasting gelatin and gelatin dynamite in which no liquid nitroglycerin is present. A cartridge of guhr dynamite 30 mm. in diameter will propagate its explosion through a distance of 30 cm. to a similar cartridge.

[10] Phokion Naoúm, "Nitroglycerine and Nitroglycerine Explosives," trans. E. M. Symmes, Baltimore, The Williams and Wilkins Company, 1928, p. 277.

Straight Dynamite

Straight dynamite containing 60% or less of mixed nitric esters—but not more because of the danger of exudation—is used extensively in the United States, but has found little favor in

FIGURE 85. Dynamite Manufacture. (Courtesy Hercules Powder Company.) Rubbing the dry ingredients of dynamite through a screen into the bowl of a mixing machine.

Europe. It is made simply by mixing the explosive oil with the absorbent materials; the resulting loose, moist-appearing or greasy mass, from which oil ought not to exude under gentle pressure, is put up in cartridges or cylinders wrapped in paraffined paper and dipped into melted paraffin wax to seal them against moisture.

The strength of straight nitroglycerin dynamite is expressed by the per cent of nitroglycerin which it contains. Thus, "40% straight nitroglycerin dynamite" contains 40% of nitroglycerin, but "40% ammonia dynamite," "40% gelatin dynamite," etc., whatever their compositions may be, are supposed to have the same strength or explosive force as 40% straight nitroglycerin dynamite. Munroe and Hall [11] in 1915 reported for typical straight nitroglycerin dynamites the compositions which are

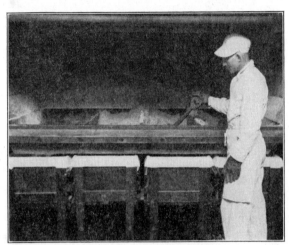

FIGURE 86. Dynamite Manufacture. (Courtesy Hercules Powder Company.) Hoppers underneath the mixing machine, showing the buggies which carry the mixed dynamite to the packing machines.

shown in the following table. Although these dynamites are not now manufactured commercially in the United States, their explosive properties, studied intensively at the U. S. Bureau of

	STRENGTH									
	15%	20%	25%	30%	35%	40%	45%	50%	55%	60%
Nitroglycerin	15	20	25	30	35	40	45	50	55	60
Combustible material	20	19	18	17	16	15	14	14	15	16
Sodium nitrate......	64	60	56	52	48	44	40	35	29	23
Calcium or magnesium carbonate ...	1	1	1	1	1	1	1	1	1	1

Mines and reported as a matter of interest, do not differ greatly from those of the l. f. dynamites by which they have been superseded in common use. The combustible material stated to be used in these compositions consists of a mixture of wood pulp,

[11] Charles E. Munroe and Clarence Hall, "A Primer on Explosives for Metal Miners and Quarrymen," *U. S. Bur. Mines Bull.* 80, Washington, 1915, p. 22.

flour, and brimstone for the grades below 40% strength, wood pulp alone for the 40% and stronger. In commercial practice the dope sometimes contains coarse combustible material, like rice hulls, sawdust, or bran, which makes the explosive more bulky and has the effect of reducing the velocity of detonation. Tests at the U. S. Bureau of Mines on standard straight dynamites in cartridges 1¼ inches in diameter showed for the 30% grade a velocity of detonation of 4548 meters per second, for the 40%

FIGURE 87. Dynamite Manufacture. (Courtesy Hercules Powder Company.) Dumping the mixed dynamite onto the conveyor belt which raises it to the hopper of the semi-automatic packing machine.

grade 4688 meters per second, and for the 60% grade 6246 meters per second. The 40% dynamite was exploded in one case out of three by an 11-cm. drop of a 2-kilogram weight, in no case out of five by a 10-cm. drop. Cartridges 1¼ inches in diameter and 8 inches long transmitted explosion from one to another through a distance of 16 inches once in two trials, but not through a distance of 17 inches in three trials. The 40% dynamite gave a small lead block compression of 16.0 mm., and an expansion (average of three) in the Trauzl test of 278 cc.[12]

[12] Clarence Hall, W. O. Snelling, and S. P. Howell, "Investigations of Explosives Used in Coal Mines," *U. S. Bur. Mines Bull.* 15, Washington, 1912, pp. 171, 173.

Munroe and Hall [13] also reported the following compositions for typical ordinary and low-freezing ammonia dynamites, the combustible material in each case being a mixture of wood pulp, flour, and brimstone. Low-freezing dynamites at present in use in this country contain nitroglycol or nitrosugar instead of the above-mentioned nitrosubstitution compounds. In Europe dinitro-chlorohydrin, tetranitrodiglycerin, and other nitric esters are used.

Strength	Ordinary					Low-Freezing				
	30%	35%	40%	50%	60%	30%	35%	40%	50%	60%
Nitroglycerin............	15	20	22	27	35	13	17	17	21	27
Nitrosubstitution compounds...............	..	..	..	..	..	3	4	4	5	6
Ammonium nitrate.......	15	15	20	25	30	15	15	20	25	30
Sodium nitrate..........	51	48	42	36	24	53	49	45	36	27
Combustible material....	18	16	15	11	10	15	14	13	12	9
Calcium carbonate or zinc oxide................	1	1	1	1	1	1	1	1	1	1

Three of the standard French ammonia dynamites, according to Naoúm,[14] have the compositions and explosive properties listed below.

Nitroglycerin	40	20	22
Ammonium nitrate	45	75	75
Sodium nitrate	5	...	...
Wood or cereal meal	10	5	...
Charcoal	...	...	3
Lead block expansion	400.0 cc.	335.0 cc.	330.0 cc.
Lead block crushing	22.0 mm.	15.5 mm.	16.0 mm.
Density	1.38	1.20	1.33

Taylor and Rinkenbach [15] report typical analyses of American ammonium nitrate dynamite (I below) and ammonium nitrate sodium nitrate dynamite (II below). These formulas really represent ammonium nitrate permissible explosives, very close in their

[13] *Op. cit.*, p. 23. [15] *Op. cit.*, pp. 136, 138.
[14] *Op. cit.*, p. 285.

compositions to Monobel (III below) which is permissible in this country for use in coal mines. Naoúm [16] reports that this

	I	II	III
Nitroglycerin	9.50	9.50	10.0
Ammonium nitrate	79.45	69.25	80.0
Sodium nitrate	...	10.20	...
Carbonaceous combustible material [17]	9.75	9.65	...
Wood meal	...	...	10.0
Anti-acid	0.40	0.50	...
Moisture	0.90	0.90	...

Monobel (density about 1.15) gives a lead block expansion of about 350 cc. and a lead block crushing of 12 mm. He states that

FIGURE 88. Dynamite Manufacture. (Courtesy Hercules Powder Company.) Cartridges of dynamite as they come from the semi-automatic packing machine.

Monobel belongs to the class of typical ammonium nitrate explosives rather than to the dynamites, and points out that no specific effect can be ascribed to the 10% nitroglycerin which it contains, for an explosive containing only a small quantity, say 4%,

[16] *Op. cit.,* p. 286,

[17] The carbonaceous combustible material contains 0.40% grease or oil which was added to the ammonium nitrate to counteract its hygroscopicity. Note that the figures in the first two columns of the table represent results of analyses; those in the third column represent the formula according to which the explosive is mixed.

of nitroglycerin, or none at all, will give essentially the same performance. But the ammonium nitrate explosive with no nitroglycerin in it is safer to handle and more difficult to detonate.

Blasting Gelatin

Blasting gelatin exists as a yellowish, translucent, elastic mass of density about 1.63. Strong pressure does not cause nitroglycerin to exude from it. Its surface is rendered milky by long contact with water, but its explosive strength is unaffected. It is less sensitive to shock, blows, and friction than nitroglycerin, guhr dynamite, and straight dynamite, for its elasticity enables it more readily to absorb the force of a blow, and a thin layer explodes under a hammer more easily than a thick one. Blasting gelatin freezes with difficulty. When frozen, it loses its elasticity and flexibility, and becomes a hard, white mass. Unlike guhr dynamite and straight dynamite, it is more sensitive to shock when frozen than when in the soft and unfrozen state.

Unlike nitroglycerin, blasting gelatin takes fire easily from a flame or from the spark of a fuse. Its combustion is rapid and violent, and is accompanied by a hissing sound. If a large quantity is burning, the combustion is likely to become an explosion, and the same result is likely to follow if even a small quantity of the frozen material is set on fire.

Pulverulent explosives or explosive mixtures are easier to initiate and propagate detonation for a greater distance than liquid explosives, especially viscous ones, and these are easier to detonate and propagate more readily than colloids. The stiffer the colloid the more difficult it becomes to initiate, until, with increasingly large proportions of nitrocellulose in the nitroglycerin gel, tough, horny colloids are formed, like ballistite and cordite, which in sizable aggregates can be detonated only with difficulty. Blasting gelatin is more difficult to detonate than any of the forms of dynamite in which the nitroglycerin exists in the liquid state. Naoúm [18] reports that a freshly prepared blasting gelatin made from 93 parts of nitroglycerin and 7 parts of collodion cotton is exploded by a No. 1 (the weakest) blasting cap and propagates detonation even in 25-mm. cartridges across a gap of about 10 mm. A blasting gelatin containing 9% of collodion cotton requires a No. 4 blasting cap to make it explode and propagates

[18] *Op. cit.,* p. 316.

its explosion to an adjacent cartridge only when initiated by a No. 6 blasting cap.

Blasting gelatin and gelatin dynamite on keeping become less sensitive to detonation, and, after long storage in a warm climate, may even become incapable of being detonated. The effect has been thought to be due to the small air bubbles which make newly prepared blasting gelatin appear practically white but which disappear when the material is kept in storage and becomes translucent and yellowish. But this cannot be the whole cause of the effect, for the colloid becomes stiffer after keeping. The loss of sensitivity is accompanied by a rapid dropping off in the velocity of detonation and in the brisance. According to Naoúm,[19] blasting gelatin containing 7% collodion cotton when newly prepared gave a lead block expansion of 600 cc., after 2 days 580 cc., and one containing 9% collodion gave when freshly made an expansion of 580 cc., after 2 days 545 cc.

Blasting gelatin under the most favorable conditions has a velocity of detonation of about 8000 meters per second. In iron pipes it attains this velocity only if its cross section exceeds 30 mm. in diameter, and it attains it only at a certain distance away from the point of initiation, so that in the Dautriche method where short lengths are used lower values are generally obtained. In tubes of 20–25 mm. diameter, and with samples of a sensitivity reduced either by storage or by an increased toughness of the colloid, values as low as 2000–2500 meters per second have been observed.

Gelatin Dynamite $0 - 5\%$

Blasting gelatin is not used very widely in the United States; the somewhat less powerful gelatin dynamite, or simply gelatin as it is called, is much more popular. Gelatin dynamite is essentially a straight dynamite in which a gel is used instead of the liquid nitroglycerin or l. f. mixture of nitric esters. It is a plastic mass which can be kneaded and shaped. The gel contains between 2 and 5.4% collodion cotton, and is not tough and really elastic like blasting gelatin. Correspondingly it is initiated more easily and has a higher velocity of detonation and better propagation. The gel is prepared by mixing the nitroglycerin and collodion cotton, allowing to stand at 40–45°C. for some hours or over

[19] *Op. cit.,* p. 322.

night, and then incorporating mechanically with the dope materials which have been previously mixed together. Munroe and Hall [20] in 1915 gave the compositions listed below as typical of gelatin dynamites offered for sale at that time in this country. Instead of straight nitroglycerin, l. f. mixtures of nitric esters are now used.

	STRENGTH						
	30%	35%	40%	50%	55%	60%	70%
Nitroglycerin	23.0	28.0	33.0	42.0	46.0	50.0	60.0
Nitrocellulose	0.7	0.9	1.0	1.5	1.7	1.9	2.4
Sodium nitrate	62.3	58.1	52.0	45.5	42.3	38.1	29.6
Combustible material [21]	13.0	12.0	13.0	10.0	9.0	9.0	7.0
Calcium carbonate	1.0	1.0	1.0	1.0	1.0	1.0	1.0

The three standard explosives which are used in Great Britain are called respectively blasting gelatin, gelatin dynamite, and *Gelignite*. Gelignite, let us note, is a variety of gelatin dynamite as the latter term is used in this country. It is the most widely used of the three and may indeed be regarded as the standard explosive.

	BLASTING GELATIN	GELATIN DYNAMITE	GELIGNITE
Nitroglycerin	92	75	60
Collodion cotton	8	5	4
Wood meal	..	5	8
Potassium nitrate	..	15	28

The gelatin dynamites most widely used in Germany contain about 65 parts of gelatinized nitroglycerin and about 35 parts of dope or absorbent material. The dope for an explosive for domestic use consists of 76.9% sodium nitrate, 22.6% wood meal, and 0.5% chalk, and for one for export of 80% potassium nitrate, 19.5% wood meal, and 0.5% chalk. A weaker *Gelignite II* and certain high-strength gelatin dynamites, as tabulated below, are also manufactured for export.

	GELIGNITE II	HIGH-STRENGTH GELATIN DYNAMITE		
		80%	81%	75%
Nitroglycerin	47.5	75	75.8	70.4
Collodion cotton	2.5	5	5.2	4.6
Potassium nitrate	37.5	15	15.2	19.3
Wood meal with chalk......	3.5	5	3.8	5.7
Rye meal	9.0	..	...	...

[20] *Op. cit.*, p. 23.

[21] Wood pulp was used in the 60% and 70% grades. Flour, wood pulp, and, in some examples, rosin and brimstone were used in the other grades.

The gelatin dynamites manufactured in Belgium are called *Forcites*. The reported compositions of several of them are tabulated below. *Forcite extra* is an ammonia gelatin dynamite.

	For- cite Extra	For- cite Per- ieure	For- cite Su- per- For- cite	For- cite No. 1	For- cite No. 1P	For- cite No. 2	For- cite No. 2P
Nitroglycerin	64	64	64	49	49	36	36
Collodion cotton	3.5	3	3	2	2	3	2
Sodium nitrate	..	24	..	36	..	35	..
Potassium nitrate	..	..	23	..	37	..	46
Ammonium nitrate	25	..	..	..	..	..	..
Wood meal	6.5	8	9	13	11	11	..
Bran	..	..	..	..	..	14	15
Magnesium carbonate	1	1	1	1	1	1	1

In France gelatin dynamites are known by the names indicated in the following table where the reported compositions of several of them are tabulated.

	Dynamite-gomme-extra-forte	Dynamite-gomme-potasse	Dynamite-gomme-soude	Gélatine A	Gélatine B-potasse	Gélatine B-soude	Gomme E	Gélignite
Nitroglycerin	92–93	82–83	82–83	64	57.5	57	49	58
Collodion cotton	8–7	6–5	6–5	3	2.5	3	2	2
Potassium nitrate	...	9–10	...	..	32.0	..	36	28
Sodium nitrate	...	...	9–10	24	..	34	..	..
Wood meal	...	2–3	2–3	8	8.0	6	10	9
Flour	...	...	...	..	..	..	3	3
Magnesium carbonate	...	...	...	1	..	..	..	..

Permissible Explosives

The atmosphere of coal mines frequently contains enough methane (fire damp) to make it explode from the flame of a black powder or dynamite blast. Dust also produces an explosive atmosphere, and it may happen, if dust is not already present, that one blast will stir up clouds of dust which the next blast will cause to explode. Accidents from this cause became more and more frequent as the industrial importance of coal increased during the nineteenth century and as the mines were dug deeper and contained more fire damp, until finally the various nations which were producers of coal appointed commissions to study and develop means of preventing them. The first of these was appointed in France in 1877, the British commission in 1879, the Prussian commission in 1881, and the Belgian and Austrian commissions at later dates. The Pittsburgh testing station of the U. S. Geological Survey was officially opened and regular work was commenced there on December 3, 1908, with the result that the first American list of explosives permissible for use in gaseous and dusty coal mines was issued May 15, 1909. On July 1, 1909, the station was taken over by the U. S. Bureau of Mines,[22] which, since January 1, 1918, has conducted its tests at the Explosives Experiment Station at Bruceton, not far from Pittsburgh, in Pennsylvania.

Explosives which are approved for use in gaseous and dusty coal mines are known in this country as *permissible* explosives, in England as *permitted* explosives, and are to be distinguished from *authorized* explosives which conform to certain conditions with respect to safety in handling, in transport, etc. Explosives which are safe for use in coal mines are known in France as *explosifs antigrisouteux*, in Belgium as *explosifs S. G. P.* (*sécurité, grisou, poussière*), in Germany as *schlagwettersichere Sprengstoffe* while the adjective *handhabungssichere* is applied to those which are safe in handling. Both kinds, permissible and authorized, are *safety explosives, explosifs de sûreté, Sicherheitssprengstoffe*.

A mixture of air and methane is explosive if the methane content lies between 5 and 14%. A mixture which contains 9.5% of methane, in which the oxygen exactly suffices for complete combustion, is the one which explodes most violently, propagates the explosion most easily, and produces the highest temperature. This mixture ignites at about 650° to 700°. Since explosives in general produce temperatures which are considerably above 1000°, explo-

[22] A few of the interesting and important publications of the U. S. Bureau of Mines are listed in the footnote, Vol. I, pp. 22–23.

sive mixtures of methane and air would always be exploded by them if it were not for the circumstance, discovered by Mallard and Le Chatelier,[23] that there is a certain delay or period of induction before the gaseous mixture actually explodes. At 650° this amounts to about 10 seconds, at 1000° to about 1 second, and at 2200° there is no appreciable delay and the explosion is presumed to follow instantaneously after the application of this temperature however momentary. Mallard and Le Chatelier concluded that an explosive having a temperature of explosion of 2200° or higher would invariably ignite fire damp. The French commission which was studying these questions at first decided that the essential characteristic of a permissible explosive should be that its calculated temperature of explosion should be not greater than 2200°, and later designated a temperature of 1500° as the maximum for explosives permissible in coal seams and 1900° for those intended to be used in the accompanying rock.

The flame which is produced by the explosion of a brisant explosive is of extremely short duration, and its high temperature continues only for a small fraction of a second, for the hot gases by expanding and by doing work immediately commence to cool themselves. If they are produced in the first place at a temperature below that of the instantaneous inflammation of fire damp, they may be cooled to such an extent that they are not sufficiently warm for a sufficiently long time to ignite fire damp at all. Black powder, burning slowly, always ignites explosive gas mixtures. But any high explosive may be made safe for use in gaseous mines by the addition to it of materials which reduce the initial temperature of the products of its explosion. Or, in cases where this initial temperature is not too high, the same safety may be secured by limiting the size of the charge and by firing the shot in a well-tamped bore hole under such conditions that the gases are obliged to do more mechanical work and are cooled the more in consequence.

Permissible explosives may be divided into two principal classes: (1) those which are and (2) those which are not based upon a high explosive which is cool in itself, such as ammonium nitrate, or guanidine nitrate, or nitroguanidine. The second class may be subdivided further, according to composition, into as

23 *Ann. Min.*, [8] 11, 274 (1887).

many classes as there are varieties in the compositions of high explosives, or it may be subdivided, irrespective of composition, according to the means which are used to reduce the explosion temperature. Thus, an explosive containing nitroglycerin, nitro-starch, chlorate or perchlorate, or tetranitronaphthalene, or an explosive which is essentially black powder, may have its temperature of explosion reduced by reason of the fact that (a) it contains an excess of carbonaceous material, (b) it contains water physically or chemically held in the mixture, or (c) it contains volatile salts or substances which are decomposed by heat. Ammonium nitrate may also be used as a means of lowering the temperature of explosion, and thus defines another subdivision (d) which corresponds to an overlapping of the two principal classes, (a) and (b).

Ammonium nitrate, although it is often not regarded as an explosive, may nevertheless be exploded by a suitable initiator. On complete detonation it decomposes in accordance with the equation

$$2NH_4NO_3 \longrightarrow 4H_2O + 2N_2 + O_2$$

but the effect of feeble initiation is to cause decomposition in another manner with the production of oxides of nitrogen. By using a booster of 20–30 grams of Bellite (an explosive consisting of a mixture of ammonium nitrate and dinitrobenzene) and a detonator containing 1 gram of mercury fulminate, Lobry de Bruyn [24] succeeded in detonating 180 grams of ammonium nitrate compressed in a 8-cm. shell. The shell was broken into many fragments. A detonator containing 3 grams of mercury fulminate, used without the booster of Bellite, produced only incomplete detonation. Lheure [25] secured complete detonation of cartridges of ammonium nitrate [26] loaded in bore holes in rock by means of a trinitrotoluene detonating fuse which passed completely through them.

The sensitiveness of ammonium nitrate to initiation is increased by the addition to it of explosive substances, such as nitroglycerin, nitrocellulose, or aromatic nitro compounds, or of

[24] *Rec. trav. chim.*, **10**, 127 (1891).

[25] *Ann. Min.*, [10] **12**, 169 (1907).

[26] On the explosibility of ammonium nitrate, see also Munroe, *Chem. Met. Eng.*, **26**, 535 (1922); Cook, *ibid.*, **31**, 231 (1924); Sherrick, *Army Ordnance*, **4**, 237, 329 (1924).

non-explosive combustible materials, such as rosin, sulfur, char-coal, flour, sugar, oil, or paraffin. Substances of the latter class react with the oxygen which the ammonium nitrate would other-wise liberate; they produce additional gas and heat, and increase both the power of the explosive and the temperature of its explo-sion. Pure ammonium nitrate has a temperature of explosion of about 1120° to 1130°. Ammonium nitrate explosives permissible in the United States generally produce instantaneous tempera-tures between 1500° and 2000°.

Among the first permissible explosives developed in France were certain ones of the Belgian Favier type which contained no nitroglycerin and consisted essentially of ammonium nitrate, sometimes with other nitrates, along with a combustible mate-rial such as naphthalene or nitrated naphthalene or other aro-matic nitro compounds. These explosives have remained the favorites in France for use in coal mines. The method of manu-facture is simple. The materials are ground together in a wheel mill, and the mass is broken up, sifted, and packed in paraffined paper cartridges. The compositions of the mixtures are those which calculations show to give the desired temperatures of ex-plosion. *Grisounites roches*, permissible for use in rock, have temperatures of explosion between 1500° and 1900°; *Grisounites couches*, for use in coal, below 1500°. Several typical composi-tions are listed below.

	Grisou-naphtalite-roche	Grisou-naphtalite-roche salpêtrée	Grisou-naphtalite-couche	Grisou-naphtalite-couche salpêtrée	Grisou-tétrylite-couche
Ammonium nitrate......	91.5	86.5	95	90	88
Potassium nitrate......	..	5.0	..	5	5
Dinitro-naphthalene.	8.5	8.5	..	..	..
Trinitro-naphthalene.	..	..	5	5	..
Tetryl........	..	..	..	..	7

The French also have permissible explosives containing both ammonium nitrate and nitroglycerin (gelatinized), with and without saltpeter. These are called *Grisou-dynamites* or *Grisoutines*.

	Grisou-dynamite-roche	Grisou-dynamite-roche salpêtrée	Grisou-dynamite-couche	Grisou-dynamite-couche salpêtrée
Nitroglycerin......	29.0	29.0	12.0	12.0
Collodion cotton....	1.0	1.0	0.5	0.5
Ammonium nitrate.	70.0	65.0	87.5	82.5
Potassium nitrate...	..	5.0	..	5.0

The effect of ammonium nitrate in lowering the temperature of explosion of nitroglycerin mixtures is nicely illustrated by the data of Naoúm [27] who reports that guhr dynamite (75% actual nitroglycerin) gives a temperature of 2940°, a mixture of equal amounts of guhr dynamite and ammonium nitrate 2090°, and a mixture of 1 part of guhr dynamite and 4 of ammonium nitrate 1468°.

In ammonium nitrate explosives in which the ingredients are not intimately incorporated as they are in the Favier explosives, but in which the granular particles retain their individual form, the velocity of detonation may be regulated by the size of the nitrate grains. A relatively slow explosive for producing lump coal is made with coarse-grained ammonium nitrate, and a faster explosive for the procurement of coking coal is made with fine-grained material.

The first explosives to be listed as permissible by the U. S. Bureau of Mines were certain *Monobels* and *Carbonites,* and Monobels are still among the most important of American permissibles. Monobels contain about 10% nitroglycerin, about 10% carbonaceous material, wood pulp, flour, sawdust, etc., by the physical properties of which the characteristics of the explosive are somewhat modified, and about 80% ammonium nitrate of which, however, a portion, say 10%, may be substituted by a volatile salt such as sodium chloride.

[27] *Op. cit.,* p. 403.

In Europe the tendency is to use a smaller amount of nitroglycerin, say 4 to 6%, or, as in the Favier explosives, to omit it altogether. Ammonium nitrate permissible explosives which contain nitroglycerin may be divided broadly into two principal classes, those of low ammonium nitrate content in which the oxygen is balanced rather accurately against the carbonaceous material and which are cooled by the inclusion of salts, and those which have a high ammonium nitrate content but whose temperature of explosion is low because of an incomplete utilization of the oxygen by a relatively small amount of carbonaceous material. Explosives of the latter class are more popular in England and in Germany. Several examples of commercial explosives of each sort are listed in the following table.

	I	II	III	IV	V	VI	VII	VIII
Ammonium nitrate	52.0	53.0	60.0	61.0	66.0	73.0	78.0	83.0
Potassium nitrate	21.0	...	...	...	...	2.8	5.0	7.0
Sodium nitrate	...	12.0	5.0	3.0	...	...	...	...
Barium nitrate	...	...	...	...	...	...	...	2.0
Na or K chloride	...	...	21.0	20.5	22.0	15.0	8.0	...
Hydrated ammonium oxalate	16.0	19.0	...	...	...	...	...	...
Ammonium chloride	6.0	...	...	...	...	...	...	...
Cereal or wood meal	...	4.0	4.0	7.5	2.0	1.0	5.0	2.0
Glycerin	...	...	...	3.0	...	...	...	...
Powdered coal	...	...	...	...	4.0	...	...	...
Nitrotoluene	...	...	6.0	1.0	...	...	...	...
Dinitrotoluene	...	...	...	...	...	5.0	...	...
Trinitrotoluene	...	6.0	...	...	...	...	...	2.0
Nitroglycerin	5.0	5.0	4.0	4.0	4.0	3.2	4.0	4.0

The *Carbonites* which are permissible are straight dynamites whose temperatures of explosion are lowered by the excess of carbon which they contain. As a class they merge, through the *Ammon-Carbonites*, with the class of ammonium nitrate explosives. The Carbonites, have the disadvantage that they produce gases which contain carbon monoxide, and for that reason have largely given way for use in coal mines to ammonium nitrate permissibles which contain an excess of oxygen. Naoúm [28] reports the compositions and explosive characteristics of four German Carbonites as follows.

[28] *Op. cit.*, p. 401.

	I	II	III	IV
Nitroglycerin	25.0	25.0	25.0	30.0
Potassium nitrate	30.5	34.0	. . .	. . .
Sodium nitrate	. . .	. . .	30.5	24.5
Barium nitrate	4.0	1.0	. . .	. . .
Spent tan bark meal	40.0	1.0	. . .	. . .
Meal	. . .	38.5	39.5	40.5
Potassium dichromate	. . .	. . .	5.0	5.0
Sodium carbonate	0.5	0.5	. . .	. . .
Heat of explosion, Cal./kg.	576	506	536	602
Temperature of explosion	1874°	1561°	1666°	1639°
Velocity of detonation, meters/sec.	2443	2700	3042	2472
Lead block expansion	235 cc.	213 cc.	240 cc.	258 cc.

The salts which are most frequently used in permissible explosives are sodium chloride and potassium chloride, both of which are volatile (the potassium chloride more readily so), ammonium chloride and ammonium sulfate, which decompose to form gases, and the hydrated salts, alum $Al_2(SO_4)_3 \cdot K_2SO_4 \cdot 24H_2O$; ammonium alum $Al_2(SO_4)_3 \cdot (NH_4)_2SO_4 \cdot 24H_2O$; chrome alum $Cr_2(SO_4)_3 \cdot K_2SO_4 \cdot 24H_2O$; aluminum sulfate $Al_2(SO_4)_3 \cdot 18H_2O$; ammonium oxalate $(NH_4)_2C_2O_4 \cdot H_2O$; blue vitriol $CuSO_4 \cdot 5H_2O$; borax $Na_2B_4O_7 \cdot 10H_2O$; Epsom salt $MgSO_4 \cdot 7H_2O$; Glauber's salt $Na_2SO_4 \cdot 10H_2O$; and gypsum $CaSO_4 \cdot 2H_2O$, all of which give off water, while the ammonium salts among them yield other volatile products in addition. Hydrated sodium carbonate is not suitable for use because it attacks both ammonium nitrate and nitroglycerin.[29]

Sprengel Explosives

Explosives of a new type were introduced in 1871 by Hermann Sprengel, the inventor of the mercury high-vacuum pump, who patented [30] a whole series of mining explosives which were prepared by mixing an oxidizing substance with a combustible one "in such proportions that their mutual oxidation and de-oxidation should be theoretically complete." The essential novelty of his invention lay in the fact that the materials were mixed just before the explosive was used, and the resultant explosive mixture was

[29] C. G. Storm, "The Analysis of Permissible Explosives," U. S. Bur. Mines Bull. 96, Washington, 1916.

[30] Brit. Pats. 921, 2642 (1871).

fired by means of a blasting cap. Among the oxidizing agents which he mentioned were potassium chlorate, strong nitric acid, and liquid nitrogen dioxide; among the combustible materials nitrobenzene, nitronaphthalene, carbon disulfide, petroleum, and picric acid.[31] Strong nitric acid is an inconvenient and unpleasant material to handle. It can eat through the copper capsule of a blasting cap and cause the fulminate to explode. Yet several explosives containing it have been patented, *Oxonite*, for example, consisting of 58 parts of picric acid and 42 of fuming nitric acid, and *Hellhoffite*, 28 parts of nitrobenzene and 72 of nitric acid. These explosives are about as powerful as 70% dynamite, but are distinctly more sensitive to shock and to blows. Hellhoffite was sometimes absorbed on kieselguhr to form a plastic mass, but it still had the disadvantage that it was intensely corrosive and attacked paper, wood, and the common metals.

The peculiarities of the explosives recommended by Sprengel so set them apart from all others that they define a class; explosives which contain a large proportion of a liquid ingredient and which are mixed *in situ* immediately before use are now known as Sprengel explosives. They have had no success in England, for the reason that the mixing of the ingredients has been held to constitute manufacture within the meaning of the Explosives Act of 1875 and as such could be carried out lawfully only on licensed premises. Sprengel explosives have been used in the United States, in France, and in Italy, and were introduced into Siberia and China by American engineers when the first railroads were built in those countries. *Rack-a-rock*, patented by S. R. Divine,[32] is particularly well known because it was used for blasting out Hell Gate Channel in New York Harbor. On October 10, 1885, 240,399 pounds of it, along with 42,331 pounds of dynamite, was exploded for that purpose in a single blast. It was prepared for use by adding 21 parts of nitrobenzene to 79 parts of potassium chlorate contained in water-tight copper cartridges.

[31] Sprengel was aware in 1871 that picric acid alone could be detonated by means of fulminate but realized also that more explosive force could be had from it if it were mixed with an oxidizing agent. Picric acid alone was evidently not used practically as an explosive until after Turpin in 1886 had proposed it as a bursting charge for shells.

[32] Brit. Pats. 5584, 5596 (1881); 1461 (1882); 5624, 5625 (1883).

The *Prométhées,* authorized in France under the name of *explosifs O No. 3,* are prepared by dipping cartridges of a compressed oxidizing mixture of potassium chlorate 80 to 95% and manganese dioxide 5 to 20% into a liquid prepared by mixing nitrobenzene, turpentine, and naphtha in the proportions 50/20/30 or 60/15/25. The most serious disadvantage of these explosives was an irregularity of behavior resulting from the circumstance that different cartridges absorbed different quantities of the combustible oil, generally between 8 and 13%, and that the absorption was uneven and sometimes caused incomplete detonation. Similar explosives are those of Kirsanov, a mixture of 90 parts of turpentine and 10 of phenol absorbed by a mixture of 80 parts of potassium chlorate and 20 of manganese dioxide, and of Fielder, a liquid containing 80 parts of nitrobenzene and 20 of turpentine absorbed by a mixture of 70 parts of potassium chlorate and 30 of potassium permanganate.

The *Panclastites,* proposed by Turpin in 1881, are made by mixing liquid nitrogen dioxide with such combustible liquids as carbon disulfide, nitrobenzene, nitrotoluene, or gasoline. They are very sensitive to shock and must be handled with the greatest caution after they have once been mixed. In the first World War the French used certain ones of them, under the name of *Anilites,* in small bombs which were dropped from airplanes for the purpose of destroying personnel. The two liquids were enclosed in separate compartments of the bomb, which therefore contained no explosive and was safe while the airplane was carrying it. When the bomb was released, a little propeller on its nose, actuated by the passage through the air, opened a valve which permitted the two liquids to mix in such fashion that the bomb was then filled with a powerful high explosive which was so sensitive that it needed no fuze but exploded immediately upon impact with the target.

Liquid Oxygen Explosives

Liquid oxygen explosives were invented in 1895 by Linde who had developed a successful machine for the liquefaction of gases. The *Oxyliquits,* as he called them, prepared by impregnating cartridges of porous combustible material with liquid oxygen or liquid air are members of the general class of Sprengel explosives, and have the unusual advantage from the point of view of safety that they rapidly lose their explosiveness as they lose their liquid oxygen by evaporation. If they have failed to fire in a bore hole, the workmen need have no fear of going into the place with a pick or a drill after an hour or so has elapsed.

Liquid oxygen explosives often explode from flame or from the spurt of sparks from a miner's fuse, and frequently need no detonator, or, putting the matter otherwise, some of them are themselves satisfactory detonators. Like other detonating explosives, they may explode from shock. Liquid oxygen explosives made from carbonized cork and from kieselguhr mixed with petroleum were used in the blasting of the Simplon tunnel in 1899. The explosive which results when a cartridge of spongy metallic aluminum absorbs liquid oxygen is of theoretical interest because its explosion yields no gas; it yields only solid aluminum oxide and heat, much heat, which causes the extremely rapid gasification of the excess of liquid oxygen and it is this which produces the explosive effect. Lampblack is the absorbent most commonly used in this country.

Liquid oxygen explosives were at first made up from liquid air more or less self-enriched by standing, the nitrogen (b.p. $-195°$) evaporating faster than the oxygen (b.p. $-183°$), but it was later shown that much better results followed from the use of pure liquid oxygen. Rice reports [33] that explosives made from liquid oxygen and an absorbent of crude oil on kieselguhr mixed with lampblack or wood pulp and enclosed in a cheesecloth bag within a corrugated pasteboard insulator were 4 to 12% stronger than 40% straight nitroglycerin dynamite in the standard Bureau of Mines test with the ballistic pendulum. They had a velocity of detonation of about 3000 meters per second. They caused the ignition of fire damp and produced a flame which lasted for 7.125 milliseconds as compared with 0.342 for an average permissible explosive (no permissible producing a flame of more than 1 millisecond duration). The length of the flame was $2\frac{1}{2}$ times that of the flame of the average permissible. In the Trauzl lead block an explosive made up from a liquid air (i.e., a mixture of liquid

[33] George S. Rice, "Development of Liquid Oxygen Explosives during the War," *U. S. Bur. Mines Tech. Paper* 243, Washington, 1920, pp. 14–16. Also, S. P. Howell, J. W. Paul, and J. L. Sherrick, "Progress of Investigations on Liquid Oxygen Explosives," *U. S. Bur. Mines Tech. Paper* 294, Washington, 1923, pp. 33, 35, 51.

oxygen and liquid nitrogen) containing 33% of oxygen gave no explosion; with 40% oxygen an enlargement of 9 cc.; with 50% 80 cc., with 55% 147 cc.; and with 98% oxygen an enlargement of 384 cc., about 20% greater than the enlargement produced by 60% straight dynamite. The higher temperatures of explosion of the liquid oxygen explosives cause them to give higher results in the Trauzl test than correspond to their actual explosive power.

Liquid oxygen explosives are used in this country for open-cut mining or strip mining, not underground, and are generally prepared near the place where they are to be used. The cartridges are commonly left in the "soaking box" for 30 minutes, and on occasions have been transported in this box for several miles.

One of the most serious faults of liquid oxygen explosives is the ease with which they inflame and the rapidity with which they burn, amounting practically and in the majority of cases to their exploding from fire. Denues [34] has found that treatment of the granular carbonaceous absorbent with an aqueous solution of phosphoric acid results in an explosive which is non-inflammable by cigarettes, matches, and other igniting agents. Mono- and diammonium phosphate, ammonium chloride, and phosphoric acid were found to be suitable for fireproofing the canvas wrappers. Liquid oxygen explosives made up from the fireproofed absorbent are still capable of being detonated by a blasting cap. Their strength, velocity of detonation, and length of life after impregnation are slightly but not significantly shorter than those of explosives made up from ordinary non-fireproofed absorbents containing the same amount of moisture.

Chlorate and Perchlorate Explosives

The history of chlorate explosives goes back as far as 1788 when Berthollet attempted to make a new and more powerful gunpowder by incorporating in a stamp mill a mixture of potassium chlorate with sulfur and charcoal. He used the materials in the proportion 6/1/1. A party had been organized to witness the manufacture, M. and Mme. Lavoisier, Berthollet, the Commissaire M. de Chevraud and his daughter, the engineer M. Lefort, and others. The mill was started, and the party went away for

[34] A. R. T. Denues, "Fire Retardant Treatments of Liquid Oxygen Explosives," *U. S. Bur. Mines Bull.* **429**, Washington, 1940.

breakfast. Lefort and Mlle. de Chevraud were the first to return. The material exploded, throwing them to a considerable distance and causing such injuries that they both died within a few minutes. In 1849 the problem of chlorate gunpowder was again attacked by Augendre who invented a *white powder* made from potassium chlorate 4 parts, cane sugar 1 part, and potassium ferrocyanide 1 part. However, no satisfactory propellent powder for use in guns has yet been made from chlorate. Chlorate powders are used in toy salutes, maroons, etc., where a sharp explosion accompanied by noise is desired, and chlorate is used in primer compositions and in practical high explosives of the Sprengel type (described above) and in the Cheddites and Silesia explosives.

Many chlorate mixtures, particularly those which contain sulfur, sulfides, and picric acid, are extremely sensitive to blows and to friction. In the *Street explosives*, later called Cheddites because they were manufactured at Chedde in France, the chlorate is phlegmatized by means of castor oil, a substance which appears to have remarkable powers in this respect. The French *Commission des Substances Explosives* in 1897 commenced its first investigation of these explosives by a study of those which are listed below, and concluded [35] that their sensitivity to shock is

	I	II	III
Potassium chlorate	75.0	74.6	80.0
Picronitronaphthalene	20.0	...	...
Nitronaphthalene	...	5.5	12.0
Starch	...	14.9	...
Castor oil	5.0	5.0	8.0

less than that of No. 1 dynamite (75% guhr dynamite) and that when exploded by a fulminate cap they show a considerable brisance which however is less than that of dynamite. Later studies showed that the Cheddites had slightly more force than No. 1 dynamite, although they were markedly less brisant because of their lower velocity of detonation. After further experimentation four Cheddites were approved for manufacture in France, but the output of the Poudrerie de Vonges where they were made consisted principally of Cheddites No. 1 and No. 4.

[35] *Mém. Poudres*, **9**, 144 (1897–1898); **11**, 22 (1901); **12**, 117, 122 (1903–1904); **13**, 144, 282 (1905–1906); **15**, 135 (1909–1910); **16**, 66 (1911–1912).

	O No. 1 Formula 41	O No. 1 Formula 60 bis	O No. 2 Formula 60 bis M Cheddite No. 4	O No. 5 Cheddite No. 1
Potassium chlorate.........	80	80	79	..
Sodium chlorate............	..	..	..	79
Nitronaphthalene...........	12	13	1	..
Dinitrotoluene.............	..	2	15	16
Castor oil.................	8	5	5	5

The Cheddites are manufactured by melting the nitro compounds in the castor oil at 80°, adding little by little the pulverized chlorate dried and still warm, and mixing thoroughly. The mixture is emptied out onto a table, and rolled to a thin layer which hardens on cooling and breaks up under the roller and is then sifted and screened.

Sodium chlorate contains more oxygen than potassium chlorate, but has the disadvantage of being hygroscopic. Neither salt ought to be used in mixtures which contain ammonium nitrate or ammonium perchlorate, for double decomposition might occur with the formation of dangerous ammonium chlorate. Potassium chlorate is one of the chlorates least soluble in water, potassium perchlorate one of the least soluble of the perchlorates. The latter salt is practically insoluble in alcohol. The perchlorates are intrinsically more stable and less reactive than the chlorates, and are much safer in contact with combustible substances. Unlike the chlorates they are not decomposed by hydrochloric acid, and they do not yield an explosive gas when warmed with concentrated sulfuric acid. The perchlorates require a higher temperature for their decomposition than do the corresponding chlorates.

SOLUBILITY: PARTS PER 100 PARTS OF WATER

	$KClO_3$	$NaClO_3$	$KClO_4$	NH_4ClO_4
At 0°	3.3	82.	0.7	12.4
At 100°	56.	204.	18.7	88.2

Mixtures of aromatic nitro compounds with chlorate are dangerously sensitive unless they are phlegmatized with castor oil or a similar material, but there are other substances, such as rosin, animal and vegetable oils, and petroleum products, which give mixtures which are not unduly sensitive to shock and friction and may be handled with reasonable safety. Some of these, such as *Pyrodialyte* [36] and the *Steelites*,[37] were studied by the *Commission des Substances Explosives*. The former consisted of 85 parts of potassium chlorate and 15 of rosin, 2 parts of alcohol being used during the incorporation. The latter, invented by Everard Steele of Chester, England, contained an oxidized rosin (*résidée* in French) which was made by treating a mixture of 90 parts of colophony and 10 of starch with 42 Bé nitric acid. After washing, drying, and powdering, the *résidée* was mixed with powdered potassium chlorate, moistened with methyl alcohol, warmed, and stirred gently while the alcohol was evaporated. *Colliery Steelite*

	Steelite No. 3	Steelite No. 5	Steelite No. 7	Colliery Steelite
Potassium chlorate	75	83.33	87.50	72.5–75.5
Résidée	25	16.67	12.50	23.5–26.5
Aluminum	..	5.00	...	...
Castor oil	..	....	....	0.5–1.0
Moisture	..	....	....	0–1

passed the Woolwich test for safety explosives and was formerly on the British permitted list but failed in the Rotherham test. In Germany the *Silesia* explosives have been used to some extent. *Silesia No. 4* consists of 80 parts of potassium chlorate and 20 of rosin, and *Silesia IV 22*, 70 parts of potassium chlorate, 8 of rosin, and 22 of sodium chloride, is cooled by the addition of the volatile salt and is on the permissible list.

The *Sebomites*,[38] invented by Eugène Louis, contained animal fat which was solid at ordinary temperature, and were inferior to the Cheddites in their ability to transmit detonation. *Explosifs P (potasse)* and *S (soude)* [39] and the *Minélites*,[40] containing petroleum hydrocarbons, were studied in considerable detail by Dautriche, some of whose results for velocities of detonation are reported in the table on pages 362–363 where they are compared with

[36] *Mém. Poudres,* **11,** 53 (1901).
[37] *Ibid.,* **15,** 181 (1909–1910).
[38] *Ibid.,* **13,** 280 (1905–1906); **15,** 137 (1909–1910).
[39] *Ibid.,* **15,** 212 (1909–1910).
[40] *Ibid.,* **16,** 224 (1911–1912).

his results for Cheddite 60, fourth formula.[41] His experimental results [42] illustrate very clearly the principle that there is an optimum density of loading at which the velocity of detonation is greatest and that at higher densities the velocity drops and the detonation is incomplete and poorly propagated. The Cheddite 60,

	Explosifs		Minélites		
	P	S	A	B	C
Potassium chlorate	90	..	90	90	89
Sodium chlorate	..	89	..	..	..
Heavy petroleum oil	..	..	3	..	..
Vaseline	..	..	..	3	4
Paraffin	10	11	7	7	5
Pitch	..	..	..	..	2

fourth formula, when ignited burns slowly with a smoky flame. *Explosifs P* and *S* and the *Minélites* burn while the flame of a Bunsen burner is played upon them but, in general, go out when the flame is removed. *Minélite B*, under the designation *O No. 6 B*, was used by the French during the first World War in grenades and mines. A similar explosive containing 90 parts of sodium chlorate instead of 90 of potassium chlorate was used in grenades and in trench mortar bombs.

Chlorate explosives which contain aromatic nitro compounds have higher velocities of detonation and are more brisant than those whose carbonaceous material is merely combustible. The addition of a small amount of nitroglycerin increases the velocity of detonation still farther. Brisant chlorate explosives of this sort were developed in Germany during the first World War and were known as *Koronit* and *Albit* (*Gesteinskoronit, Kohlenkoronit, Wetteralbit*, etc.). They found considerable use for a time but have now been largely superseded by low-percentage dynamites and by perchlorate explosives. Two of them, manufactured by the Dynamit A.-G., had according to Naoúm [43] the compositions and explosive characteristics which are indicated

[41] The composition of this explosive was the same as that which is given in the table on page 359 as that of *O No. 2*, formula 60 *bis* M, or Cheddite No. 4.

[42] In several cases Dautriche reported temperatures, but the velocity of detonation appears to be unaffected by such temperature variations as those between summer and winter.

[43] *Op. cit.*, p. 428.

Explosive	In Tubes of	Diameter	Density of Loading	Velocity of Detonation, M./Sec.
Explosif P	copper	20–22 mm.	0.62	2137
			1.00	3044
			1.05	3185
			1.36	3621
			1.48	3475
			1.54	Incomplete
			0.99	2940
			1.24	3457
			1.45	3565
			1.59	Incomplete
Explosif P	paper	29 mm.	0.95	2752
			1.30	3406
			1.35	3340
			0.90	2688
			1.21	3308
			1.36	3259
			1.41	Incomplete
Explosif S	copper	20–22 mm.	0.88	2480
			1.25	2915
			0.81	2191
			0.92	2457
			1.33	2966
			1.45	2940
			1.54	2688
			1.56	Incomplete
			1.58	Incomplete
Explosif S	paper	29 mm.	1.05	2335
			1.16	2443
			1.29	2443
			1.39	Incomplete
			1.47	Incomplete
Cheddite 60 4th formula	copper	20–22 mm.	1.51	3099
			1.62	2820
			0.84	2457
			1.39	3045
			1.48	3156
Cheddite 60 4th formula	paper	29 mm.	1.25	2774
			1.31	2915
			1.40	2843
			1.50	Incomplete

Minélite A in powder	copper	20–22 mm.	0.87	2800
			0.99	2930
			1.17	3125
			1.24	3235
			1.38	Incomplete
			1.52	Incomplete
			0.89	2435
			0.95	2835
			1.20	3235
			1.39	3125
			1.45	Incomplete
			0.87	2395
			1.27	3355
			1.39	Incomplete
Minélite A in powder	paper	29 mm.	1.08	2670
			1.19	2835
			1.25	Incomplete
			1.28	Incomplete
			1.19	2895
			1.24	Incomplete
Minélite A in grains	copper	20–22 mm.	0.87	2150
			1.12	2415
			1.20	2550
			1.29	3025
			1.33	2480
			1.35	Incomplete
			1.30	2895
			0.85	2100
			1.17	2415
			1.27	2750
Minélite B in powder	copper	20–22 mm.	0.97	2350
			1.07	2895
			1.24	3235
			1.33	3090
			1.45	Incomplete
			1.57	Incomplete
			1.00	2925
			1.12	2925
			1.26	3165
			1.02	2585
			1.14	2910
			1.30	3180
			1.41	Complete
			1.38	3160
Minélite C in powder	copper	20–22 mm.	1.28	3125
			1.37	Incomplete
			1.48	Incomplete

below. It is interesting that the explosive which contained a small amount of nitroglycerin was more brisant, as well as softer and more plastic, and less sensitive to shock, to friction, and to initiation than the drier explosive which contained no nitroglycerin. It required a No. 3 blasting cap to explode it, but the material which contained no nitroglycerin was exploded by a weak No. 1.

	Gesteins-Koronit T1	Gesteins-Koronit T2
Sodium chlorate	72.0	75.0
Vegetable meal	1.0–2.0	1.0–2.0
Di- and trinitrotoluene	20.0	20.0
Paraffin	3.0–4.0	3.0–4.0
Nitroglycerin	3.0–4.0	...
Heat of explosion, Cal./kg.	1219.0	1241.0
Temperature of explosion	3265.0°	3300.0°
Velocity of detonation, m./sec.	5000.0	4300.0
Density of cartridge	1.57	1.46
Lead block expansion	290.0 cc.	280.0 cc.
Lead block crushing	20.0 mm.	19.5 mm.

During the first World War when Germany needed to conserve as much as possible its material for military explosives, blasting explosives made from perchlorate came into extensive use. The Germans had used in their trench mortar bombs an explosive, called *Perdit*, which consisted of a mixture of potassium perchlorate 56%, with dinitrobenzene 32% and dinitronaphthalene 12%. After the War, the perchlorate recovered from these bombs and that from the reserve stock came onto the market, and perchlorate explosives, *Perchlorit, Perchloratit, Persalit, Perkoronit*, etc., were used more widely than ever. The sale of these explosives later ceased because the old supply of perchlorate became exhausted and the new perchlorate was too high in price. Each of these explosives required a No. 3 cap for its initiation. Perchlorate explosives in general are somewhat less sensitive to initiation than chlorate explosives. A small amount of nitroglycerin in perchlorate explosives plays a significant part in propagating the explosive wave and is more important in these compositions than it is in ammonium nitrate explosives. Naoúm [44] reports the following particulars concerning two of the Perkoronites.

[44] *Op. cit.*, p. 430.

	PERKORONIT A	PERKORONIT B
Potassium perchlorate	58	59
Ammonium nitrate	8	10
Di- and trinitrotoluene, vegetable meal....	30	31
Nitroglycerin	4	..
Heat of explosion, Cal./kg.	1170.0	1160.0
Temperature of explosion	3145.0°	3115.0°
Velocity of detonation, m./sec.	5000.0	4400.0
Density of cartridge	1.58	1.52
Lead block expansion	340.0 cc.	330.0 cc.
Lead block crushing	20.0 mm.	18.0 mm.

Potassium perchlorate and ammonium perchlorate permissible explosives, cooled by means of common salt, ammonium oxalate, etc., and containing either ammonium nitrate or alkali metal nitrate with or without nitroglycerin, are used in England, Belgium, and elsewhere. They possess no novel features beyond the explosives already described. Explosives containing ammonium perchlorate yield fumes which contain hydrogen chloride. Potassium perchlorate produces potassium chloride.

Early in the history of these explosives the French *Commission des Substances Explosives* published a report on two ammonium perchlorate Cheddites.[45] The manufacture of these explosives,

	I	II
Ammonium perchlorate	82	50
Sodium nitrate	..	30
Dinitrotoluene	13	15
Castor oil	5	5

however, was not approved for the reason that the use of castor oil for phlegmatizing was found to be unnecessary. Number I took fire easily and burned in an 18-mm. copper gutter at a rate of 4.5 mm. per second, and produced a choking white smoke. Cheddite 60, for comparison, burned irregularly in the copper gutter, with a smoke which was generally black, at a rate of 0.4–0.5 mm. per second. Number II took fire only with the greatest difficulty, and did not maintain its own combustion. The maximum velocities of detonation in zinc tubes 20 mm. in diameter were about 4020 meters per second for No. I and about 3360 for No. II.

[45] *Mém. poudres,* **14,** 206 (1907–1908).

The *Commission* published in the same report a number of interesting observations on ammonium perchlorate. Pieces of cotton cloth dipped into a solution of ammonium perchlorate and dried were found to burn more rapidly than when similarly treated with potassium chlorate and less rapidly than when similarly treated with sodium chlorate. Ammonium perchlorate inflamed in contact with a hot wire and burned vigorously with the production of choking white fumes, but the combustion ceased as soon as the hot wire was removed. Its sensitivity to shock, as determined by the drop test, was about the same as that of picric acid, but its sensitivity to initiation was distinctly less. A 50-cm. drop of a 5-kilogram weight caused explosions in about 50% of the trials. A cartridge, 16 cm. long and 26 mm. in diameter, was filled with ammonium perchlorate gently tamped into place (density of loading about 1.10) and was primed with a cartridge of the same diameter containing 25 grams of powdered picric acid (density of loading about 0.95) and placed in contact with one end of it. When the picric acid booster was exploded, the cartridge of perchlorate detonated only for about 20 mm. of its length and produced merely a slight and decreasing furrow in the lead plate on which it was resting. When a booster of 75 grams of picric acid was used, the detonation was propagated in the perchlorate for 35 mm. The temperature of explosion of ammonium perchlorate was calculated to be 1084°.

The French used two ammonium perchlorate explosives during the first World War.

	I	II
Ammonium perchlorate	86	61.5
Sodium nitrate	..	30.0
Paraffin	14	8.5

The first of these was used in 75-mm. shells, the second in 58-mm. trench mortar bombs.

Hydrazine perchlorate melts at 131–132°, burns tranquilly, and explodes violently from shock.

Guanidine perchlorate is relatively stable to heat and to mechanical shock but possesses extraordinary explosive power and sensitivity to initiation. Naoúm [46] states that it gives a lead block expansion of about 400 cc. and has a velocity of detonation of about 6000 meters per second at a density of loading of 1.15.

[46] Naoúm, "Schiess- und Sprengstoffe," Dresden and Leipzig, 1927, p. 137.

Ammonium Nitrate Military Explosives

The *Schneiderite* (*Explosif S* or *Sc*) which the French used during the first World War in small and medium-size high-explosive shells, especially in the 75 mm., was made by incorporating 7 parts of ammonium nitrate and 1 of dinitronaphthalene in a wheel mill, and was loaded by compression. Other mixtures, made in the same way, were used in place of Schneiderite or as a substitute for it.

	NX	NT	NTN	NDNT	N2TN
Ammonium nitrate	77	70	80	85	50
Sodium nitrate	..	..	..	..	30
Trinitrotoluene	..	30	..	5	..
Trinitroxylene	23	..	..	..	..
Dinitronaphthalene	..	..	..	10	..
Trinitronaphthalene	..	..	20	..	20

Amatol, developed by the British during the first World War, is made by mixing granulated ammonium nitrate with melted trinitrotoluene, and pouring or extruding the mixture into the shells where it solidifies. The booster cavity is afterwards drilled out from the casting. The explosive can be cut with a hand saw. It is insensitive to friction and is less sensitive to initiation and more sensitive to impact than trinitrotoluene. It is hygroscopic, and in the presence of moisture attacks copper, brass, and bronze.

Amatol is made up in various proportions of ammonium nitrate to trinitrotoluene, such as 50/50, 60/40, and 80/20. The granulated, dried, and sifted ammonium nitrate, warmed to about 90°, is added to melted trinitrotoluene at about 90°, and the warm mixture, if 50/50 or 60/40, is ladled into the shells which have been previously warmed somewhat in order that solidification may not be too rapid, or, if 80/20, is *stemmed* or extruded into the shells by means of a screw operating within a steel tube. Synthetic ammonium nitrate is preferred for the preparation of amatol. The pyridine which is generally present in gas liquor and tar liquor ammonia remains in the ammonium nitrate which is made from these liquors and causes frothing and the formation of bubbles in the warm amatol—with the consequent probability of cavitation in the charge. Thiocyanates which are often present in ammonia from the same sources likewise cause frothing, and phenols if present tend to promote exudation.

The velocity of detonation of TNT-ammonium nitrate mixtures decreases regularly with increasing amounts of ammonium

nitrate, varying from about 6700 meters per second for TNT to
about 4500 meters per second for 80/20 amatol. The greater the
proportion of ammonium nitrate the less the brisance and the
greater the heaving power of the amatol. 50/50 Amatol does not
contain oxygen enough for the complete combustion of its trinitrotoluene, and gives a smoke which is dark colored but less
black than the smoke from straight TNT. 80/20 Amatol is less
brisant than TNT. It gives an insignificant white smoke. Smoke
boxes are usually loaded with 80/20 amatol in order that the
artilleryman may observe the bursting of his shells. The best
smoke compositions for this purpose contain a large proportion
of aluminum and provide smoke by day and a brilliant flash of
light by night.

The name of *ammonal* is applied both to certain blasting explosives which contain aluminum and to military explosives, based
upon ammonium nitrate, which contain this metal. Military am-
monals are brisant and powerful explosives which explode with
a bright flash. They are hygroscopic, but the flake aluminum
which they contain behaves somewhat in the manner of the
shingles on a roof and helps materially to exclude moisture. At
the beginning of the first World War the Germans were using
in major caliber shells an ammonal having the first of the compositions listed below. After the War had advanced and TNT

	GERMAN I	AMMONAL II	FRENCH AMMONAL
Ammonium nitrate	54	72	86
Trinitrotoluene	30	12	..
Aluminum flakes	16	16	8
Stearic acid	..	..	6

had become more scarce, ammonal of the second formula was
adopted. The French also used ammonal in major caliber shells
during the first World War. All three of the above-listed explosives were loaded by compression. Experiments have been tried
with an ammonal containing ammonium thiocyanate; the mixture was melted, and loaded by pouring but was found to be
unsatisfactory because of its rapid decomposition. Ammonal
yields a flame which is particularly hot, and consequently gives
an unduly high result in the Trauzl lead block test.

CHAPTER VIII

NITROAMINES AND RELATED SUBSTANCES

The nitroamines are substituted ammonias, substances in which a nitro group is attached directly to a trivalent nitrogen atom. They are prepared in general either by the nitration of a nitrogen base or of one of its salts, or they are prepared by the splitting off of water from the nitrate of the base by the action of concentrated sulfuric acid upon it. At present two nitroamines are of particular interest to the explosives worker, namely, nitroguanidine and cyclotrimethylenetrinitramine (cyclonite). Both are produced from synthetic materials which have become available in large commercial quantities only since the first World War, the first from cyanamide, the second from formaldehyde from the oxidation of synthetic methyl alcohol.

Nitroamide (Nitroamine)

Nitroamide, the simplest of the nitroamines, is formed by the action of dilute acid on potassium nitrocarbamate, which itself results from the nitration of urethane and the subsequent hydrolysis of the nitro ester by means of alcoholic potassium hydroxide.

$$NH_2\!-\!COOC_2H_5 \qquad NO_2\!-\!NH\!-\!COOK \qquad NH_2\!-\!NO_2 + CO_2$$

$$NO_2\!-\!NH\!-\!COOC_2H_5 \qquad [NO_2\!-\!NH\!-\!COOH]$$

Nitroamide is strongly acidic, a white crystalline substance, melting at 72–73° with decomposition, readily soluble in water, alcohol, and ether, and insoluble in petroleum ether. It explodes on contact with concentrated sulfuric acid. The pure material decomposes slowly on standing, forming nitrous oxide and water; it cannot be preserved for more than a few days. When an aqueous solution of nitroamide is warmed, gas bubbles begin to come off at about 60–65°, and decomposition is complete after boiling for a short time.

The solution which results when ammonium nitrate is dissolved in a large excess of concentrated sulfuric acid evidently contains nitroamide.[1] If the solution is warmed directly, no nitric acid distils from it but at about 150° it gives off nitrous oxide which corresponds to the dehydration of the nitroamide by the action of the strong acid. The nitroamide moreover, by the action of the same acid, may be hydrated to yield nitric acid, slowly if the solution is digested at 90° to 120°, under which conditions the nitric acid distils out, and rapidly at ordinary temperature in the nitrometer where mercury is present which reacts with the nitric acid as fast as it is formed.

$$NH_3 \cdot HONO_2 \text{ minus } H_2O \longrightarrow NH_2\text{—}NO_2 \begin{cases} \text{minus } H_2O \longrightarrow N_2O \\ \text{plus } H_2O \longrightarrow NH_3 + HONO_2 \end{cases}$$

The two reactions, hydration and dehydration, or, more exactly, the formation of nitrous oxide and of nitric acid, are more or less general reactions of the substituted nitroamines. The extent to which one or the other occurs depends largely upon the groups which are present in the molecule. Thus, tetryl on treatment with concentrated sulfuric acid forms nitric acid, and it gives up one and only one of its nitro groups in the nitrometer, but the reaction is not known by which nitrous oxide is eliminated from it. Methylnitramine, on the other hand, gives nitrous oxide readily enough but shows very little tendency to produce nitric acid.

Solutions of nitrourea and nitroguanidine in concentrated sulfuric acid contain actual nitroamide, and these substances give up their nitro group nitrogen in the nitrometer. Nitroamide has been isolated [2] both from an aqueous solution of nitrourea and from a solution of the same substance in concentrated sulfuric acid.

$$NH_2\text{—}CO\text{—}NH\text{—}NO_2 \rightleftharpoons HNCO + NH_2\text{—}NO_2$$

The reaction is reversible, for nitroamide in aqueous solution combines with cyanic acid to form nitrourea.

[1] Davis and Abrams, *J. Am. Chem. Soc.*, **47**, 1043 (1925).
[2] Davis and Blanchard, *J. Am. Chem. Soc.*, **51**, 1790 (1929).

Methylnitramine

Methylnitramine is produced when aniline reacts with tetryl in benzene solution, and when ammonia water or barium hydroxide solution acts upon dinitrodimethyloxamide. The structure of tetryl was first proved by its synthesis from picryl chloride and the potassium salt of methylnitramine.

Methylnitramine is a strong monobasic acid, very readily soluble in water, alcohol, chloroform, and benzene, less soluble in ether, and sparingly soluble in petroleum ether. It crystallizes from ether in flat needles which melt at 38°. It is not decomposed by boiling in aqueous solution even in the presence of an excess of alkali. On distillation it yields dimethylnitramine, m.p. 57°, methyl alcohol, nitrous oxide and other products. Methylnitramine owes its acidity to the fact that it is tautomeric.

$$CH_3-N \Big\langle {}^{H}_{NO_2} \rightleftharpoons CH_3-N=N \Big\langle {}^{O}_{OH}$$

Dimethylnitramine, in which there is no hydrogen atom attached to the atom which carries the nitro group, cannot tautomerize, and is not acidic.

Methylnitramine decomposes explosively in contact with concentrated sulfuric acid. If the substance is dissolved in water, and if concentrated sulfuric acid is added little by little until a considerable concentration is built up, then the decomposition proceeds more moderately, nitrous oxide is given off, and dimethyl ether (from the methyl alcohol first formed) remains dissolved in the sulfuric acid. The same production of nitrous oxide occurs even in the nitrometer in the presence of mercury. If methylnitramine and a small amount of phenol are dissolved together in water, and if concentrated sulfuric acid is then added little by little, a distinct yellow color shows that a trace of nitric acid has been formed. The fact that methylnitramine gives a blue color with the diphenylamine reagent shows the same thing.

Methylnitramine is conveniently prepared [3] by nitrating methylurethane with absolute nitric acid, drowning in water, neutralizing with sodium carbonate, extracting with ether, and

[3] Franchimont and Klobbie, *Rec. trav. chim.*, **7**, 354 (1887).

then passing ammonia gas into the ether solution of methyl-nitrourethane.

$$H\!\!-\!\!NH_2$$

$$CH_3-NH-COOC_2H_5 \qquad\qquad CH_3-N\!\!-\!\!COOC_2H_5 + NH_3$$
$$\qquad\qquad\qquad\qquad\qquad\qquad\qquad\qquad\quad NO_2$$

$$CH_3-N-COOC_2H_5 \qquad\qquad CH_3-NH-NO_2\cdot NH_3$$
$$\qquad\quad\; NO_2 \qquad\qquad\qquad\qquad\qquad\qquad CH_3-N\!\!<^{H}_{NO_2}$$

A white crystalline precipitate of the ammonium salt of methyl-nitramine is deposited. This is dissolved in alcohol, and the solution is boiled—whereby ammonia is driven off—and con-centrated to a small volume. The product is procured by com-pleting the evaporation in a vacuum desiccator over sulfuric acid.

The heavy metal salts of methylnitramine are primary explo-sives, but have not been investigated extensively.

Urea Nitrate

Although urea has the properties of an amide (carbamide) rather than those of an amine, it nevertheless acts as a monoacid base in forming salts among which the nitrate and the oxalate are noteworthy because they are sparingly soluble in cold water, particularly in the presence of an excess of the corresponding acid. The nitrate, white monoclinic prisms which melt at 152° with decomposition, is procured by adding an excess of nitric acid (1.42) to a strong aqueous solution of urea. The yield is increased if the mixture is chilled and allowed to stand for a time. Urea nitrate is stable and not deliquescent. It has interest as a powerful and cool explosive, but suffers from the disadvan-tage that it is corrosively acidic in the presence of moisture.

Pure urea is manufactured commercially by pumping ammonia and carbon dioxide into an autoclave where they are heated together under pressure while more of each gas is pumped in. Ammonium carbamate is formed at first, this loses water from its molecule to form urea, and the autoclave finally becomes filled with a strong solution of urea which is drawn off and crystallized.

$$2NH_3 + CO_2 \longrightarrow NH_3 \cdot HO—CO—NH_2 \longrightarrow H_2O + NH_2—CO—NH_2$$

Urea is sometimes incorporated in blasting explosives for the purpose of lowering the temperature of explosion. Its use as a stabilizer has already been mentioned.

Nitrourea

Nitrourea is a cool but powerful explosive, and would be useful if it were not for the fact that it tends to decompose spontaneously in the presence of moisture. The mechanism of its reactions is the same as that of the reactions of nitroguanidine, which differs from it in containing an $>NH$ group where nitrourea contains a $>CO$, but the reactions of nitrourea are very much more rapid. The nitro group promotes the *urea dearrangement*, so that nitrourea when dissolved in water or when warmed breaks down into cyanic acid and nitroamide much more readily than urea breaks down under like conditions into cyanic acid and ammonia. The imido group in place of the carbonyl hinders it; guanidine dearranges less readily than urea, and nitroguanidine is substantially as stable as urea itself.

Nitrourea is prepared by adding dry urea nitrate (200 grams) in small portions at a time with gentle stirring to concentrated sulfuric acid (1.84) (300 cc.) while the temperature of the mixture is kept below 0°. The milky liquid is poured without delay into a mixture of ice and water (1 liter), the finely divided white precipitate is collected on a filter, sucked as dry as may be, and, without washing, is immediately dissolved while still wet in boiling alcohol.[4] The liquid on cooling deposits pearly leaflets of nitrourea. It is chilled and filtered, and the crystals are rinsed with cold alcohol and dried in the air. The product, which melts at 146° to 153° with decomposition, is sufficiently pure for use in synthesis, and may be preserved for several years unchanged in hard glass bottles. If slightly moist nitrourea is allowed to stand in contact with soft glass, that is, in contact with a trace

[4] The product at this point contains acid enough to prevent it from decomposing in boiling alcohol. For a second recrystallization it is unsafe to heat the alcohol above 60°.

of alkali, it decomposes completely within a short time forming water, ammonia, nitrous oxide, urea, biuret, cyanuric acid, etc. Pure nitrourea, recrystallized from benzene, ether, or chloroform, in which solvents it is sparingly soluble, melts with decomposition at 158.4–158.8°.

In water and in hydrophilic solvents nitrourea dearranges rapidly into cyanic acid and nitroamide. Alkalis promote the reaction. If an aqueous solution of nitrourea is warmed, bubbles of nitrous oxide begin to come off at about 60°. If it is allowed to stand over night at room temperature, the nitrourea disappears completely and the liquid is found to be a solution of cyanic acid. Indeed, nitrourea is equivalent to cyanic acid for purposes of synthesis. It reacts with alcohols to form carbamic esters (urethanes) and with primary and second amines to form mono- and *unsym*-di-substituted ureas.

Guanidine Nitrate

Guanidine nitrate is of interest to us both as an explosive itself and a component of explosive mixtures, and as an intermediate in the preparation of nitroguanidine. All other salts of guanidine require strong mixed acid to convert them to nitroguanidine, but the nitrate is converted by dissolving it in concentrated sulfuric acid and pouring the solution into water.

Guanidine is a strong monoacid base, indistinguishable from potassium hydroxide in an electrometric titration. There is considerable evidence [5] which indicates that the charge of the guanidonium ion resides upon its carbon atom.

$$
\begin{array}{ccc}
\text{NH}_2 & & \text{NH}_2 \\
| & & | \\
\text{NH}_2\text{---C} & + \text{H}^+ \rightleftharpoons \text{NH}_2\text{---C}^+ \\
\| & & | \\
\text{NH} & & \text{NH}_2 \\
\text{Guanidine} & & \text{Guanidonium ion}
\end{array}
$$

Guanidine itself is crystalline, deliquescent, and strongly caustic, and takes up carbon dioxide from the air.

Guanidine was first obtained by Strecker in 1861 by the oxidation with hydrochloric acid and potassium chlorate of guanine (a substance found in guano and closely related to uric acid).

[5] Davis, Yelland, and Ma, *J. Am. Chem. Soc.*, **59**, 1993 (1937).

Guanidine or its salts may be prepared, among other ways, by the interaction (1) of orthocarbonic ester or (2) of chloropicrin

1. $CCl_3 \cdot NO_2 + 3NH_3 \longrightarrow NH_2—C(NH)—NH_2 + HNO_2 + 3HCl$

2. $C(OC_2H_5)_4 + 3NH_3 \longrightarrow NH_2—C(NH)—NH_2 + 4C_2H_5—OH$

with aqueous ammonia at 150°, by the interaction (3) of carbon tetrabromide with alcoholic ammonia in a sealed tube at 100°,

3. $CBr_4 + 3NH_3 \longrightarrow NH_2—C(NH)—NH_2 + 4HBr$

by the interaction (4) of cyanogen iodide with alcoholic ammonia in a sealed tube at 100°, whereby cyanamide and ammonium iodide are formed first and then combine with one another to

4. $I—C \equiv N + 2NH_3 \longrightarrow NH_2—C \equiv N + NH_3 \cdot HI \longrightarrow$
$$NH_2—C(NH)—NH_2 \cdot HI$$

form guanidine iodide, by the combination (5) of cyanamide, already prepared, with an ammonium salt by heating the materials with alcohol in a sealed tube at 100°, and (6) by heating

6. $NH_4NCS \rightleftharpoons NH_3 + HNCS \rightleftharpoons NH_2—CS—NH_2 \rightleftharpoons NH_2—C \equiv N + H_2S$
$$NH_4NCS + NH_2—C \equiv N \longrightarrow NH_2—C(NH)—NH_2 \cdot HNCS$$

ammonium thiocyanate at 170–190° for 20 hours, or until hydrogen sulfide no longer comes off, whereby the material is converted into guanidine thiocyanate. The reaction depends upon the fact that the ammonium thiocyanate is in part converted into thiourea, and that this breaks down into hydrogen sulfide, which escapes, and cyanamide which combines with the unchanged ammonium thiocyanate to form the guanidine salt. The yield from this process is excellent.

For many years guanidine thiocyanate was the most easily prepared and the most commonly used of the salts of guanidine. Other salts were made from it by metathetical reactions. Nitroguanidine, prepared from the thiocyanate by direct nitration with mixed acids, was found to contain traces of sulfur compounds which attacked nitrocellulose and affected the stability of smokeless powder, and this is one of the reasons why nitroguanidine powders did not come into early use. Guanidine thiocyanate is deliquescent. Strong solutions of it dissolve filter paper.

Cyanamide itself is not a suitable raw material for the preparation of guanidine salts, for it is difficult to prepare and to purify, and it polymerizes on keeping. The evaporation of an aqueous solution of cyanamide yields the dimer, dicyandiamide, and the heating, or even the long keeping, of the dry substance produces the trimer, melamine.

$$NH_2\!-\!C(NH)\!-\!NH\!-\!C\!\equiv\!N$$
Dicyandiamide

$$NH_2\!-\!C\!\equiv\!N$$
Cyanamide

$$
\begin{array}{c}
NH \\
\parallel \\
C \\
NH \quad NH \\
| \qquad | \\
HN\!=\!C \qquad C\!=\!NH \\
\diagdown \quad \diagup \\
NH
\end{array}
$$
Melamine

Cyanamide, colorless crystals, m.p. 40°, is readily soluble in water, alcohol, and ether. An aqueous solution of cyanamide gives a black precipitate of copper cyanamide with ammoniacal copper sulfate solution, and a yellow precipitate of silver cyanamide with ammoniacal silver nitrate. The precipitates are almost unique among the compounds of copper and silver in the respect that they are insoluble in ammonia water.

Before the development of the cyanamide process for the fixation of nitrogen, cyanamide was prepared by the interaction of cyanogen chloride or bromide (from the action of the halogen on potassium cyanide) with ammonia in water or ether solution.

$$KCN + Cl_2 \longrightarrow KCl + Cl\!-\!CN$$

$$2NH_3 + Cl\!-\!CN \longrightarrow NH_4Cl + NH_2\!-\!CN$$

If the reaction, say, with cyanogen chloride, is carried out in ether solution, ammonium chloride precipitates and is filtered off, and the cyanamide is procured as a syrup by allowing the ether solution to evaporate spontaneously and later as crystals by allowing the syrup to stand over sulfuric acid in a desiccator. Cyanamide may also be prepared by removing the component atoms of hydrogen sulfide from thiourea by means of mercuric oxide. Thionyl chloride effects the corresponding removal of water from urea.

$$NH_2\!-\!CS\!-\!NH_2 \text{ minus } H_2S \text{ (HgO)} \longrightarrow NH_2\!-\!CN + HgS + H_2O$$

$$NH_2\!-\!CO\!-\!NH_2 \text{ minus } H_2O \text{ (Cl}_2SO) \longrightarrow NH_2\!-\!CN + SO_2 + 2HCl$$

The cyanamide process has made cyanamide and its derivatives more easily available for commercial synthesis. Coke and limestone are heated together in the electric furnace for the production of calcium carbide. This substance, along with a small amount of calcium chloride which acts as a catalyst, is then heated at 800–1000° in a stream of nitrogen gas.

$$2CaCO_3 + 5C \longrightarrow 2Ca{\Large\langle}\begin{smallmatrix}C\\ \|\|\\ C\end{smallmatrix} + 3CO_2$$

$$Ca{\Large\langle}\begin{smallmatrix}C\\ \|\|\\ C\end{smallmatrix} + N_2 \longrightarrow CaNCN + C$$

The resulting dark-colored mixture of calcium cyanamide and carbon is known as *lime nitrogen* (*Kalkstickstoff*) and is used in fertilizers. If steam is passed through it, it yields ammonia.

$$CaNCN + 3H_2O \text{ (steam)} \longrightarrow CaCO_3 + 2NH_3$$

Water, whether cool or warm, produces some cyanamide, which is readily soluble, and some calcium hydrogen cyanamide, white, microcrystalline, and sparingly soluble, but water plus acid for the removal of the calcium (sulfuric acid, oxalic acid, or carbon dioxide) yields a solution of cyanamide which is directly applicable for use in certain reactions.

$$2CaNCN + 2H_2O \longrightarrow Ca(OH)_2 + Ca{\Large\langle}\begin{smallmatrix}NH-CN\\ NH-CN\end{smallmatrix}$$

$$Ca{\Large\langle}\begin{smallmatrix}NH-CN\\ NH-CN\end{smallmatrix} + CO_2 + H_2O \longrightarrow CaCO_3 + 2NH_2-CN$$

On hydrolysis with dilute sulfuric acid it yields urea. On treatment with ammonium sulfide it prefers to react with the hydrogen sulfide part of the molecule to form thiourea, not with the ammonia part to form guanidine, and the reaction is the commercial source of many tons of thiourea for the rubber industry. On evaporation for crystals, the solution yields dicyandiamide which constitutes a convenient source for the preparation of guanidine nitrate.

Dicyandiamide crystallizes from water in handsome flat needles or plates which melt at 208.0–208.1° and decompose if heated slightly above the melting point. A saturated aqueous solution contains—

Temperature, °C.	Grams per 100 cc. of Solution
0	1.3
10	2.0
20	3.4
30	5.0
40	7.6
50	11.4
60	16.1
70	22.5
80	30.0
90	37.9
100	46.7

The preparation of guanidine nitrate from dicyandiamide by the action of aqua regia has been patented,[6] but the reaction evidently depends solely upon the hydrolysis of the cyan group and does not require the use of a vigorous oxidizing agent. Marqueyrol and Loriette in a French patent of September 26, 1917, described a process for the preparation of nitroguanidine direct from dicyandiamide without the isolation of any intermediate products. The process depends upon the hydrolysis of the dicyandiamide by means of 61% sulfuric acid to form guanylurea or dicyandiamidine (sulfate) which is then further hydrolyzed to form carbon dioxide, which escapes, and guanidine and ammonia, which remain in the reaction mixture in the form of sulfates.

$$NH_2—C(NH)—NH—CN + H_2O \longrightarrow$$
Dicyandiamide

$$NH_2—C(NH)—NH—CO—NH_2 + H_2O \longrightarrow$$
Guanylurea

$$NH_2—C(NH)—NH_2 + CO_2 + NH_3$$
Guanidine

The guanidine sulfate, without removal from the mixture, is then nitrated to nitroguanidine.[7] The process yields a nitroguanidine which is suitable for use in nitrocellulose powder, but it suffers from the disadvantages that the dicyandiamide, which corresponds after all to two molecules of cyanamide, yields in theory

[6] Ulpiani, Ger. Pat. 209,431 (1909).

[7] The procedure, under conditions somewhat different from those described in the patent, is illustrated by our process for the preparation of β-nitroguanidine; see page 383.

only one molecular equivalent of guanidine, that the actual yield is considerably less than the theory because of the loss of guanidine by hydrolysis to carbon dioxide and ammonia, and that the final nitration of the guanidine sulfate, which is carried out in the presence of water and of ammonium sulfate, requires strong and expensive mixed acid.

Werner and Bell [8] reported in 1920 that dicyandiamide heated for 2 hours at 160° with 2 mols of ammonium thiocyanate gives 2 mols of guanidine thiocyanate in practically theoretical yield. Ammonium thiocyanate commends itself for the reaction because it is readily fusible. The facts suggest that another fusible ammonium salt might work as well, ammonium nitrate melts at about 170°, and, of all the salts of guanidine, the nitrate is the one which is most desired for the preparation of nitroguanidine. When dicyandiamide and 2 mols of ammonium nitrate are mixed and warmed together at 160°, the mixture first melts to a colorless liquid which contains biguanide (or guanylguanidine) nitrate, which presently begins to deposit crystals of guanidine nitrate, and which after 2 hours at 160° solidifies completely to a mass of that substance.[9] The yield is practically theoretical. The reaction consists, first, in the addition of ammonia to the cyan group of the dicyandiamide, then in the ammoniolytic splitting of the biguanide to form two molecules of guanidine.

$$NH_2—C(NH)—NH—CN + NH_3 \cdot HNO_3 \longrightarrow$$
Dicyandiamide

$$NH_2—C(NH)—NH—C(NH)—NH_2 \cdot HNO_3 + NH_3 \cdot HNO_3 \longrightarrow$$
Biguanide nitrate

$$2NH_2—C(NH)—NH_2 \cdot HNO_3$$
Guanidine nitrate

The nitric acid of the original 2 mols of ammonium nitrate is exactly sufficient for the formation of 2 mols of guanidine nitrate. But the intermediate biguanide is a strong diacid base; the ammonium nitrate involved in its formation supplies only one equivalent of nitric acid; and there is a point during the early part of the process when the biguanide mononitrate tends to attack the unchanged ammonium nitrate and to liberate ammonia from it. For this reason the process works best if a small excess of

[8] *J. Chem. Soc.*, **118**, 1133 (1920).

[9] Davis, *J. Am. Chem. Soc.*, **43**, 2234 (1921); Davis, U. S. Pat. 1,440,063 (1922), French Pat. 539,125 (1922).

ammonium nitrate is used. The preparation may be carried out by heating the materials together either in the dry state or in an autoclave in the presence of water or of alcohol.

Guanidine nitrate is not deliquescent. It is readily soluble in alcohol, very readily in water, and may be recrystallized from either solvent. The pure material melts at 215–216°.

Preparation of Guanidine Nitrate. An intimate mixture of 210 grams of dicyandiamide and 440 grams of ammonium nitrate is placed in a 1 liter round-bottom flask, and the flask is arranged for heating in an oil bath which has a thermometer in the oil. The oil bath is warmed until the thermometer indicates 160°, and the temperature is held at this point for 2 hours. At the end of that time the flask is removed and allowed to cool, and its contents is extracted on the steam bath by warming with successive portions of water. The combined solution is filtered while hot for the removal of white insoluble material (ammeline and ammelide), concentrated to a volume of about a liter, and allowed to crystallize. The mother liquors are concentrated to a volume of about 250 cc. for a second crop, after the removal of which the residual liquors are discarded. The crude guanidine nitrate may be recrystallized by dissolving it in the least possible amount of boiling water and allowing to cool, etc., or it may be dried thoroughly and used directly for the preparation of nitroguanidine. A small amount of ammonium nitrate in it does not interfere with its conversion to nitroguanidine by the action of concentrated sulfuric acid.

Nitroguanidine

Nitroguanidine exists in two forms.[10] The α-form invariably results when guanidine nitrate is dissolved in concentrated sulfuric and the solution is poured into water. It is the form which is commonly used in the explosives industry. It crystallizes from water in long, thin, flat, flexible, lustrous needles which are tough and extremely difficult to pulverize; $N_\alpha = 1.518$, $N_\beta = $ a little greater than 1.668, $N_\gamma = $ greater than 1.768, double refraction 0.250. When α-nitroguanidine is decomposed by heat, a certain amount of β-nitroguanidine is found among the products.

β-Nitroguanidine is produced in variable amount, usually along with some of the α-compound, by the nitration of the mixture of guanidine sulfate and ammonium sulfate which results from the hydrolysis of dicyandiamide by sulfuric acid. Conditions have

[10] Davis, Ashdown, and Couch, *J. Am. Chem. Soc.*, **47**, 1063 (1925).

been found, as described later, which have yielded exclusively the β-compound in more than thirty trials. It crystallizes from water in fernlike clusters of small, thin, elongated plates; $N_\alpha = 1.525$, N_β not determined, $N_\gamma = 1.710$, double refraction 0.185. It is converted into the α-compound by dissolving in concentrated sulfuric acid and pouring the solution into water.

Both α- and β-nitroguanidine, if dissolved in hot concentrated nitric acid and allowed to crystallize, yield the same nitrate, thick, rhomb-shaped prisms which melt at 147° with decomposition. The nitrate loses nitric acid slowly in the air, and gives α-nitroguanidine when recrystallized from water. Similarly, both forms recrystallized from strong hydrochloric acid yield a hydrochloride which crystallizes in needles. These lose hydrogen chloride rapidly in the air, and give α-nitroguanidine when recrystallized from water. The two forms are alike in all their chemical reactions, in their derivatives and color reactions.

Both forms of nitroguanidine melt at 232° if the temperature is raised with moderate slowness, but by varying the rate of heating melting points varying between 220° and 250° may be obtained.

Neither form can be converted into the other by solution in water, and the two forms can be separated by fractional crystallization from this solvent. They appear to differ slightly in their solubility in water, the two solubility curves lying close together but apparently crossing each other at about 25°, where the solubility is about 4.4 grams per liter, and again at about 100°, where the solubility is about 82.5 grams per liter. Between these temperatures the β-form appears to be the more soluble.

Preparation of α-*Nitroguanidine.* Five hundred cc. of concentrated sulfuric acid in a 1-liter beaker is cooled by immersing the beaker in cracked ice, and 400 grams of well-dried guanidine nitrate is added in small portions at a time, while the mixture is stirred with a thermometer and the temperature is not allowed to rise above 10°. The guanidine nitrate dissolves rapidly, with very little production of heat, to form a milky solution. As soon as all crystals have disappeared, the milky liquid is poured into 3 liters of cracked ice and water, and the mixture is allowed to stand with chilling until precipitation and crystallization are complete. The product is collected on a filter, rinsed with water for the removal of sulfuric acid, dissolved in boiling water (about 4 liters), and allowed to crystallize by standing over night. Yield 300–310 grams, about 90% of the theory.

The rapid cooling of a solution of α-nitroguanidine produces small needles, which dry out to a fluffy mass but which are still too coarse to be incorporated properly in colloided powder. An

FIGURE 89. α-Nitroguanidine (25×). Small crystals from the rapid cooling of a hot aqueous solution.

extremely fine powder may be procured by the rapid cooling of a mist or spray of hot nitroguanidine solution, either by spraying it against a cooled surface from which the material is removed continuously, or by allowing the spray to drop through a tower up which a counter current of cold air is passing.

Preparation of β-Nitroguanidine. Twenty-five cc. of 61% aqueous sulfuric acid is poured upon 20 grams of dicyandiamide contained in a 300-cc. round-bottom flask equipped with a reflux condenser. The mixture warms up and froths considerably. After the first vigorous reaction has subsided, the material is heated for 2 hours in an oil bath at 140° (thermometer in the oil). The reaction mass, chilled in a freezing mixture, is treated with ice-cold nitrating acid prepared by mixing 20 cc. of fuming nitric acid (1.50) with 10 cc. of concentrated sulfuric acid (1.84). After the evolution of red fumes has stopped, the mixture is heated for 1 hour in the boiling-water bath, cooled, and drowned in 300 cc. of cracked ice and water. The precipitate, collected on a filter, rinsed with water for the removal of acid, and recrystallized from water, yields about 6 grams of β-nitroguanidine, about 25% of the theory.

Saturated solutions of nitroguanidine in sulfuric acid of various concentrations contain [11] the amounts indicated below.

| | NITROGUANIDINE (GRAMS) PER | |
| | 100 CC. | |
CONCENTRATION OF SOLVENT SULFURIC ACID, %	at 0°	at 25°
45	5.8	10.9
40	3.4	8.0
35	2.0	5.2
30	1.3	2.9
25	0.75	1.8
20	0.45	1.05
15	0.30	0.55
0	0.12	0.42

Nitroguanidine on reduction is converted first into nitroso-guanidine and then into aminoguanidine (or guanylhydrazine). The latter substance is used in the explosives industry for the preparation of tetracene. In organic chemical research it finds use because of the fact that it reacts readily with aldehydes and ketones to form products which yield crystalline and easily characterized nitrates.

$NO_2-NH-C(NH)-NH_2$
Nitroguanidine

N—NH—C(NH)—NH₂
Aminoguanidine

CH=NH—NH—C(NH)—NH₂
Benzalaminoguanidine

Preparation of Benzalaminoguanidine Nitrate (Benzaldehyde Guanylhydrazone Nitrate). Twenty-six grams of zinc dust and 10.4 grams of nitroguanidine are introduced into a 300-cc. Erlenmeyer flask, 150 cc. of water is added, then 42 cc. of glacial acetic acid at such a rate that the temperature of the mixture does not rise above 40°. The liquid at first turns yellow because of the formation of nitrosoguanidine but

[11] Davis, *J. Am. Chem. Soc.*, **44**, 868 (1922).

becomes colorless again when the reduction is complete. After all the zinc has disappeared, 1 mol of concentrated nitric acid is added, then 1 mol of benzaldehyde, and the mixture is shaken and scratched to facilitate the separation of the heavy granular precipitate of benzalaminoguanidine nitrate. The product, recrystallized from water or from alcohol, melts when pure at 160.5°.

Nitroguanidine and nitrosoguanidine both give a blue color with the diphenylamine reagent, and both give the tests described below, but the difference in the physical properties of the substances is such that there is no likelihood of confusing them.

Tests for Nitroguanidine. To 0.01 gram of nitroguanidine in 4 cc. of cold water 2 drops of saturated ferrous ammonium sulfate solution is added, then 1 cc. of 6 N sodium hydroxide solution. The mixture is allowed to stand for 2 minutes, and is filtered. The filtrate shows a fuchsine color but fades to colorless on standing for half an hour. Larger quantities of nitroguanidine give a stronger and more lasting color.

One-tenth gram of nitroguanidine is treated in a test tube with 5 cc. of water and 1 cc. of 50% acetic acid, and the mixture is warmed at 40–50° until everything is dissolved. One gram of zinc dust is added, and the mixture is set aside in a beaker of cold water for 15 minutes. After filtering, 1 cc. of 6% copper sulfate solution is added. The solution becomes intensely blue, and, on boiling, gives off gas, becomes turbid, and presently deposits a precipitate of metallic copper. If, instead of the copper sulfate solution, 1 cc. of a saturated solution of silver acetate [12] is added, and the solution is boiled, then a precipitate of metallic silver is formed.

Many of the reactions of nitroguanidine, particularly its decomposition by heat and the reactions which occur in aqueous and in sulfuric acid solutions, follow directly from its dearrangement.[13] Nitroguanidine dearranges in two modes, as follows.

$$\text{(H}\!\!\!\!\quad \text{N-C(NH)-N}\begin{smallmatrix}\text{NO}_2\\ \text{H}\end{smallmatrix} \rightleftharpoons NH_2-NO_2 + \underset{\text{Cyanamide}}{HNCNH} \rightleftharpoons NH_2CN$$

$$\text{(H}\!\!\!\!\quad \text{N-C(NH)-N}\begin{smallmatrix}\text{NO}_2\\ \text{H}\end{smallmatrix} \rightleftharpoons NH_3 + \underset{\text{Nitrocyanamide}}{HNCN-NO_2} \rightleftharpoons NC-N\begin{smallmatrix}\text{NO}_2\\ \text{H}\end{smallmatrix}$$

[12] Two grams of silver acetate, 2 cc. of glacial acetic acid, diluted to 100 cc., warmed, filtered, and allowed to cool.

[13] Davis and Abrams, *Proc. Am. Acad. Arts and Sciences,* **61,** 437 (1926).

A solution of nitroguanidine in concentrated sulfuric acid comports itself as if the nitroguanidine had dearranged into nitroamide and cyanamide. When it is warmed, nitrous oxide containing a small amount of nitrogen comes off first (from the dehydration of the nitroamide) and carbon dioxide (from the hydrolysis of the cyanamide) comes off later and more slowly. Long-continued heating at an elevated temperature produces ammonia and carbon dioxide quantitatively according to the equation,

$$NH_2—C(NH)—NH—NO_2 + H_2O \longrightarrow N_2O + 2NH_3 + CO_2$$

The production of nitrous oxide is not exactly quantitative because of secondary reactions. A solution of nitroguanidine in concentrated sulfuric acid, after standing for some time, no longer gives a precipitate of nitroguanidine when it is diluted with water.

A freshly prepared solution of nitroguanidine in concentrated sulfuric acid contains no nitric acid, for none can be distilled out of it, but it is ready to produce nitric acid (by the hydration of the nitroamide) if some material is present which will react with it. Thus, it gives up its nitro group quantitatively in the nitrometer, and it is a reagent for the nitration of such substances as aniline, phenol, acet-p-toluide, and cinnamic acid which are conveniently nitrated in sulfuric acid solution.

In aqueous solution nitroguanidine dearranges in both of the above-indicated modes, but the tendency toward dearrangement is small unless an acceptor for the product of the dearrangement is present. It results that nitroguanidine is relatively stable in aqueous solution; after many boilings and recrystallizations the same solution finally becomes ammoniacal. Ammonia, being alkaline, tends to promote the decomposition of nitroamide in aqueous solution. Also, because of its mass action effect, it tends to inhibit dearrangement in the second mode which produces ammonia. If nitroguanidine is warmed with aqueous ammonia, the reaction is slow. But, if it is warmed with water and a large excess of ammonium carbonate, nitrous oxide comes off rapidly, the ammonia combines with the cyanamide from the dearrangement, and guanidine carbonate is formed in practically quantitative amount.

Preparation of Guanidine Carbonate from Nitroguanidine. Two hundred and eight grams of nitroguanidine, 300 grams of ammonium carbonate, and 1 liter of water are heated together in a 2-liter flask in the water bath. The flask is equipped with a reflux condenser and with a thermometer dipping into the mixture. When the thermometer indicates 65–70°, nitrous oxide escapes rapidly, and it is necessary to shake the flask occasionally to prevent the undissolved nitroguanidine from being carried up into the neck. The temperature is raised as rapidly as may be done without the reaction becoming too violent. After all the material has gone into solution, the flask is removed from the water bath and the contents boiled under reflux for 2 hours by the application of a free flame. The liquid is then transferred to an evaporating dish and evaporated to dryness on the steam or water bath. During this process all the remaining ammonium carbonate ought to be driven off. The residue is taken up in the smallest possible amount of cold water, filtered for the removal of a small amount of melamine, and the filtrate is stirred up with twice its volume of 95% alcohol which causes the precipitation of guanidine carbonate (while the traces of urea which will have been formed remain in solution along with any ammonium carbonate which may have survived the earlier treatment). The guanidine carbonate is filtered off, rinsed with alcohol, and dried. The filtrate is evaporated to dryness, taken up in water, and precipitated with alcohol for a second crop—total yield about 162 grams or 90% of the theory. The product gives no color with the diphenylamine reagent; it is free from nitrate and of a quality which would be extremely difficult to procure by any process involving the double decomposition of guanidine nitrate.

In the absence of ammonia and in the presence of a primary aliphatic amine, nitroguanidine in aqueous solution dearranges in the second of the above-indicated modes, ammonia is liberated, and the nitrocyanamide combines with the amine to form an alkylnitroguanidine.

$$HNCN—NO_2 + CH_3—NH_2 \longrightarrow CH_3—NH—C(NH)—NH—NO_2$$
Nitrocyanamide   Methylnitroguanidine

The structure of the N-alkyl,N′-nitroguanidine is demonstrated by the fact that it yields the amine and nitrous oxide on hydrolysis, indicating that the alkyl group and the nitro group are attached to different nitrogen atoms.

$$CH_3—NH—C(NH)—NH—NO_2 + H_2O \longrightarrow$$
$$CH_3—NH_2 + NH_3 + N_2O + CO_2$$

The same N-alkyl,N′-nitroguanidines are produced by the nitration of the alkyl guanidines.[14]

[14] Davis and Elderfield, *J. Am. Chem. Soc.*, **55**, 731 (1933).

Nitroguanidine, warmed with an aqueous solution of hydrazine, yields N-amino,N'-nitroguanidine,[15] white crystals from water, m. p. 182°. This substance explodes on an iron anvil if struck with a heavy sledge hammer allowed to drop through a distance of about 8 inches. It may perhaps have some interest as an explosive.

Flashless colloided powder containing nitroguanidine produces a considerable amount of gray smoke made up of solid materials from the decomposition of the substance. The gases smell of ammonia. The powder produces more smoke than the other flashless powders which are used in this country.

Nitroguanidine decomposes immediately upon melting and cannot be obtained in the form of a liquid, as can urea, dicyandiamide, and other substances which commence to decompose when heated a few degrees above their melting points. A small quantity heated in a test tube yields ammonia, water vapor, a white sublimate in the upper part of the tube, and a yellow residue of mellon which is but little affected if warmed to a bright red heat. The products which are formed are precisely those which would be predicted from the dearrangements,[16] namely, water and nitrous oxide (from nitroamide), cyanamide, melamine (from the polymerization of cyanamide), ammonia, nitrous oxide again and cyanic acid (from nitrocyanamide), cyanuric acid (from the polymerization of cyanic acid), ammeline and ammelide (from the co-polymerization of cyanic acid and cyanamide) and, from the interaction and decomposition of these substances, carbon dioxide, urea, melam, melem, mellon, nitrogen, prussic acid, cyanogen, and paracyanogen. All these substances have been detected in, or isolated from, the products of the decomposition of nitroguanidine by heat.

There is no doubt whatever that nitroguanidine is a cool explosive, but there appears to be a disagreement as to the temperature which it produces. A package of nitroguanidine, exploded at night by means of a blasting cap, produces no visible flash. If 10 or 15% of the substance is incorporated in nitrocellulose powder, it makes the powder flashless. Vieille [17] found that the gases from the explosion of nitroguanidine were much less erosive

15 Phillips and Williams, *J. Am. Chem. Soc.,* **50,** 2465 (1928).
16 Davis and Abrams, *Proc. Am. Acad. Arts and Sciences,* **61,** 443 (1926).
17 *Mém. poudres,* **11,** 195 (1901).

than those from other explosives of comparable force, and considered the fact to be in harmony with his general conclusion that the hotter explosives are the more erosive. In his experiments the explosions were made to take place in a steel bomb equipped with a crusher gauge and with a removable, perforated, steel plug through the perforation in which the hot gases from the explosion were allowed to escape. They swept away, or eroded off, a certain amount of the metal. The plug was weighed before and after the experiment, its density had been determined, and the number of cubic millimeters of metal lost was reported as a measure of the erosion. Some of Vieille's results are indicated in the following table.

EXPLOSIVE	CHARGE (Grams)	PRESSURE (Kg./sq. cm.)	EROSION	EROSION PER GRAM	FORCE
Poudre BF	3.45	2403	20.3	5.88	
	3.50	2361	22.7	6.58	
	3.55	2224	24.7	6.96 6.4	9,600
	3.55	2253	25.5	7.19	
	3.55	2143	20.1	5.66	
Cordite	3.55	2500	64.2	18.1	10,000
Ballistite VF	3.47	2509	84.5	24.3	
	3.51	2370	83.2	23.7	
	3.55	2542	90.2	25.4 24.3	10,000
	3.55	2360	85.9	24.2	
	3.55	2416	84.5	23.8	
Black military	10.00	2167	22.3	2.2	3,000
Black sporting	8.88	1958	40.0	4.5	3,000
Blasting gelatin	3.35	2458	105.0	31.4	10,000
Nitromannite	3.54	2361	83.5	23.6	10,000
Nitroguanidine	3.90	2019	8.8	2.3	9,000

These experiments [18] were carried out in a bomb of 17.8 cc. capacity, which corresponds, for the example cited, to a density of loading of 0.219 for the nitroguanidine which was pulverulent

[18] The cordite used in these experiments was made from 57% nitroglycerin, 5% vaseline, and 38% high nitration guncotton colloided with acetone; the ballistite VF of equal amounts by weight of nitroglycerin and high nitration guncotton colloided with ethyl acetate. The black military powder was made from saltpeter 75, sulfur 10, and charcoal 15; the black sporting powder from saltpeter 78, sulfur 10, and charcoal 12. The blasting gelatin contained 94% nitroglycerin and 6% soluble nitrocotton.

material "firmly agglomerated in a manner to facilitate the naturally slow combustion of that substance."

An experiment with 18.11 grams nitroguanidine in a bomb of 75.0 cc. capacity (density of loading 0.241) showed an erosion of 2.29 per gram of explosive.

The temperature (907°) which Vieille accepted as the temperature produced by the explosion of nitroguanidine had been determined earlier by Patart [19] who published in 1904 an account of manometric bomb experiments with guanidine nitrate and with nitroguanidine. The explosives were agglomerated under a pressure of 3600 kilograms per square centimeter, broken up into grains 2 or 3 mm. in diameter, and fired in a bomb of 22 cc. capacity. Some of Patart's experimental results are tabulated below. Calculated from these data, Patart reported for guanidine

	PRESSURE, KILOGRAMS PER SQUARE CENTIMETER		
DENSITY OF LOADING	Guanidine Nitrate	Nitroguanidine
0.15...............	1128 1038 } 1083 ...	1304 1584 } 1435 1416
0.20...............	1556 1416 } 1486	2060 2122 } 2091
0.25...............	2168 2028 } 2098	3092 3068 } 3080
0.30...............	3068 2814 } 2941	4118 4038 } 4078
0.35...............	3668 3730 } 3699	... ...

nitrate, covolume 1.28, force 5834, and temperature of explosion 929°; for nitroguanidine, covolume 1.60, force 7140, and temperature of explosion 907°. He appears to have felt that these calculated temperatures of explosion were low, for he terminated his article by calling attention to the extraordinary values of the covolume deduced from the pressures in the closed vessel, and subpended a footnote:

It may be questioned whether the rapid increase of the pressure with the density of loading, rather than being the consequence of a constant reaction giving place to a considerable covolume, is not due simply to the mode of de-

[19] Mém. poudres, 13, 153 (1905–1906).

composition being variable with the density of loading and involving a more and more complete decomposition of the explosive. Only an analysis of the gases produced by the reaction can determine this point, as it also can determine the actual temperature of the deflagration.

The later studies of Muraour and Aunis [20] have shown that the temperature of explosion of nitroguanidine may be much higher than Patart calculated, and have given probability to his hypothesis that the density of loading has an effect upon the mode of the explosive decomposition. These investigators found that a platinum wire 0.20 mm. in diameter, introduced into the bomb along with the nitroguanidine, was melted by the heat of the explosion—a result which indicates a temperature of at least 1773°C. They pointed out that nitroguanidine, if compressed too strongly, may take fire with difficulty and may undergo an incomplete decomposition, and hence at low densities of loading may produce unduly low pressures corresponding to a covolume which is too large and to a temperature of explosion which is too low. The pressure of 3600 kilograms per square centimeter, under which Patart compressed his nitroguanidine, is much too high. Nitroguanidine compressed under 650 kilograms per square centimeter, and fired in a manometric bomb of 22 cc. capacity, at a density of loading of 0.2, and with a primer of 1 gram of black powder, gave a pressure of 1737 kilograms per square centimeter; compressed under 100 kilograms per square centimeter and fired in the same way nitroguanidine gave a pressure of 1975 kilograms per square centimeter, or a difference of 238 kilograms. In an experiment with a bomb of 139 cc. capacity, density of loading 0.2, Muraour and Aunis observed a pressure which, correction being made for various heat losses, corresponded to a temperature of 1990°.

Assuming that nitroguanidine explodes to produce carbon dioxide, water, carbon monoxide, hydrogen, and nitrogen,[21] assuming that the equilibrium constant for the reaction, $CO + H_2O \rightleftharpoons CO_2 + H_2$, is 6, and that the molecular heat of formation at con-

[20] *Annales des Mines*, **9**, 178, 180 (1920); *Comp. rend.*, **190**, 1389, 1547 (1930); *Mém. poudres*, **25**, 91 (1932–1933).

[21] This assumption however is not true, for powder which contains nitroguanidine produces a gray smoke consisting of solid decomposition products and yields gases which smell of ammonia.

stant volume of nitroguanidine is 17.9 Calories, and taking the values of Nernst and Wohl for the specific heats of the various gases, Muraour and Aunis calculated the following values for the explosion of nitroguanidine, temperature 2098°, covolume 1.077, force 9660, and pressure (at density of loading 0.20) 2463 kilograms per square centimeter. They have also calculated the temperature of explosion of ammonium nitrate 1125°,[22] of "explosive NO" (ammonium nitrate 78.7, trinitrotoluene 21.3) 2970°, and of explosive N4 (ammonium nitrate 90, potassium nitrate 5, trinitronaphthalene 5) 1725°, and have found by experiment that the last named of these explosives, fired at a density of loading of 0.30, did not fuse a platinum wire (0.06-mm. diameter) which had been introduced along with it into the bomb.

Nitroguanidine detonates completely under the influence of a detonator containing 1.5 gram of fulminate. According to Patart [23] 40 grams exploded on a lead block 67 mm. in diameter produced a shortening of 7 mm. Picric acid under the same conditions produced a shortening of 10.5 mm., and Favier explosive (12% dinitronaphthalene, 88% ammonium nitrate) one of 8 mm. Muraour and Aunis [24] experimented with nitroguanidine compressed under 100 kilograms per square centimeter and with trinitrotoluene compressed under 1000 kilograms per square centimeter, in a manometric bomb of 22-cc. capacity and at densities of loading of 0.13, 0.20, 0.25, and 0.30, and reported that the two explosives gave the same pressures.

During the first World War the Germans used in trench mortar bombs an explosive consisting of nitroguanidine 50%, ammonium nitrate, 30%, and paraffin 20%.

Nitrosoguanidine

Nitrosoguanidine is a cool and flashless primary explosive, very much more gentle in its behavior than mercury fulminate and lead azide. It is a pale yellow crystalline powder which explodes on contact with concentrated sulfuric acid or on being heated in a melting point tube at 165°. It explodes from the blow of a car-

[22] The temperature of 1121° was calculated by Hall, Snelling, and Howell, "Investigations of Explosives Used in Coal Mines," U. S. Bur. Mines Bull. 15, Washington, 1912, p. 32.

[23] Mém. poudres, 13, 159 (1905–1906).

[24] Ibid., 25, 92–93, footnote (1932–1933).

penter's hammer on a concrete block. Its sensitivity to shock, to friction, and to temperature, and the fact that it decomposes slowly in contact with water at ordinary temperatures, militate against its use as a practical explosive. It may be kept indefinitely in a stoppered bottle if it is dry.

The reactions of nitrosoguanidine in aqueous solution are similar to those of nitroguanidine except that nitrogen and nitrous acid respectively are formed under conditions which correspond to the formation of nitrous oxide and nitric acid from nitroguanidine. It dearranges principally as follows.

$$NH_2\text{—}C(NH)\text{—}NH\text{—}NO \rightleftharpoons NH_2\text{—}NO + HNCNH \rightleftharpoons NH_2\text{—}CN$$

If it is warmed in aqueous solution, the nitrosoamide breaks down into water and nitrogen, and the cyanamide polymerizes to dicyandiamide. The evaporation of the solution yields crystals of the latter substance. A cold aqueous solution of nitrosoguanidine acidified with hydrochloric acid yields nitrous acid, and may be used for the introduction of a nitroso group into dimethylaniline or some similar substance which is soluble in the acidified aqueous liquid.

Preparation of Nitrosoguanidine.[25] Twenty-one grams of nitroguanidine, 11 grams of ammonium chloride, 18 grams of zinc dust, and 250 cc. of water in an 800-cc. beaker are stirred together mechanically while external cooling is applied to prevent the temperature from rising above 20–25°. After 2 hours or so the gray color of the zinc disappears, the mixture is yellow, and on settling shows no crystals of nitroguanidine. The mixture is then cooled to 0° or below by surrounding the beaker with a mixture of cracked ice and salt; it is filtered, and the filtrate is discarded. The yellow residue, consisting of nitrosoguanidine mixed with zinc oxide or hydroxide and basic zinc chloride, is extracted with 4 successive portions of 250 cc. each of water at 65°. The combined extracts, allowed to stand over night at 0°, deposit nitrosoguanidine which is collected, rinsed with water, and dried at 40°. Yield 8.0–9.2 grams, 45–52% of the theory.

The flashlessness of nitrosoguanidine may be demonstrated safely by igniting about 0.5 gram of it on the back of the hand. The experiment is most striking if carried out in a darkened room. The sample being poured out in a conical heap on the back of the left hand, a match held in the right hand is scratched and allowed to burn until the mate-

[25] Davis and Rosenquist, *J. Am. Chem. Soc.,* **59**, 2114 (1937).

rial which composes the burnt head of the match has become thoroughly heated, it is extinguished by shaking, and the burnt head is then touched to the heap of nitrosoguanidine. The nitrosoguanidine explodes with a zishing sound and with a cloud of gray smoke, but with no visible flash whatsoever. The place on the hand where the nitrosoguanidine was fired will perhaps itch slightly, and the next day will perhaps show a slight rash and peeling of the skin. There is no sensation of being burned, and the explosion is so rapid that the hand remains steady and makes no reflex movement.

Ethylenedinitramine

Ethylenedinitramine, m.p. 174–176° with decomposition, is produced when dinitroethyleneurea is refluxed with water,[26] or it

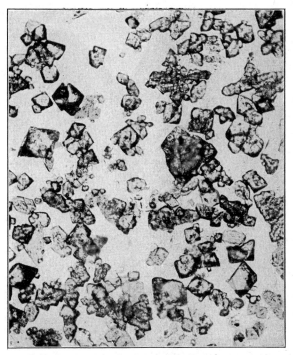

Figure 90. Ethylenedinitramine Crystals (60×).

may be prepared directly, without isolating this intermediate, by the nitration of ethyleneurea with mixed acid.

[26] Franchimont and Klobbie, *Rec. trav. chim.*, **7**, 17, 244 (1887).

$$
\begin{array}{c}
\text{CH}_2\text{—NH} \\
| \qquad\qquad \text{CO} \\
\text{CH}_2\text{—NH} \\
\text{Ethyleneurea}
\end{array}
\longrightarrow
\begin{array}{c}
\text{CH}_2\text{—N(NO}_2) \\
| \qquad\qquad \text{CO} \\
\text{CH}_2\text{—N(NO}_2) \\
\text{Dinitroethyleneurea}
\end{array}
\longrightarrow
\begin{array}{c}
\text{CH}_2\text{—NH—NO}_2 \\
| \\
\text{CH}_2\text{—NH—NO}_2 \\
\text{Ethylenedinitramine}
\end{array}
$$

It is a dibasic acid and forms neutral salts, the silver salt a pulverulent precipitate, the potassium salt needles from alcohol. It is sparingly soluble in water, about 1 part in 200 at 25°, and is not affected by refluxing with this solvent. On refluxing with dilute sulfuric acid it gives nitrous oxide, acetaldehyde, and glycol. Hale [27] has reported that it explodes spontaneously when heated to 180°, in which respect it resembles mercury fulminate and nitroglycerin, but that it corresponds in resistance to shock more nearly to the relatively insensitive high explosives, like TNT and picric acid, which are used as the bursting charges of shells. He found that it is exploded by a 10-inch drop of a 2-kilogram weight, the same as picric acid, and reported that it withstands the standard 120° stability test as well as tetryl.

Dinitrodimethyloxamide

This substance was prepared by Franchimont [28] by dissolving dimethyloxamide in very strong nitric acid (specific gravity 1.523) without cooling, allowing to stand, and pouring into water, and by Thiele and Meyer [29] by dissolving dimethyloxamide in crude nitric acid, adding fuming sulfuric acid to the chilled solution, and pouring onto ice. Dimethyloxamide is prepared readily by the interaction of methylamine with an ester of oxalic acid.

$$
\begin{array}{c}
\text{COOR} \\
| \\
\text{COOR}
\end{array}
+ 2\text{NH}_2\text{—CH}_3 \longrightarrow
\begin{array}{c}
\text{CO—NH—CH}_3 \\
| \\
\text{CO—NH—CH}_3 \\
\text{Dimethyloxamide}
\end{array}
\longrightarrow
\begin{array}{c}
\text{CO—N(NO}_2)\text{—CH}_3 \\
| \\
\text{CO—N(NO}_2)\text{—CH}_3 \\
\text{Dinitrodimethyloxamide}
\end{array}
$$

Dinitrodimethyloxamide is very slightly soluble in water, sparingly in ether and chloroform, and soluble in alcohol from which it crystallizes in needles which melt at 124° and decompose at a higher temperature. By reduction with zinc and acetic acid in alcohol solution it yields dimethyloxamide. It is not destroyed by refluxing with concentrated hydrochloric acid. Concentrated sulfuric acid splits off nitric acid, and the substance accordingly

[27] U. S. Pat. 2,011,578 (1935).
[28] *Rec. trav. chim.*, 2, 96 (1882); 4, 197 (1884); 13, 311 (1893).
[29] *Ber.*, 29, 961 (1896).

gives up its nitro group in the nitrometer. On treatment with an excess of aqueous ammonia or on refluxing with a slight excess of barium hydroxide solution, it yields the corresponding salt of methylnitramine. Haid, Becker, and Dittmar [30] have reported that dinitrodimethyloxamide, like PETN, tetryl, TNT, and picric acid, gives no red fumes after 30 days at 100° while nitrocellulose in their experiments gave red fumes after 36 hours and dipentaerythrite hexanitrate after 8 days.

Dinitrodimethyloxamide has interesting explosive properties, but it is limited in its use because it develops an acidity when wet with water. It has been reported [31] that 30 parts of dinitrodimethyloxamide and 70 parts of PETN yield a eutectic which melts at 100° and can be poured as a homogeneous liquid. The cast explosive has a velocity of detonation of 8500 meters per second which is equal to that of PETN under the best conditions. The further addition of dimethyl oxalate or of camphor [32] lowers the melting point still more and affects the brisance only slightly but has a significant phlegmatizing action. A mixture of PETN 60%, dinitrodimethyloxamide 30%, and dimethyl oxalate 10% melts at 82°, and has, when cast, a velocity of detonation of 7900 meters per second which is higher than the velocity of detonation of cast picric acid.

Dinitrodimethylsulfamide

This substance was first prepared by Franchimont [33] by dissolving 1 part of dimethylsulfamide in 10 parts of the strongest nitric acid, and drowning in water. Dimethylsulfamide is prepared by the interaction of methylamine and sulfuryl chloride in chilled absolute ether solution.

$$O_2S\begin{smallmatrix}Cl\\Cl\end{smallmatrix} + 2NH_2-CH_3 \longrightarrow O_2S\begin{smallmatrix}NH-CH_3\\NH-CH_3\end{smallmatrix} \longrightarrow O_2S\begin{smallmatrix}N(NO_2)-CH_3\\N(NO_2)-CH_3\end{smallmatrix}$$

Dimethylsulfamide   Dinitrodimethylsulfamide

Dinitrodimethylsulfamide is very slightly soluble in water, very readily in hot alcohol, and moderately in chloroform and benzene. Crystals from benzene, m.p. 90°. The vapor of the substance

[30] Z. ges. Schiess- u. Sprengstoffw., **30**, 68 (1935).

[31] Ger. Pat. 499,403, cited by Foulon, Z. ges. Schiess- u. Sprengstoffw., **27**, 191 (1932).

[32] Ger. Pat. 505,852.

[33] Rec. trav. chim., **3**, 419 (1883).

explodes if heated to about 160°. Dinitrodimethylsulfamide has been suggested as an addition to PETN for the preparation of a fusible explosive which can be loaded by pouring.

Cyclotrimethylenetrinitramine (Cyclonite, Hexogen, T4).

The name of *cyclonite*, given to this explosive by Clarence J. Bain because of its cyclic structure and cyclonic nature, is the one by which it is generally known in the United States. The Germans call it *Hexogen*, the Italians *T4*.

Figure 91. George C. Hale. Has studied cyclonite, ethylenedinitramine, and many other explosives. Author of numerous inventions and publications in the field of military powder and explosives. Chief Chemist, Picatinny Arsenal, 1921-1929; Chief of the Chemical Department, Picatinny Arsenal, 1929—.

Cyclonite, prepared by the nitration of hexamethylenetetramine, is derived ultimately from no other raw materials than coke, air, and water. It has about the same power and brisance as PETN, and a velocity of detonation under the most favorable conditions of about 8500 meters per second.

Hexamethylenetetramine, $C_6H_{12}N_4$, is obtained in the form of colorless, odorless, and practically tasteless crystals by the evaporation of an aqueous solution of formaldehyde and ammonia. It is used in medicine under the names of *Methenamine, Hexamine, Cystamine, Cystogen,* and *Urotropine,* administered orally as an antiseptic for the urinary tract, and in industry in the manufacture of plastics and as an accelerator for the vulcanization of rubber. It has feebly basic properties and forms a nitrate, $C_6H_{12}N_4 \cdot 2HNO_3$, m.p. 165°, soluble in water, insoluble in alcohol, ether, chloroform, and acetone. The product, $C_3H_6O_6N_6$, prepared by nitrating this nitrate and patented by Henning [34] for possible use in medicine, was actually cyclonite. Herz later patented [35] the same substance as an explosive compound, cyclotrimethylenetrinitramine, which he found could be prepared by treating hexamethylenetetramine directly with strong nitric acid. In his process the tetramine was added slowly in small portions at a time to nitric acid (1.52) at a temperature of 20–30°. When all was in solution, the liquid was warmed to 55°, allowed to stand for a few minutes, cooled to 20°, and the product precipitated by the addition of water. The nitration has been studied further by Hale [36] who secured his best yield, 68%, in an experiment in which 50 grams of hexamethylenetetramine was added during 15 minutes to 550 grams of 100% nitric acid while the temperature was not allowed to rise above 30°. The mixture was then cooled to 0°, held there for 20 minutes, and drowned.

Hexamethylenetetramine   Cyclotrimethylenetrinitramine

The formaldehyde which is liberated by the reaction tends to be oxidized by the nitric acid if the mixture is allowed to stand or is warmed. It remains in the spent acid after drowning and interferes with the recovery of nitric acid from it.

[34] Ger. Pat. 104,280 (1899).
[35] Brit. Pat. 145,791 (1920); U. S. Pat. 1,402,693 (1922).
[36] *J. Am. Chem. Soc.,* **47,** 2754 (1925).

Cyclonite is a white crystalline solid, m.p. 202°. It is insoluble in water, alcohol, ether, ethyl acetate, petroleum ether, and carbon tetrachloride, very slightly soluble in hot benzene, and soluble 1 part in about 135 parts of boiling xylene. It is readily soluble in hot aniline, phenol, ethyl benzoate, and nitrobenzene, from all of which it crystallizes in needles. It is moderately soluble in hot acetone, about 1 part in 8, and is conveniently recrystallized from this solvent from which it is deposited in beautiful, transparent, sparkling prisms. It dissolves very slowly in cold concentrated sulfuric acid, and the solution decomposes on standing. It dissolves readily in warm nitric acid (1.42 or stronger) and separates only partially again when the liquid is cooled. The chemical reactions of cyclonite indicate that the cyclotrimethylenetrinitramine formula which Herz suggested for it is probably correct.

Cyclonite is hydrolyzed slowly when the finely powdered material is boiled with dilute sulfuric acid or with dilute caustic soda solution.

$$C_3H_6O_6N_6 + 6H_2O \longrightarrow 3NH_3 + 3CH_2O + 3HNO_3$$

Quantitative experiments have shown that half of its nitrogen appears as ammonia. If the hydrolysis is carried out in dilute sulfuric acid solution, the formaldehyde is oxidized by the nitric acid and nitrous acid is formed.

If cyclonite is dissolved in phenol at 100° and reduced by means of sodium, it yields methylamine, nitrous acid, and prussic acid. Finely powdered cyclonite, suspended in 80% alcohol and treated with sodium amalgam, yields methylamine, ammonia, nitrous acid, and formaldehyde, a result which probably indicates that both hydrolysis and reduction occur under these conditions.

When a large crystal of cyclonite is added to the diphenylamine reagent, a blue color appears slowly on the surface of the crystal. Powdered cyclonite gives within a few seconds a blue color which rapidly becomes more intense. If cinnamic acid is dissolved in concentrated sulfuric acid, and if finely powdered cyclonite is added while the mixture is stirred, gas comes off at a moderate rate, and the mixture, after standing over night and drowning, gives a precipitate which contains a certain amount of p-nitrocinnamic acid.

In the drop test cyclonite is exploded by a 9-inch drop of a 2-kilogram weight. For the detonation of 0.4 gram, the explosive requires 0.17 gram of mercury fulminate. It fails to detonate when struck with a fiber shoe, and detonates when struck with a steel shoe, in the standard frictional impact test of the U. S. Bureau of Mines. In 5 seconds it fumes off at 290°, but at higher temperatures, even as high as 360°, it does not detonate.

CHAPTER IX

PRIMARY EXPLOSIVES, DETONATORS, AND PRIMERS

Primary explosives explode from shock, from friction, and from heat. They are used in primers where it is desired by means of shock or friction to produce fire for the ignition of powder, and they are used in detonators where it is desired to produce shock for the initiation of the explosion of high explosives. They are also used in toy caps, toy torpedoes, and similar devices for the making of noise. Indeed, certain primary explosives were used for this latter purpose long before the history of modern high explosives had yet commenced.

Discovery of Fulminating Compounds

Fulminating gold, silver, and platinum (Latin, *fulmen*, lightning flash, thunderbolt) are formed by precipitating solutions of these metals with ammonia. They are perhaps nitrides or hydrated nitrides, or perhaps they contain hydrogen as well as nitrogen and water of composition, but they contain no carbon and must not be confused with the fulminates which are salts of fulminic acid, HONC. They are dangerously sensitive, and are not suited to practical use.

Fulminating gold is described in the writings of the pseudonymous Basil Valentine,[1] probably written by Johann Thölde (or Thölden) of Hesse and actually published by him during the years 1602–1604. The author called it *Goldkalck,* and prepared it by dissolving gold in an *aqua regia* made by dissolving sal ammoniac in nitric acid, and then precipitating by the addition of potassium carbonate solution. The powder was washed by decantation 8 to 12 times, drained from water, and dried in the air where no sunlight fell on it, "and not by any means over the

---

[1] We find the description on page 289 of the second part of the third German edition of the collected writings of Basil Valentine, Hamburg, 1700.

fire, for, as soon as this powder takes up a very little heat or warmth, it kindles forthwith, and does remarkably great damage, when it explodes with such vehemence and might that no man would be able to restrain it." The author also reported that warm distilled vinegar converted the powder into a material which was no longer explosive. The name of *aurum fulminans* was given to the explosive by Beguinus who described its preparation in his *Tyrocinium Chymicum*, printed in 1608.

Fulminating gold precipitates when a solution of pure gold chloride is treated with ammonia water. The method of preparation described by Basil Valentine succeeds because the sal ammoniac used for the preparation of the *aqua regia* supplies the necessary ammonia. If gold is dissolved in an *aqua regia* prepared from nitric acid and common salt, and if the solution is then treated with potassium carbonate, the resulting precipitate has no explosive properties. Fulminating gold loses its explosive properties rapidly if it is allowed to stand in contact with sulfur.

Fulminating gold was early used both for war and for entertainment. The Dutch inventor and chemist, Cornelis Drebbel, being in the service of the British Navy, devoted considerable time to the preparation of fulminating gold and used his material as a detonator in petards and torpedoes in the English expedition against La Rochelle in 1628. Pepys, in his diary for November 11, 1663, reports a conversation with a Dr. Allen concerning *aurum fulminans* "of which a grain . . . put in a silver spoon and fired, will give a blow like a musquett and strike a hole through the silver spoon downward, without the least force upward."

Fulminating silver was prepared in 1788 by Berthollet who precipitated a solution of nitrate of silver by means of lime water, dried the precipitated silver oxide, treated it with strong ammonia water which converted it into a black powder, decanted the liquid, and left the powder to dry in the open air. Fulminating silver is more sensitive to shock and friction than fulminating gold. It explodes when touched; it must not be enclosed in a bottle or transferred from place to place, but must be left in the vessel, or better upon the paper, where it was allowed to dry.

The black material which deposits in a reagent bottle of ammoniacal silver nitrate, and sometimes collects on the rim and around the stopper, contains fulminating silver. Explosions are reported to have been caused by the careless turning of the glass stopper of a bottle containing this reagent. After a test (for aldehyde, for example) has been made with ammoniacal silver nitrate solution, the liquid ought promptly to be washed down the sink, and all insoluble matter left in the vessel ought to be dissolved out with dilute nitric acid.

Fulminating platinum was first prepared by E. Davy, about 1825, by adding ammonia water to a solution of platinum sulfate, boiling the precipitate with a solution of potash, washing, and allowing to dry. It was exploded by heat, but not easily by percussion or friction.

Fourcroy prepared a *fulminating mercury* by digesting red oxide of mercury in ammonia water for 8 or 10 days. The material became white and finally assumed the form of crystalline scales. The dried product exploded loudly from fire, but underwent a spontaneous decomposition when left to itself. At slightly elevated temperatures it gave off ammonia and left a residue of mercury oxide.

In the *Journal de physique* for 1779 the apothecary, Bayen, described a fulminating mercurial preparation of another kind. Thirty parts of precipitated, yellow oxide of mercury, washed and dried, was mixed with 4 or 5 parts of sulfur; the mixture exploded with violence when struck with a heavy hammer or when heated on an iron plate. Other mixtures which react explosively when initiated by percussion have been studied more recently,[2] metallic sodium or potassium in contact with the oxide or the chloride of silver or of mercury or in contact with chloroform or carbon tetrachloride.

The explosion of chloroform in contact with an alkali metal may be demonstrated by means of the apparatus illustrated in Figure 92. About 0.3 gram of sodium or of potassium or of the liquid alloy of the two is introduced into a thin-wall glass tube, or, better yet, is sealed up in a small glass bulb, 6 to 8 mm. in diameter, which has a capillary 15 to 20 mm. in length. The tube or bulb containing the alkali metal is placed in the bottom of a narrow test tube into which 1 or 2 cc. of chloroform has already been introduced, and the apparatus is then

[2] Staudinger, *Z. Elektrochem.*, **31**, 549 (1925); Davis and McLean, *J. Am. Chem. Soc.*, **60**, 720 (1938).

ready for the experiment. Or, if it is desired to prepare in advance an explosive capsule which can safely be kept as long as desired, then the bulb is held in place at the bottom of the test tube by a collar of glass (a section of glass tubing) sintered to the inner wall of the test tube, and the top of the test tube is drawn down and sealed. When the prepared test tube or capsule is dropped onto a concrete pavement from

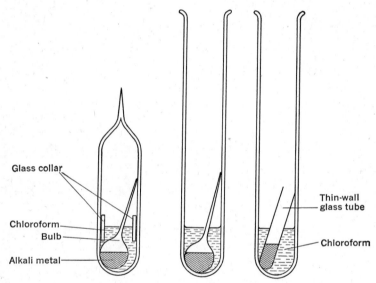

FIGURE 92. Apparatus for Demonstrating the Explosion of Chloroform with an Alkali Metal.

a height of 6 feet, a loud explosion is produced accompanied by a bright flash which is visible even in the direct sunlight. The chemical reaction is as follows, each one of the three chlorine atoms of the chloroform reacting in a different manner.

$$6CHCl_3 + 6Na \longrightarrow 6NaCl + 6HCl +$$

Mercury fulminate appears to have been prepared for the first time by Johann Kunckel von Löwenstern (1630–1703), the same chemist who discovered phosphorus and applied the purple of

Cassius practically to the manufacture of ruby glass. In his post-humous *Laboratorium Chymicum* he says: [3]

> Further evidence that mercury is cold is to be seen when you dissolve it in *aqua fortis* (nitric acid), evaporate the solution to dryness, pour highly rectified *spiritum vini* (alcohol) over the residue, and then warm it slightly so that it begins to dissolve. It commences to boil with amazing vigor. If the glass is somewhat stopped up, it bursts into a thousand pieces, and, in consequence, it must by no means be stopped up. I once dissolved silver and mercury together in *aqua fortis* and poured over it an excess of *spiritum vini*, and set the mixture to putrify *in fimum equinum* (horse manure) after having stopped up the glass with mere sealing wax only. When it happened a few days later that the manure became a little warm, it made such a thunder-crack, with the shattering of the glass, that the stable-servant imagined, since I had put it in a box, either that someone had shot at him through the window or that the Devil himself was active in the stable. As soon as I heard this news, I was able easily to see that the blame was mine, that it must have been my glass. Now this was with silver and mercury, 2 *loth* of each. Mercury does the same thing [4] alone, but silver not at all.

The preparation and properties of mercury fulminate were described in much detail by Edward Howard [5] in 1800 in a paper presented to the Royal Society of London. The method of preparation which he found to be most satisfactory was as follows: 100 grains of mercury was dissolved by heating in 1½ drams of nitric acid (specific gravity 1.3), the solution was cooled and added to 2 ounces of alcohol (specific gravity 0.849) in a glass vessel, the mixture was warmed until effervescence commenced, the reaction was allowed to proceed to completion, and the precipitate which formed was collected on a filter, washed with distilled water, and dried at a temperature not exceeding that of the water bath. Howard found that the fulminate was exploded by means of an electric spark or by concentrated sulfuric acid brought into contact with it. When a few grains were placed on a

[3] Kunckel, "Collegium Physico-Chymicum Experimentale, oder Laboratorium Chymicum," ed. Engelleder, Hamburg, 1716, p. 213. Cf. Davis, *Army Ordnance,* **7,** 62 (1926).

[4] Kunckel's meaning in the last sentence is evidently that mercury nitrate reacts with alcohol on warming, and that silver nitrate does not react with alcohol under the same conditions.

[5] *Phil. Trans. Roy. Soc.,* 204 (1800).

cold anvil and struck with a cold hammer, a very stunning dis-
agreeable noise was produced and the faces of the hammer and
anvil were indented. A few grains floated in a tinfoil capsule on
hot oil exploded at 368°F. (186.7°C.). When a mixture of fine-
and coarse-grain black powder was placed on top of a quantity
of fulminate and the fulminate was fired, the black powder was
blown about but it was not ignited and was recovered unchanged.
Howard also attempted by means of alcohol to produce fulminating compounds from gold, platinum, antimony, tin, copper, iron,
lead, nickel, bismuth, cobalt, arsenic, and manganese, but silver
was the only one of these metals with which he had any success.

Brugnatelli in 1802 worked out a satisfactory method for the
preparation of silver fulminate by pouring onto 100 grains of
powdered silver nitrate first an ounce of alcohol and then an
ounce of nitric acid. After the fulminate had precipitated, the
mixture was diluted with water to prevent it from dissolving
again and immediately filtered. Silver fulminate explodes more
easily from heat and from friction than mercury fulminate and
is more spectacular in its behavior. It quickly became an object
of amateur interest and public wonderment, one of the standard
exhibits of street fakirs and of mountebanks at fairs. Liebig, who
was born in 1803, saw a demonstration of silver fulminate in the
market place at Darmstadt when he was a boy. He watched the
process closely, recognized by its odor the alcohol which was
used, went home, and succeeded in preparing the substance for
himself. He retained his interest in it, and in 1823 carried out
studies on the fulminates in the laboratory of Gay-Lussac at
Paris.

Mercury Fulminate

The commercial preparation of mercury fulminate is carried
out by a process which is essentially the same as that which
Howard originally recommended. Five hundred or 600 grams of
mercury is used for each batch, the operation is practically on
the laboratory scale, and several batches are run at the same
time. Since the reaction produces considerable frothing, capacious
glass balloons are used. The fumes, which are poisonous and
inflammable, are passed through condensers, and the condensate,
which contains alcohol, acetaldehyde, ethyl nitrate, and ethyl
nitrite, is utilized by mixing it with the alcohol for the next batch.

Pure fulminate is white, but the commercial material is often grayish in color. The color is improved if a small amount of cupric chloride is added to the nitric acid solution of mercury before it is poured into the alcohol in the balloon, but the resulting white fulminate is actually less pure than the unbleached material.

Preparation of Mercury Fulminate. Five grams of mercury is added to 35 cc. of nitric acid (specific gravity 1.42) in a 100-cc. Erlenmeyer

FIGURE 93. Fulminate Manufacture. (Courtesy Atlas Powder Company.) At left, flasks in which mercury is dissolved in nitric acid. At right, balloons in which the reaction with alcohol occurs.

flask, and the mixture is allowed to stand without shaking until the mercury has gone into solution. The acid liquid is then poured into 50 cc. of 90% alcohol in a 500-cc. beaker in the hood. The temperature of the mixture rises, a vigorous reaction commences, white fumes come off, and crystals of fulminate soon begin to precipitate. Red fumes appear and the precipitation of the fulminate becomes more rapid, then white fumes again as the reaction moderates. After about 20 minutes the reaction is over; water is added, and the crystals are washed with water repeatedly by decantation until the washings are no longer acid to litmus. The product consists of grayish-yellow crystals, and corresponds to a good grade of commercial fulminate. It may be obtained white and entirely pure by dissolving in strong ammonia water, filtering, and reprecipitating by the addition of 30% acetic acid. The pure fulminate is filtered off, washed several times with cold water, and stored under water, or, if a very small amount is desired for experimental purposes, it is dried in a desiccator.

The chemical reactions in the preparation appear to be as follows. (1) The alcohol is oxidized to acetaldehyde, and (2) the nitrous acid which is formed attacks the acetaldehyde to form a nitroso derivative which goes over to the more stable, tautomeric, isonitroso form.

$$CH_3-CH_2-OH \rightarrow CH_3-CHO \longrightarrow \begin{array}{c} CH_2-CHO \\ | \\ NO \end{array} \rightleftharpoons \begin{array}{c} CH-CHO \\ \| \\ N-OH \end{array}$$

Nitrosoacetaldehyde   Isonitrosoacetaldehyde

(3) The isonitrosoacetaldehyde is oxidized to isonitrosoacetic acid, and (4) this is nitrated by the nitrogen dioxide which is present to form nitroisonitrosoacetic acid.

$$\begin{array}{c} CH-CHO \\ \| \\ N-OH \end{array} \longrightarrow \begin{array}{c} CH-COOH \\ \| \\ N-OH \end{array} \longrightarrow \begin{array}{c} NO_2 \\ | \\ C-COOH \\ \| \\ N-OH \end{array}$$

Isonitrosoacetic acid   Nitroisonitrosoacetic acid

(5) The nitroisonitrosoacetic acid loses carbon dioxide to form formonitrolic acid which (6) decomposes further into nitrous acid and fulminic acid, and (7) the fulminic acid reacts with the mercury nitrate to form the sparingly soluble mercury fulminate which precipitates.

$$\begin{array}{c} NO_2 \\ | \\ C-[COO]H \\ \| \\ N-OH \end{array} \longrightarrow \begin{array}{c} [NO_2] \\ [\uparrow] \\ C[H] \\ \| \\ N-OH \end{array} \nearrow \begin{array}{c} HONC \\ \downarrow \\ Hg(ONC)_2 \end{array}$$

Formonitrolic acid   Mercury fulminate

Fulminate can be prepared from acetaldehyde instead of from alcohol, and from substances which are convertible into acetaldehyde, such as paraldehyde, metaldehyde, dimethyl- and diethylacetal. Methyl alcohol, formaldehyde, propyl alcohol, butyraldehyde, glycol, and glyoxal do not yield fulminate.[6]

Fulminate can, however, be prepared from a compound which contains only one carbon atom. The sodium salt of nitromethane gives with an aqueous solution of mercuric chloride at 0° a white

[6] Wöhler and Theodorovits, *Ber.*, **38**, 1345 (1905).

precipitate of the mercuric salt of nitromethane which gradually becomes yellow and which, digested with warm dilute hydro-chloric acid, yields mercury fulminate.[7]

$$CH_2=N \begin{array}{c} O \\ ONa \end{array} \longrightarrow C \begin{array}{c} H_2=N \\ OHgO \end{array} \begin{array}{c} O \\ N=C H_2 \end{array} \longrightarrow Hg \begin{array}{c} ONC \\ ONC \end{array}$$

Sodium fulminate, soluble in water, has a molecular weight which corresponds[8] to the simple monomolecular formula, NaONC. These facts, taken together with the fact that mercury fulminate warmed with concentrated aqueous hydrochloric acid yields hy-droxylamine and formic acid,[9] prove that fulminic acid is the oxime of carbon monoxide.

$$HO—N=C \quad + 2H_2O \longrightarrow HO—NH_2 + H—COOH$$

Mercury fulminate dissolves readily in an aqueous solution of potassium cyanide to form a complex compound from which it is reprecipitated by the addition of strong acid. It dissolves in pyridine and precipitates again if the solution is poured into water. A sodium thiosulfate solution dissolves mercury fulminate with the formation of mercury tetrathionate and other inert compounds, and this reagent is used both for the destruction of fulminate and for its analysis.[10] The first reaction appears to be as follows.

$$Hg(ONC)_2 + 2Na_2S_2O_3 + H_2O \longrightarrow HgS_4O_6 + 2NaOH + NaCN + NaNCO$$

The cyanide and cyanate are salts of weak acids and are largely hydrolyzed, and the solution, if it is titrated immediately, ap-pears to have developed four molecules of sodium hydroxide for every molecule of mercury in the sample which was taken. If the solution is allowed to stand, the alkalinity gradually decreases because of a secondary reaction whereby sulfate and thiocyanate are formed.

[7] Nef, Ann., **280**, 275 (1894); Jones, Am. Chem. J., **20**, 33 (1898).

[8] Wöhler, Ber., **43**, 754 (1910).

[9] Carstenjen and Ehrenberg, J. prak. Chem., [2] **25**, 232 (1883); Steiner, Ber., **16**, 1484, 2419 (1883); Divers and Kawita, J. Chem. Soc., **45**, 17 (1884).

[10] Brownsdon, Chem. News, **89**, 303 (1904); Philip, Z. ges. Schiess- u. Sprengstoffw., **7**, 109, 156, 180, 198, 221 (1912); Taylor and Rinkenbach, "Explosives, Their Materials, Constitution, and Analysis," U. S. Bureau of Mines Bulletin 219, Washington, 1923, p. 62.

$$HgS_4O_6 + NaCN + NaNCO + 2NaOH \longrightarrow$$
$$HgSO_4 + Na_2SO_4 + 2NaNCS + H_2O$$

This reaction is restrained by a large excess of thiosulfate, and even more effectively by potassium iodide. A moderate excess of thiosulfate is commonly used, and an amount of potassium iodide

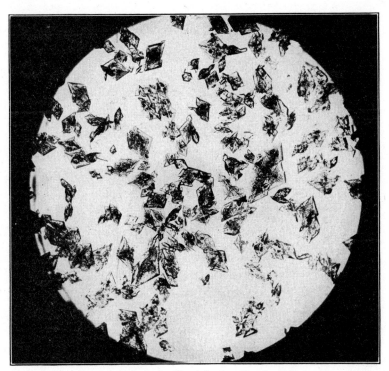

FIGURE 94. Mercury Fulminate Crystals for Use in Primer Composition (30×).

equal to 10 times the weight of the fulminate, and the titration for acidity (methyl orange indicator) is made as rapidly as possible. After that, the same solution is titrated with iodine (starch indicator) to determine the amount of unused thiosulfate and hence, by another method, the amount of actual fulminate in the sample. Speed is not essential in the second titration, for the iodine value does not change greatly with time as does the alkalinity. Blank determinations ought to be made because of the possibility that the iodide may contain iodate, and the apparent analytical results ought to be corrected accordingly.

Mercury fulminate has a specific gravity of 4.45, but a mass of the crystals when merely shaken down has an apparent density (gravimetric density) of about 1.75. In detonators the material is usually compressed to a density of about 2.5, but densities as high as 4.0 have been obtained by vigorous compression. Mercury fulminate crystallizes from water in crystals which contain $\frac{1}{2}H_2O$, from alcohol in crystals which are anhydrous. One liter of water at 12° dissolves 0.71 gram, at 49° 1.74 grams, and at 100° 7.7 grams.

Mercury fulminate is usually stored under water, or, where there is danger of freezing, under a mixture of water and alcohol. When wet it is not exploded by a spark or by ordinary shock, but care must be taken that no part of the individual sample is allowed to dry out, for wet fulminate is exploded by the explosion of dry fulminate. It is not appreciably affected by long storage, either wet or dry, at moderate temperatures. At the temperature of the tropics it slowly deteriorates and loses its ability to explode. At 35°C. (95°F.) it becomes completely inert after about 3 years, at 50°C. (122°F.) after about 10 months. The heavy, dark-colored product of the deterioration of fulminate is insoluble in sodium thiosulfate solution.

When loaded in commercial detonators mercury fulminate is usually compressed under a pressure of about 3000 pounds per square inch, and in that condition has a velocity of detonation of about 4000 meters per second, explodes from a spark, and, in general, has about the same sensitivity to fire and to shock as the loosely compressed material. When compressed under greater and greater pressures, it gradually loses its property of detonating from fire. After being pressed at 25,000–30,000 pounds per square inch, mercury fulminate becomes "dead pressed" and no longer explodes from fire but merely burns. Dead-pressed fulminate however is exploded by loosely pressed fulminate or other initial detonating agent, and then shows a higher velocity of detonation than when compressed at a lower density.

The temperature at which mercury fulminate explodes depends upon the rate at which it is heated and, to some extent, upon the state of subdivision of the sample. Wöhler and Matter [11] experi-

[11] *Z. ges. Schiess- u. Sprengstoffw.*, 2, 181, 203, 244, 265 (1907).

mented with small particles of various primary explosives, heated
in copper capsules in a bath of Wood's metal. If a sample did not
explode within 20 seconds, the temperature of the bath was
raised 10° and a new sample was tried. The temperatures at
which explosions occurred were as follows.

Mercury fulminate	190°
Sodium fulminate	150°
Nitrogen sulfide	190°
Benzenediazonium nitrate	90°
Chloratotrimercuraldehyde	130°
Silver azide	290°
Basic mercury nitromethane	160°

In a later series of experiments Wöhler and Martin [12] studied a
large number of fulminates and azides. The materials were in
the form of microcrystalline powders, and all were compressed
under the same pressure into pellets weighing 0.02 gram. The
temperatures at which explosions occurred within 5 seconds were
as follows.

Mercury fulminate	215°
Silver fulminate	170°
Copper fulminate	205°
Cadmium fulminate	215°
Sodium fulminate	215°
Potassium fulminate	225°
Thallium fulminate	120°
Cobalt azide	148°
Barium azide	152°
Calcium azide	158°
Strontium azide	169°
Cuprous azide	174°
Nickel azide	200°
Manganese azide	203°
Lithium azide	245°
Mercurous azide	281°
Zinc azide	289°
Cadmium azide	291°
Silver azide	297°
Lead azide	327°

Wöhler and Martin [13] in the same year also reported determinations of the smallest amounts of certain fulminates and

[12] *Z. angew. Chem.*, **30**, 33 (1917).
[13] *Z. ges. Schiess- u. Sprengstoffw.*, **12**, 1, 18 (1917).

azides necessary to cause the detonation of various high explosives.

SMALLEST AMOUNT (GRAMS) WHICH WILL CAUSE DETONATION OF:	Tetryl	Picric Acid	Trinitro-toluene	Trinitro-anisol	Trinitro-xylene
Cadmium azide........	0.01	0.02	0.04	0.1	..
Silver azide..........	0.02	0.035	0.07	0.26	0.25
Lead azide...........	0.025	0.025	0.09	0.28	..
Cuprous azide........	0.025	0.045	0.095	0.375	0.40
Mercurous azide.......	0.045	0.075	0.145	0.55	0.50
Thallium azide........	0.07	0.115	0.335	...	..
Silver fulminate........	0.02	0.05	0.095	0.23	0.30
Cadmium fulminate....	0.008	0.05	0.11	0.26	0.35
Copper fulminate......	0.025	0.08	0.15	0.32	0.43
Mercury fulminate.....	0.29	0.30	0.36	0.37	0.40
Thallium fulminate.....	0.30	0.43	...	...	..

From these data it is apparent that mercury fulminate is by no means the most efficient initiating agent among the fulminates and azides. Silver fulminate is about 15 times as efficient as mercury fulminate for exploding tetryl, but only about $\frac{4}{3}$ as efficient for exploding trinitroxylene. Mercury fulminate however will tolerate a higher temperature, and is much less sensitive to shock and friction, than silver fulminate. Lead azide, which has about the same initiating power as silver fulminate, has an explosion temperature more than 100° higher than that of mercury fulminate. Many other interesting inferences are possible from the data. Among them we ought especially to note that the order of the several fulminates and azides with respect to their efficiency in detonating one explosive is not always the same as their order with respect to their efficiency in detonating another.

Silver Fulminate

Silver fulminate is so sensitive and so dangerous to handle that it has not been used for practical purposes in blasting or in the military art. It early found use in toys, in tricks, and in such devices for entertainment as those which Christopher Grotz described in 1818 in his book on "The Art of Making Fireworks, Detonating Balls, &c."

Amusements with Fulminating Silver. . . .
Segars.
Are prepared by opening the smoking end, and inserting
a little of the silver; close it carefully up, and it is done.
Spiders.
A piece of cork cut into the shape of the body of a spider,
and a bit of thin wire for legs, will represent with tolerable
exactness this insect. Put a small quantity of the silver underneath it; and on any female espying it, she will naturally
tread on it, to crush it, when it will make a loud report.

Silver fulminate is still used for similar purposes in practical
jokes, in toy torpedoes (see Vol. I, p. 106), and in the snaps or
pull-crackers which supply the noise for bon-boms, joy-boms,
and similar favors.

Silver fulminate is insoluble in nitric acid, and is decomposed
by hydrochloric acid. It darkens on exposure to light. One liter
of water at 13° dissolves 0.075 gram of the salt, and at 30°
0.18 gram. The double fulminate of silver and potassium,
$AgONC \cdot KONC$, is soluble in 8 parts of boiling water.

Detonators

The discovery of the phenomenon of initiation by Alfred Nobel
and the invention of the blasting cap [14] stand at the beginning
of the development of modern explosives, perhaps the most important discovery and invention in the history of the art. The
phenomenon has supplied a basis for the definition of high explosives, that is to say, of those explosives, whether sensitive or
insensitive, which are incapable, without the invention, of being
used safely and controllably or perhaps even of being used at all.

Nobel's experiments quickly led him to the form of the blasting
cap which is now in use, a cylindrical capsule, generally of copper
but sometimes of aluminum or zinc, filled for about half of its
length with a compressed charge of primary explosive. The charge
is fired either by an electric igniter or by a fuse, crimped into place,
its end held firmly against the charge in order that the chances of
a misfire may be reduced. Its action depends upon the development of an intense pressure or shock. Fulminate of mercury was
the only substance known at the time of Nobel's invention which
could be prepared and loaded for the purpose with reasonable
safety, and caps loaded with straight fulminate were the first to

[14] Nobel, Brit. Pat. 1345 (1867).

be manufactured. The original fulminate detonators were numbered according to the amount of fulminate which they contained,

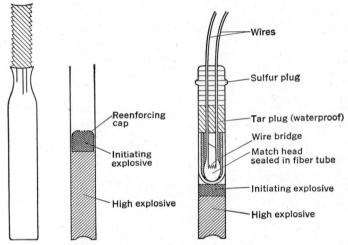

FIGURE 95. Blasting Caps. Detonator crimped to miner's fuse. Compound detonator. Compound electric detonator.

the same numbers being used throughout the world. The charges of fulminate for the various sizes are shown in the following table,

Detonator	Weight of Mercury Fulminate		External Dimensions of Capsule	
	Grams	Grains	Diameter, mm.	Length, mm.
No. 1	0.30	4.6	5.5	16
No. 2	0.40	6.2	5.5	22
No. 3	0.54	8.3	5.5	26
No. 4	0.65	10.0	6	28
No. 5	0.80	12.3	6	30–32
No. 6	1.00	15.4	6	35
No. 7	1.50	23.1	6	40–45
No. 8	2.00	30.9	6–7	50–55

along with the usual (but not universal) dimensions of the cylindrical copper capsules. The same numbers are now applied to commercial blasting caps of the same sizes, whatever the weights and characters of the charges. A No. 6 cap, for example, is a cap of the same size as one which contains 1 gram of straight fulminate. No. 6 caps of different manufacturers may differ in their power

FIGURE 96. Manufacture of Detonators. (Courtesy Hercules Powder Company.) The safe mixing of the primary explosive charge for blasting caps is accomplished mechanically behind a concrete barricade by lifting slowly and then lowering first one corner of the triangular rubber tray, then the next corner, then the next, and so on. In the background, the rubber bowl or box in which the mixed explosive is carried to the building where it is loaded into caps.

as they differ in their composition. No. 6, 7, and 8 caps are the only ones which are manufactured regularly in the United States, and the No. 6 cap is the one which is most commonly used.

The fulminate in detonators was first modified by mixing it with black powder, then with potassium nitrate, and later with

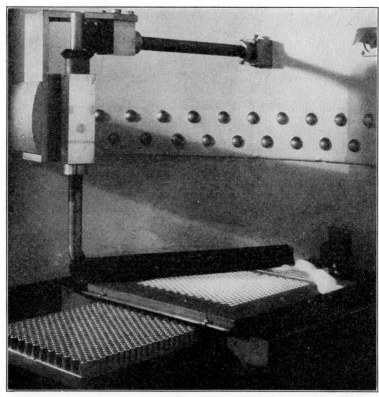

FIGURE 97. Manufacture of Detonators. (Courtesy Hercules Powder Company.) Charging the capsules. Each of the holes in the upper steel plate (*charging plate*) is of the right size to contain exactly enough explosive for the charging of one detonator. The mixed explosive is emptied onto the plate, the rubber-faced arm sweeps the material over the charging plate filling all the holes and throwing the excess into the box at the right. Under the charging plate is the thin *indexing plate* which supplies a bottom to all the holes in the charging plate. The detonator capsules, seen at the left, are placed under the indexing plate and in line with the holes in the charging plate; the indexing plate is then removed, the explosive falls down into the capsules, exactly the right amount into each, and is later pressed into place.

potassium chlorate.[15] The chlorate mixtures soon attained commercial importance in the United States, and by 1910 had largely displaced straight fulminate. Detonators containing them dominated the market until recently, and are now largely, but not yet wholly, displaced by compound detonators in which use is made of the principle of the booster. Mixtures of fulminate and potassium chlorate are distinctly more hygroscopic than straight fulminate, but are cheaper and slightly safer to handle and to load. Weight for weight they make better detonators. Storm and Cope [16] in a series of experiments in the sand test bomb found that 80/20 fulminate-chlorate pulverizes more sand than the same weight of the 90/10 mixture and that this pulverizes more than straight fulminate. The results show that the sand test is an instrument of considerable precision. A difference of $\frac{1}{40}$ gram in the size of the charge of fulminate generally caused a difference of more than 1 gram in the weight of sand which was pulverized.

	WEIGHT OF SAND (GRAMS) PULVERIZED FINER THAN 30-MESH BY		
WEIGHT OF CHARGE, GRAMS	Mercury Fulminate	90/10 Fulminate-Chlorate	80/20 Fulminate-Chlorate
2.0000	56.94	58.57	59.68
1.5000	47.71	51.11	52.54
1.0000	38.33	40.13	41.42
0.7500	29.65	32.30	34.28
0.5000	22.45	23.07	23.22
0.4000	17.91	17.90	18.13
0.3500	14.16	15.13	15.94
0.3250	12.20	12.90	13.13
0.3000	10.01	12.71	12.61
0.2500	8.84	9.57	11.94
0.2250	6.93	8.71	10.29
0.2000	5.48	8.33	9.44

Storm and Cope [17] also used the sand test to determine the

[15] Detonators were manufactured abroad and sold for a time under Nobel's patent, A. V. Newton (from A. Nobel, Paris), Brit. Pat. 16,919 (1887), covering the use, instead of fulminate, of a granulated mixture of lead picrate, potassium picrate, and potassium chlorate, but the invention apparently contributed little to the advance of the explosives art.

[16] C. G. Storm and W. C. Cope, "The Sand Test for Determining the Strength of Detonators," *U. S. Bur. Mines Tech. Paper* 125, Washington, 1916, p. 43.

[17] *Ibid.*, p. 59.

minimum amounts of fulminate and of the fulminate-chlorate mixtures which were necessary to detonate several high explosives in reenforced detonators. It is necessary to specify that the tests were made with reenforced detonators, for the results would have been quite different if reenforcing caps had not been used. In an ordinary detonator TNA required 0.3125 gram of 80/20 fulminate-chlorate instead of the 0.1700 gram which was sufficient when a reenforced detonator was used.

	MINIMUM INITIATING CHARGE (GRAMS) NECESSARY FOR EXPLOSION OF 0.4 GRAM OF		
PRIMARY EXPLOSIVE	TNT	TNA	Picric Acid
Mercury fulminate	0.26	0.20	0.25
90/10 Fulminate-chlorate	0.25	0.17	0.23
80/20 Fulminate-chlorate	0.24	0.17	0.22

The reenforced detonators which were used in this work were made by introducing the weighed charge of high explosive into the detonator shell and the weighed charge of primary explosive into the small reenforcing cap while the latter was held in a cavity in a brass block which served to prevent the explosive from falling through the hole in the end of the cap. The primary explosive was then pressed down gently by means of a wooden rod, the cap was filled by adding a sufficient quantity of the high explosive from the detonator shell, this was similarly pressed down, and the reenforcing cap was then removed from the brass block and inserted carefully in the detonator shell with its perforated end upward. The detonator was then placed in a press block, a plunger inserted, and the contents subjected to a pressure of 200 atmospheres per square inch maintained for 1 minute. The pressure expanded the reenforcing cap against the detonator shell and fixed it firmly in place.

The minimum initiating charge was determined as follows. The amount of sand pulverized by a detonator loaded, say, with TNT and with fulminate insufficient to explode the TNT was determined. Another experiment with a slightly larger amount of fulminate was tried. If this showed substantially the same amount of sand pulverized, then the charge of fulminate was increased still further, and so on, until a sudden large increase in the amount of sand pulverized showed that the TNT had detonated. After this point had been reached, further increases in the amount of fulminate caused only slight increases in the amount of sand pulverized. The magnitude of the effects, and the definiteness of the results, are shown by the following data of Storm and Cope.[18]

WEIGHT OF SAND (GRAMS) PULVERIZED FINER THAN 30-MESH BY REENFORCED DETONATOR CONTAINING 0.40 GRAM TNT AND A PRIMING CHARGE (GRAMS) OF

PRIMARY EXPLOSIVE	0.3000	0.2800	0.2600	0.2500	0.2400	0.2300
Mercury fulminate	34.20	34.70	33.00	13.55	12.60	...
	...	...	31.50	...	...	...
	...	...	30.00	...	...	...
	...	...	32.70	...	...	...
	...	...	32.00	...	...	...
90/10 Fulminate-chlorate	...	...	33.55	34.45	32.95	13.90
	...	...	34.05	34.67	13.20	...
	...	...	34.35	34.07	...	...
	...	...	34.42	35.07	...	...
	...	...	34.70	33.80	...	...
80/20 Fulminate-chlorate	...	...	...	...	34.40	16.80
	...	...	...	...	34.60	...
	...	...	...	...	34.60	...
	...	...	...	...	33.80	...
	...	...	...	...	34.85	...

Fulminate owes its success as an initiating agent primarily to the fact that it explodes easily from fire—and it catches the fire more readily than do lead azide and many another primary explosive—to the fact that it quickly attains its full velocity of detonation within a very short length of material, and probably also to the fact that the heavy mercury atom which it contains enables it to deliver an especially powerful blow. Its maximum velocity of detonation is much lower than that of TNT and similar substances, and its power to initiate the detonation of high explosives is correspondingly less. Wöhler [19] in 1900 patented detonators in which a main charge of TNT or other nitro compound is initiated by a relatively small charge of fulminate.

[18] Ibid., p. 55.
[19] Brit. Pat. 21,065 (1900). For an account of Wöhler's theory of initiation see Z. ges. Schiess- u. Sprengstoffw., 6, 253 (1911) and Z. angew. Chem., 24, 1111, 2089 (1911).

Detonators which thus make use of the principle of the booster are known as compound detonators and are made both with and without reenforcing caps. Some manufacturers insert the reenforcing cap with the perforated end down, others with the perforated end up.[20]

Not long after Curtius [21] had discovered and described hydrazoic (hydronitric) acid and its salts, Will and Lenze [22] experimented with the azides (hydronitrides, hydrazotates) at the military testing station at Spandau, but a fatal accident put an end to their experiments and their results were kept secret by the German war office. Wöhler and Matter [23] later studied several primary explosives in an effort to find a substitute for fulminate, and in 1907, in ignorance of the earlier work of Will and Lenze, published experiments which demonstrated the great effectiveness of the azides. At about the same time, the first attempt to use lead azide practically in the explosives industry was made by F. Hyronimus in France who secured a patent [24] in February, 1907, for the use of lead azide in detonators, to replace either wholly or in part the mercury fulminate which had theretofore been used, and this whether or not the fulminate would ordinarily be used alone or in conjunction with some other explosive substance such as picric acid or trinitrotoluene. In March of the same year Wöhler in Germany patented,[25] as a substitute for fulminate, the heavy metal salts of hydrazoic acid, "such as silver and mercury azides." He pointed out, as the advantages of these substances, that a smaller weight of them is necessary to produce detonation than is necessary of mercury fulminate, as, for example, that a No. 8 blasting cap containing 2 grams of mercury fulminate can be replaced, for use in detonating explosives, by a No. 8 copper capsule containing 1 gram of picric acid on top of which 0.023 gram of silver azide has been com-

---

[20] In addition to its other functions, the reenforcing cap tends toward greater safety by preventing actual contact between the primary explosive and the squarely cut end of the miner's fuse to which the detonator is crimped.

[21] *Ber.,* **23**, 3023 (1890); *ibid.,* **24**, 3341 (1891).

[22] Cf. Will, *Z. ges. Schiess- u. Sprengstoffw.,* **9**, 52 (1914).

[23] *Loc. cit.*

[24] French Pat. 384,792 (February 14, 1907), Supplement No. 8872 (process of manufacture), January 13, 1908.

[25] Ger. Pat. 196,824 (March 2, 1907).

pressed. In February of the next year Wöhler was granted a French patent [26] in which lead azide was specifically mentioned, but the use of this substance had already been anticipated by the patent of Hyronimus. Lead azide was soon afterwards manufactured commercially in Germany and in France, and compound detonators containing this material were used fairly generally in Europe at the time of the first World War. A few years later the manufacture of lead azide detonators was commenced in the United States. In this country compound detonators having a base charge of tetryl and primed with 80/20 fulminate-chlorate or with lead azide have been superseded in part by detonators loaded with a more powerful high-explosive charge of nitromannite, PETN, or diazodinitrophenol and primed with lead azide, alone or sensitized to flame by the addition of lead styphnate or tetracene, or with diazodinitrophenol as the primary explosive.

Testing of Detonators

Among the tests which are used for determining the relative efficiency of detonators,[27] the lead block or small Trauzl test, in which the detonators are fired in holes drilled in lead blocks and the resulting expansions of the holes are measured, and the lead or aluminum plate test in which the detonators are stood upright upon the plates and fired, and the character and extent of the effects upon the plates are observed, have already been mentioned.[28] The first of these gives results which are expressible by numbers, and in that sense quantitative, and it is evident that both methods may be applied, for example, to the determination of the minimum amount of primary explosive necessary for the initiation of a high explosive, for both show notably different effects according as the high explosive explodes or not. Another useful test is the determination of the maximum distance through which the detonator is capable of initiating the explosion of some standard material, say, a piece of cordeau loaded with TNT. In the *nail test*,[29] a wire nail is fastened to the side of the detonator, the detonator is fired, and the angle of the bend which the ex-

[26] French Pat. 387,640 (February 28, 1908).

[27] Clarence Hall and Spencer P. Howell, "Investigations of Detonators and Electric Detonators," *U. S. Bur. Mines Bull.* 59, Washington, 1913.

[28] Vol. I, p. 26.

[29] Hall and Howell, *op. cit.,* p. 25.

plosion imparts to the nail is measured. The sand test, in which the detonator is fired in the center of a mass of carefully screened sand contained in a suitable bomb and the sand which has been pulverized is screened off and weighed, is the most precise and significant of the tests on detonators. It is a real test of brisance, and its usefulness is not limited to the study of detonators but may be extended to the study of high explosives as well. Thus,

FIGURE 98. U. S. Bureau of Mines Sand Test Bomb No. 1. (Courtesy U. S. Bureau of Mines.) At left, assembled for making the test. At right, disassembled showing the parts. Two covers, one with a single hole for miner's fuse, the other with two holes for the two wires of an electric detonator.

two explosives may be compared by loading equal amounts in detonator shells, priming with equal amounts of the same initiator, firing in the sand test bomb, and comparing the amounts of sand pulverized.

The sand test was devised in 1910 by Walter O. Snelling, explosives chemist of the U. S. Bureau of Mines, who worked out the technique of its operation and designed the standard Bureau of Mines sand test bomb No. 1 which was used in his own investigations and in those of Storm and Cope.[30] Munroe and Taylor [31]

[30] Snelling, *Proc. Eng. Soc. Western Pennsylvania,* **28,** 673 (1912); Storm and Cope, *loc. cit.*

[31] C. E. Munroe and C. A. Taylor, "Methods of Testing Detonators," *U. S. Bur. Mines Repts. of Investigations* 2558, December, 1923.

later recommended a bomb of larger diameter, Bureau of Mines sand test bomb No. 2, as being able to differentiate more exactly between the different grades of detonators in commercial use. The test grew out of an earlier test which Snelling had developed in 1908 for measuring the strength of detonating agents. Starting

FIGURE 99. Walter O. Snelling. (Metzger & Son.) Devised the sand test. Has worked extensively with nitrostarch explosives and has patented many improvements in military and in mining explosives. Chemist at the U. S. Bureau of Mines, 1908-1916; Director of Research, Trojan Powder Company, 1917—.

with the thought that true explosives, when subjected to a sufficiently strong initiating influence, detonate in such manner as to set free more energy than that which had been applied to them by the initiating charge, he tested several materials which failed to be true explosives and, although decomposed by the detonating agent, did not give off energy enough to continue their own decomposition and to propagate a detonation wave. Copper oxalate was the best of the "near explosives" which he tried. He found it possible to measure the initiating effect of mercury fulminate and of other initial detonators by firing them in compositions consisting partly or wholly of copper oxalate, and then by chemical means determining the amount of the oxalate which had been decomposed. The experiments were carried out in a small steel bomb, the detonator was placed in the middle of a mass of oxalate or of oxalate composition, and sand was put in on top to fill the bomb completely. The fact that part of the sand was pulverized by the force of the explosion suggested that the mechanical effect of the initiator might perhaps serve as an approximate measure of the detonating efficiency; the oxalate was omitted, the bomb was filled entirely with sand, and the sand test was devised. Before Snelling left the Bureau of Mines in 1912 he had made about 40 tests on ordinary and electric detonators. Storm and Cope extended the usefulness of the test and applied it not only to the study of detonators but also to the study of the materials out of which detonators are constructed, both initial detonating agents and high explosives.

Lead Azide

Lead azide is a more efficient detonating agent than mercury fulminate. It requires a higher temperature for its spontaneous explosion, and it does not decompose on long continued storage at moderately elevated temperatures. It cannot be dead-pressed by any pressure which occurs in ordinary manufacturing operations. Lead azide pressed into place in a detonator capsule takes the fire less readily, or explodes from spark less readily, than mercury fulminate. For this reason the main initiating charge of lead azide in a blasting cap is generally covered with a layer of lead styphnate, or of styphnate-azide mixture or other *sensitizer*, which explodes more easily, though less violently, from fire, and serves to initiate the explosion of the azide.

Lead azide is not used in primers where it is desired to produce fire or flame from impact. Fulminate mixtures and certain mixtures which contain no fulminate are preferred for this purpose. Lead azide is used where it is desired to produce, either from flame or from impact, an initiatory shock for the detonation of a high explosive—in compound detonators as already described, and in the detonators of artillery fuzes. For the latter purpose, caps containing azide and tetryl (or other booster explosive) are used; the azide is exploded by impact, and the tetryl communicates the explosion to the booster or perhaps to the main charge of the shell.

Lead azide is produced as a white precipitate by mixing a solution of sodium azide with a solution of lead acetate or lead nitrate. It is absolutely essential that the process should be carried out in such manner that the precipitate consists of very small particles. The sensitivity of lead azide to shock and to friction increases rapidly as the size of the particles increases. Crystals 1 mm. in length are liable to explode spontaneously because of the internal stresses within them. The U. S. Ordnance Department specifications require that the lead azide shall contain no needle-shaped crystals more than 0.1 mm. in length. Lead azide is about as sensitive to impact when it is wet as when it is dry. Dextrinated lead azide can apparently be stored safely under water for long periods of time. The belief exists, however, that crystalline "service azide" becomes more sensitive when stored under water because of an increase in the size of the crystals.

The commercial preparation of lead azide is carried out on what is practically a laboratory scale, 300 grams of product constituting an ordinary single batch. There appear to be diverse opinions as to the best method of precipitating lead azide in a finely divided condition. According to one, fairly strong solutions are mixed while a gentle agitation is maintained, and the precipitate is removed promptly, and washed, and dried. According to another, dilute solutions ought to be used, with extremely violent agitation, and a longer time ought to be devoted to the process. The preparation is sometimes carried out by adding one solution to the other in a nickel vessel, which has corrugated sides, and is rotated around an axis which makes a considerable angle with the vertical, thereby causing turbulence in the liquid. The precipitation is sometimes carried out in the presence of dissolved colloidal material, such as gelatin or dextrin, which tends to prevent the formation of large crystals. Sometimes the lead azide is precipitated on starch or wood pulp, either of which will take up about 5 times its own weight of the material, and the impregnated starch is worked up, say, by tumbling in a sweetie barrel with a little dextrine, to form a free-flowing granular mass which can conveniently be loaded into detonators, or the impregnated wood pulp is converted into pasteboard which is cut into discs for loading. A small amount of basic salt in the lead azide makes it somewhat less sensitive to impact and slightly safer to handle, but has no appreciable effect upon its efficacy as an initiator.

The commercial preparation of the azides is carried out either by the interaction of hydrazine with a nitrite or by the interaction of sodamide with nitrous oxide. The first of these methods

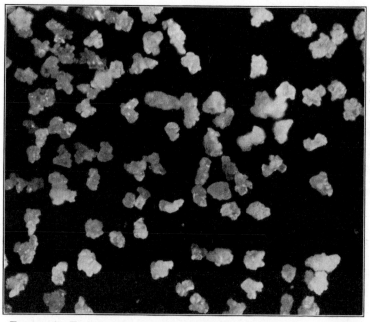

Figure 100. Technical Lead Azide, 90-95% pure (75×). For use in detonators. Precipitated in the presence of dextrin, it shows no crystal faces under the microscope.

follows from the original work of Curtius,[32] the second from a reaction discovered by Wisliscenus [33] in 1892 and later developed for plant scale operation by Dennis and Browne.[34] Curtius first prepared hydrazoic acid by the action of aqueous or alcoholic alkali or ammonia on acyl azides prepared by the action of nitrous acid on acyl hydrazides. The hydrazides are formed by

[32] Loc. cit.; also J. prak. Chem., [2] 50, 275 (1894); Ber., 29, 759 (1896); cf. survey by Darapsky in Z. ges. Schiess- u. Sprengstoffw., 2, 41, 64 (1907).

[33] Ber., 25, 2084 (1892).

[34] Z. anorg. allgem. Chem., 40, 68 (1904).

the interaction of hydrazine with esters just as the amides are formed by the corresponding interaction of ammonia.

$$R{-}COOC_2H_5 + NH_2{-}NH_2 \longrightarrow C_2H_5OH + R{-}CO{-}NH{-}NH_2$$

Acyl hydrazide

$$R{-}CO{-}NH{-}NH_2 + HONO \longrightarrow 2H_2O + R{-}CO{-}N_3$$

Acyl azide

$$R{-}CO{-}N_3 + H_2O \longrightarrow R{-}COOH + HN_3$$

$$R{-}CO{-}N_3 + NH_3 \longrightarrow R{-}CO{-}NH_2 + HN_3$$

Hydrazoic acid

By acidifying the hydrolysis mixture with sulfuric acid and by fractionating the product, Curtius procured anhydrous hydrazoic as a colorless liquid which boils at 37°. Hydrazoic acid is intensely poisonous and bad smelling. It is easily exploded by flame, by a brisant explosive, or by contact with metallic mercury. The anhydrous substance is extremely dangerous to handle, but dilute solutions have been distilled without accident.

Angeli [35] obtained a white precipitate of insoluble silver azide by mixing saturated solutions of silver nitrite and hydrazine sulfate and allowing to stand in the cold for a short time. Dennstedt and Göhlich [36] later procured free hydrazoic acid by the interaction of hydrazine sulfate and potassium nitrite in aqueous solution.

$$NH_2{-}NH_2 \cdot H_2SO_4 + KONO \longrightarrow KHSO_4 + 2H_2O + HN_3$$

Hydrazine sulfate

The yield from this reaction is greatest if the medium is alkaline, for nitrous acid attacks hydrazoic acid oxidizing it with the liberation of nitrogen. If hydrazine sulfate [37] is used in the mixture, the resulting hydrazoic acid is not available for the preparation of lead azide until it has been distilled out of the solution. (Lead ions added to the solution would cause the precipitation of lead sulfate.) The reaction mixture may be acidified with sulfuric acid, a little ammonium sulfate may be added in order that the

[35] *Rend. acc. Lincei,* [5] **2,** I, 599 (1893).

[36] *Chem.-Ztg.,* **21,** 876 (1897).

[37] Hydrazine is produced commercially by treating ammonia in aqueous solution with sodium hypochlorite to form chloramine, $NH_2{-}Cl$, and by coupling this with another molecule of ammonia to form hydrazine and hydrochloric acid. Sulfuric acid is added to the liquid, sparingly soluble hydrazine sulfate crystallizes out, and it is in the form of this salt that hydrazine generally occurs in commerce.

ammonia may react with any unchanged nitrous acid which may
be present, and the hydrazoic acid may be distilled directly into
a solution of a soluble lead salt; but methods involving the distillation of hydrazoic acid present many dangers and have not
found favor for commercial production. The alternative is to
work with materials which contain no sulfate, and to isolate the
azide by precipitation from the solution, and it is by this method
that sodium azide (for the preparation of lead azide) is generally manufactured in this country and in England.

Hydrazine [38] reacts in alcohol solution with ethyl nitrite [39] and
caustic soda to form sodium azide which is sparingly soluble in
alcohol (0.315 gram in 100 grams of alcohol at 16°) and precipitates out.

$$NH_2-NH_2 + C_2H_5ONO + NaOH \longrightarrow NaN_3 + C_2H_5OH + 2H_2O$$

The sodium azide is filtered off, washed with alcohol, and dried.
It is soluble in water to the extent of 42 grams in 100 grams of
water at 18°. It is not explosive, and requires no particular precaution in its handling.

Azide has been manufactured in France and in Germany by
the sodamide process. Metallic sodium is heated at about 300°
while dry ammonia gas is bubbled through the molten material.

$$2Na + 2NH_3 \longrightarrow 2NaNH_2 + H_2$$

The sodamide which is formed remains liquid (m.p. 210°) and
does not prevent contact between the remaining sodium and the
ammonia gas. The progress of the reaction is followed by passing the effluent gas through water which absorbs the ammonia
and allows the hydrogen to pass; if there is unabsorbed gas which
forms an explosive mixture with air, the reaction is not yet complete. For the second step, the sodamide is introduced into a
nickel or nickel-lined, trough-shaped autoclave along the bottom

---

[38] Hydrazine hydrate is actually used. It is an expensive reagent procured
by distilling hydrazine sulfate with caustic soda in a silver retort. It is
poisonous, corrosive, strongly basic, and attacks glass, cork, and rubber.
Pure hydrazine hydrate is a white crystalline solid which melts at 40° and
boils at 118°, but the usual commercial material is an 85% solution of the
hydrate in water.

[39] It is necessary to use ethyl nitrite or other alcohol-soluble nitrous
ester, instead of sodium nitrite, in order that advantage may be taken of a
solvent from which the sodium azide will precipitate out.

of which there extends a horizontal shaft equipped with teeth. The air in the apparatus is displaced with ammonia gas, the autoclave is heated to about 230°, and nitrous oxide is passed in while the horizontal stirrer is rotated. The nitrous oxide reacts with one equivalent of sodamide to form sodium azide and water. The water reacts with a second equivalent of sodamide to form sodium hydroxide and ammonia.

$$NaNH_2 + N_2O \longrightarrow NaN_3 + H_2O$$
$$NaNH_2 + H_2O \longrightarrow NaOH + NH_3$$

The reaction is complete when no more ammonia is evolved. The product, which consists of an equimolecular mixture of sodium hydroxide and sodium azide, may be taken up in water and neutralized carefully with nitric acid, and the resulting solution may be used directly for the preparation of lead azide, or the product may be fractionally crystallized from water for the production of sodium azide. The same material may be procured by washing the product with warm alcohol which dissolves away the sodium hydroxide.

The different methods by which hydrazoic acid and the azides may be prepared indicate that the acid may properly be represented by any one or by all of the following structural formulas.

$$H-N{\Large<}^{N}_{N}\Big| \qquad H-N{\Large<}^{N}_{N}\Big\| \qquad H-N{=}N{\equiv}N$$

Hydrazoic acid is a weak acid; its ionization constant at 25°, 1.9×10^{-5}, is about the same as that of acetic acid at 25°, 1.86×10^{-5}. It dissolves zinc, iron, magesium, and aluminum, forming azides with the evolution of hydrogen and the production of a certain amount of ammonia. It attacks copper, silver, and mercury, forming azides without evolving hydrogen, and is reduced in part to ammonia and sometimes to hydrazine and free nitrogen. Its reaction with copper, for example, is closely analogous to the reaction of nitric acid with that metal.

$$Cu + 3HN_3 \longrightarrow Cu(N_3)_2 + N_2 + NH_3$$
$$3Cu + 8HNO_3 \longrightarrow 3Cu(NO_3)_2 + 2NO + 4H_2O$$

So also, like nitric acid, it oxidizes hydrogen sulfide with the liberation of sulfur.

$$H_2S + HN_3 \longrightarrow S + N_2 + NH_3$$
$$3H_2S + 2HNO_3 \longrightarrow 3S + 2NO + 4H_2O$$

Mixed with hydrochloric acid it forms a liquid, comparable to *aqua regia,* which is capable of dissolving platinum.

$$Pt + 2HN_3 + 4HCl \longrightarrow PtCl_4 + 2N_2 + 2NH_3$$
$$3Pt + 4HNO_3 + 12HCl \longrightarrow 3PtCl_4 + 4NO + 8H_2O$$

Hydrazoic acid and permanganate mutually reduce each other with the evolution of a mixture of nitrogen and oxygen. The acid and its salts give with ferric chloride solution a deep red coloration, similar to that produced by thiocyanates, but the color is discharged by hydrochloric acid.

The solubilities of the azides in general are similar to those of the chlorides. Thus, silver azide is soluble in ammonia water and insoluble in nitric acid. Lead azide, like lead chloride, is sparingly soluble in cold water, but hot water dissolves enough of it so that it crystallizes out when the solution is cooled. One hundred grams of water at 18° dissolve 0.03 gram, at 80° 0.09 gram.

The true density of lead azide is 4.8, but the loose powder has an apparent density of about 1.2.

Lead azide is dissolved by an aqueous solution of ammonium acetate, but it is not destroyed by it. The solution contains azide ions and lead ions, the latter quantitatively precipitable as lead chromate, $PbCrO_4$, by the addition of potassium dichromate solution. Lead azide in aqueous suspension is oxidized by ceric sulfate with the quantitative production of nitrogen gas which may be collected in an azotometer and used for the determination of the azide radical.

$$Pb(N_3)_2 + 2Ce(SO_4)_2 \longrightarrow PbSO_4 + 3N_2 + Ce_2(SO_4)_3$$

Nitrous acid oxidizes hydrazoic acid with the evolution of nitrogen. A dilute solution of nitric or acetic acid, in which a little sodium nitrite has been dissolved, dissolves and destroys lead azide. Such a solution may conveniently be used for washing floors, benches, etc., on which lead azide may have been spilled.

Silver Azide

Silver azide is a more efficient initiator than mercury fulminate, and about as efficient as lead azide. It melts at 251° and decomposes rapidly above its melting point into silver and nitrogen. Its temperature of spontaneous explosion varies somewhat according to the method of heating, but is considerably higher than that of mercury fulminate and slightly lower than that of lead azide. Taylor and Rinkenbach [40] reported 273°. Its sensitivity to shock, like that of lead azide, depends upon its state of subdivision.

FIGURE 101. William H. Rinkenbach. Has published many studies on the physical, chemical, and explosive properties of pure high-explosive substances and primary explosives. Research Chemist, U. S. Bureau of Mines, 1919-1927; Assistant Chief Chemist, Picatinny Arsenal, 1927-1929; Chief Chemist, 1929—.

Taylor and Rinkenbach prepared a "colloidal" silver azide which required a 777-mm. drop of a 500-gram weight to cause detonation. Mercury fulminate required a drop of 127 mm. According to the same investigators 0.05 gram of silver azide was necessary to cause the detonation of 0.4 gram of trinitrotoluene in a No. 6 detonator capsule, whether the charge was confined by a reenforcing cap or not, as compared with 0.24 gram of mercury ful-

minate when the charge was confined by a reenforcing cap and
0.37 gram when it was not confined. They also measured the
sand-crushing power of silver azide when loaded into No. 6 detonator capsules and compressed under a pressure of 1000 pounds
per square inch, and compared it with that of mercury fulminate,
with the results which are tabulated below. It thus appears that

WEIGHT OF CHARGE, GRAMS	WEIGHT OF SAND CRUSHED (GRAMS) BY	
	Silver Azide	Mercury Fulminate
0.05	1.4	0.00
0.10	3.3	0.00
0.20	6.8	4.2
0.30	10.4	8.9
0.50	18.9	16.0
0.75	30.0	26.1
1.00	41.1	37.2

the sand-crushing power of silver azide is not as much greater
than the sand-crushing power of mercury fulminate as the difference in their initiatory powers would suggest. Storm and Cope [41]
in their studies on the sand test found that the powers of fulminate and of fulminate-chlorate mixtures to crush sand were
about proportional to the initiatory powers of these materials, but
the present evidence indicates that the law is not a general one.

Cyanuric Triazide

Cyanuric triazide,[42] patented as a detonating explosive by
Erwin Ott in 1921, is prepared by adding powdered cyanuric
chloride, slowly with cooling and agitation, to a water solution
of slightly more than the equivalent quantity of sodium azide.

Cyanuric triazide

[41] Loc. cit.

[42] Ott, Ber., **54**, 179 (1921); Ott, U. S. Pat. 1,390,378 (1921); Taylor and
Rinkenbach, U. S. Bur. Mines Repts. of Investigation 2513, August, 1923;
Kast and Haid, Z. angew. Chem., **38**, 43 (1925).

The best results are secured if pure and finely powdered cyanuric chloride is used, yielding small crystals of pure cyanuric triazide in the first instance, in such manner that no recrystallization, which might convert them into large and more sensitive crystals, is necessary. Cyanuric chloride, m.p. 146°, b.p. 190°, is prepared by passing a stream of chlorine into a solution of hydrocyanic acid in ether or chloroform or into liquid anhydrous hydrocyanic acid exposed to sunlight. It is also formed by distilling cyanuric acid with phosphorus pentachloride and by the polymerization of cyanogen chloride, Cl—CN, after keeping in a sealed tube.

Cyanuric triazide is insoluble in water, slightly soluble in cold alcohol, and readily soluble in acetone, benzene, chloroform, ether, and hot alcohol. It melts at 94°, and decomposes when heated above 100°. It may decompose completely without detonation if it is heated slowly, but it detonates immediately from flame or from sudden heating. The melted material dissolves TNT and other aromatic nitro compounds. Small crystals of cyanuric triazide are more sensitive than small crystals of mercury fulminate, and have exploded while being pressed into a detonator capsule. Large crystals from fusion or from recrystallization have detonated when broken by the pressure of a rubber policeman.[43]

Cyanuric triazide is not irritating to the skin, and has no poisonous effects on rats and guinea pigs in fairly large doses.[43]

Taylor and Rinkenbach have reported sand test data which show that cyanuric triazide is much more brisant than mercury fulminate.[43]

WEIGHT OF EXPLOSIVE, GRAMS	WEIGHT OF SAND CRUSHED (GRAMS) BY	
	Cyanuric Triazide	Mercury Fulminate
0.050	2.6	...
0.100	4.8	...
0.200	12.2	3.8
0.400	33.2	12.2
0.600	54.4	20.1
0.800	68.9	28.2
1.000	78.6	36.8

In conformity with these results are the findings of Kast and Haid who reported that cyanuric triazide has a higher velocity of detonation than mercury fulminate. They made their measure-

[43] Taylor and Rinkenbach, *loc. cit.*, footnote 42.

ments on several primary explosives loaded into detonator capsules 7.7 mm. in internal diameter and compressed to the densities which they usually have in commercial detonators.[44]

EXPLOSIVE	DENSITY	VELOCITY OF DETONATION, METERS PER SECOND
Cyanuric triazide	1.15	5545
Lead azide	3.8	4500
Mercury fulminate	3.3	4490
Mixture: Hg(ONC)$_2$ 85%, KClO$_3$ 15%....	3.1	4550
Lead styphnate	2.6	4900

Taylor and Rinkenbach found that cyanuric triazide is a more efficient initiator of detonation than mercury fulminate. This result cannot properly be inferred from its higher velocity of detonation, for there is no direct correlation between that quality and initiating efficiency. Lead azide is also a much more efficient initiator than mercury fulminate but has about the same velocity of detonation as that substance. The following results [43] were secured by loading 0.4 gram of the high explosive into detonator capsules, pressing down, adding an accurately weighed amount of the initiator, covering with a short reenforcing cap, and pressing with a pressure of 200 atmospheres per square inch. The size of the initiating charge was reduced until it was found that a further reduction resulted in a failure of the high explosive to detonate.

HIGH EXPLOSIVE	MINIMUM INITIATING CHARGE (GRAMS) OF	
	Cyanuric Triazide	Mercury Fulminate
Trinitrotoluene	0.10	0.26
Picric acid	0.05	0.21
Tetryl	0.04	0.24
Tetranitroaniline	0.09	0.20
Ammonium picrate	0.15	0.85

Cyanuric triazide is slightly more hygroscopic and distinctly more sensitive in the drop test than fulminate of mercury.[44] It is slightly volatile, and must be dried at as low a temperature as possible, preferably in vacuum.[44] Detonators in which it is used

[44] Kast and Haid, loc. cit., footnote 42.

TEMPERATURE OF EXPLOSION

EXPLOSIVE	When temperature is raised 20° per minute in Glass Tube	Iron Tube	In Iron Tube Temp., °C.	Elapsed time, seconds	
Cyanuric triazide	206°	205°	200	40,	2
	208°	207°	205	0,	
Lead azide	338°	337°	335	12,	9
			340	5,	7
			345	7,	6
			350	4,	5
			355	0	
			360	0	
Mercury fulminate	175°	166°	145	480,	331
			150	275,	255
			155	135,	165
			160	64,	85
			170	40,	35
			180	15,	13
			190	10,	8
			195	8,	7
			200	7,	8
			205	5,	5
			210	1,	3
			215	0	
Mixture:	168°	169°	145	370,	365
$Hg(ONC)_2$ 85%	171°	170°	150	210,	215
$KClO_3$ 15%			155	155,	145
			160	125,	74
			170	45,	50
			180	23,	22
			190	8,	8
			195	7,	7
			200	7,	8
			205	7,	6
			210	4,	3
			215	0	
Lead styphnate	276°	275°	250	90,	85
	277°	276°	265	65,	45
		275°	270	0	

must be manufactured in such a way that they are effectively
sealed.

Kast and Haid have determined the temperatures at which
cyanuric triazide and certain other initiators explode spontaneously, both by raising the temperature of the samples at a constant rate and by keeping the samples at constant temperatures
and noting the times which elapsed before they exploded. When
no measurable time elapsed, the temperature was "the temperature of instantaneous explosion." Their data are especially interesting because they show the rate of deterioration of the materials at various temperatures.[44]

Trinitrotriazidobenzene

1,3,5-Trinitro-2,4,6-triazidobenzene [45] is prepared from aniline
by the reactions indicated below.

Aniline is chlorinated to form trichloroaniline. The amino group
is eliminated from this substance by means of the diazo reaction,
and the resulting *sym*-trichlorobenzene is nitrated. The nitration,
as described by Turek, is carried out by dissolving the material
in warm 32% oleum, adding strong nitric acid, and heating at
140–150° until no more trinitrotrichlorobenzene, m.p. 187°, precipitates out. The chlorine atoms of this substance are then
replaced by azido groups. This is accomplished by adding an
acetone solution of the trinitrotrichlorobenzene, or better, the
powdered substance alone, to an actively stirred solution of sodium
azide in moist alcohol. The precipitated trinitrotriazidobenzene
is filtered off, washed with alcohol and with water, and, after
drying, is sufficiently pure for technical purposes. It may be

[45] Turek, *Chimie et industrie*, **26**, 781 (1931); Ger. Pat. 498,050; Brit.
Pat. 298,981. Muraour, *Mém. artillerie franç.*, **18**, 895 (1939).

purified further by dissolving in chloroform and allowing to cool, greenish-yellow crystals, m.p. 131° with decomposition. It is decomposed slowly by boiling in chloroform solution.

Trinitrotriazidobenzene is readily soluble in acetone, moderately soluble in chloroform, sparingly in alcohol, and insoluble in water. It is not hygroscopic, is stable toward moisture, and does not attack iron, steel, copper, or brass in the presence of moisture. It is not appreciably volatile at 35–50°. It darkens in color superficially on exposure to the light. It decomposes on melting with the evolution of nitrogen and the formation of hexanitrosobenzene.

$$
\begin{array}{c}
\text{NO}_2 \\
\text{N}_3 - \boxed{} - \text{N}_3 \\
\text{NO}_2 - \boxed{} - \text{NO}_2 \\
\text{N}_3
\end{array}
\longrightarrow 3\text{N}_2 +
\begin{array}{c}
\text{NO} \\
\text{NO} - \boxed{} - \text{NO} \\
\text{NO} - \boxed{} - \text{NO} \\
\text{NO}
\end{array}
$$

The same reaction occurs at lower temperatures: 0.665% of a given portion of the material decomposes in 3 years at 20°, 2.43% in 1 year at 35°, 0.65% in 10 days at 50°, and 100% during 14 hours heating at 100°. The decomposition is not self-catalyzed. The product, hexanitrosobenzene, m.p. 159°, is stable, not hygroscopic, not a primary explosive, and is comparable to tetryl in its explosive properties.

Trinitrotriazidobenzene, if ignited in the open, burns freely with a greenish flame; enclosed in a tube and ignited, it detonates with great brisance. It is less sensitive to shock and to friction than mercury fulminate. It gives a drop test of 30 cm., but it may be made as sensitive as fulminate by mixing with ground glass. The specific gravity of the crystalline material is 1.8054. Under a pressure of 3000 kilograms per square centimeter it yields blocks having a density of 1.7509, under 5000 kilograms per square centimeter 1.7526. One gram of TNT compressed in a No. 8 detonator shell under a pressure of 500 kilograms per square centimeter, with trinitrotriazidobenzene compressed on top of it under 300 kilograms per square centimeter, required 0.02 gram of the latter substance for complete detonation. Tetryl under similar conditions required only 0.01 gram. Trinitrotriazidobenzene may be dead-pressed and in that condition burns or puffs when it is ignited. It is a practical primary explosive and is prepared for loading in the granular form by mixing the moist material with nitrocellulose, adding a small amount of amyl acetate, kneading, rubbing through a sieve, and allowing to dry.

In the Trauzl test, trinitrotriazidobenzene gives 90% as much net expansion as PETN; tetryl gives 70%, TNT 60%, mercury fulminate 23%, and lead azide 16%. Used as a high explosive in compound detonators and initiated with lead azide, trinitrotriazidobenzene is about as strong as PETN and is stronger than tetryl.

Nitrogen Sulfide

Nitrogen sulfide was first prepared by Soubeiran in 1837 by the action of ammonia on sulfur dichloride dissolved in benzene.

$$6SCl_2 + 16NH_3 \longrightarrow N_4S_4 + 2S + 12NH_4Cl$$

It is conveniently prepared by dissolving 1 volume of sulfur chloride in 8 or 10 volumes of carbon disulfide, cooling, and passing in dry ammonia gas until the dark brown powdery precipitate which forms at first has dissolved and an orange-yellow solution results which contains light-colored flocks of ammonium chloride. These are filtered off and rinsed with carbon disulfide, the solution is evaporated to dryness, and the residue is extracted with boiling carbon disulfide for the removal of sulfur. The undissolved material is crude nitrogen sulfide. The hot extract on cooling deposits a further quantity in the form of minute golden-yellow crystals. The combined crude product is recrystallized from carbon disulfide.

The same product is also produced by the action of ammonia on disulfur dichloride in carbon disulfide, benzene, or ether solution.

$$6S_2Cl_2 + 16NH_3 \longrightarrow N_4S_4 + 8S + 12NH_4Cl$$

Nitrogen sulfide has a density of 2.22 at 15°. It is insoluble in water, slightly soluble in alcohol and ether, somewhat more soluble in carbon disulfide and benzene. It reacts slowly with water at ordinary temperature with the formation of pentathionic acid, sulfur dioxide, free sulfur, and ammonia.[46] It melts with sublimation at 178°, and explodes at a higher temperature which, however, is variable according to the rate at which the substance is heated. Berthelot found that it deflagrates at 207° or higher, and remarked that this temperature is about the same as the temperature of combustion of sulfur in the open air. Berthelot and Vieille [47] studied the thermochemical properties of nitrogen sulfide. Their data, recalculated to conform to our present notions of atomic and molecular weight, show that the substance is strongly endothermic and has a heat of formation of −138.8 Calories per mol. It detonates with vigor under a hammer blow, but is less sensitive to shock and less violent in its effects than mercury fulminate. Although its rate of acceleration is considerably less than that of mercury fulminate, it has been recommended as a filling for fuses, primers, and detonator caps, both alone and in mixtures with oxidizing agents such as lead peroxide, lead nitrate, and potassium chlorate.[48]

Nitrogen selenide was first prepared by Espenschied [49] by the action of ammonia gas on selenium chloride. His product was an orange-red, amorphous powder which exploded violently when heated and was dangerous to handle. Verneuil [50] studied the substance further and supplied a sample of it to Berthelot and Vieille [51] for thermochemical experiments. It detonates when brought into contact with a drop of concentrated sulfuric acid or when warmed to about 230°. It also detonates from friction, from a very gentle blow of iron on iron, and from a slightly stronger blow of wood on iron. It has a heat of formation of −169.2 Calories per mol, and, with nitrogen sulfide, illustrates the principle, as Berthelot pointed out, that in analogous series (such as that of the halides and that of the oxides, sulfides, and selenides) "the explosive character of the endothermic compounds becomes more and more pronounced as the molecular weight becomes larger."

[46] Van Valkenburgh and Bailor, *J. Am. Chem. Soc.*, **47**, 2134 (1925).

[47] Berthelot, "Sur la force des matières explosives," 2 vols., third edition, Paris, 1883, Vol. 1, p. 387.

[48] Claessen, Brit. Pat. 6057 (1913); Carl, U. S. Pat. 2,127,106 (1938).

[49] *Ann.*, **113**, 101 (1860).

[50] *Bull. soc. chim.*, [2] **38**, 548 (1882).

[51] Berthelot, *op. cit.*, p. 389.

Lead Styphnate (Lead trinitroresorcinate)

Lead styphnate is commonly prepared by adding a solution of magnesium styphnate [52] at 70° to a well-stirred solution of lead acetate at 70°. A voluminous precipitate of the basic salt separates. The mixture is stirred for 10 or 15 minutes; then dilute

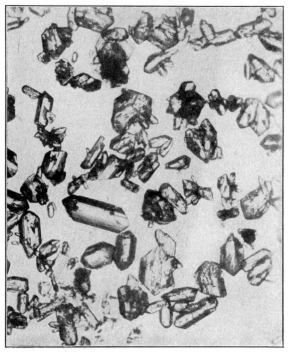

FIGURE 102. Lead Styphnate Crystals (90×).

nitric acid is added with stirring to convert the basic to the normal salt, and the stirring is continued while the temperature drops to about 30°. The product, which consists of reddish-brown, short, rhombic crystals, is filtered off, washed with water, sieved through silk, and dried.

Lead styphnate is a poor initiator, but it is easily ignited by fire or by a static discharge. It is used as an ingredient of the priming layer which causes lead azide to explode from a flash.

[52] Prepared by adding magnesium oxide to a suspension of styphnic acid in water until a clear solution results and only a very small portion of the styphnic acid remains undissolved.

A 0.05-gram sample of lead styphnate in a test tube in a bath of Wood's metal heated at a rate of 20° per minute explodes at 267–268°.

Wallbaum [53] determined the minimum charges of several primary explosives necessary for initiating the explosion of PETN. In the first series of tests, the PETN (0.4 gram) was tamped down or pressed loosely into copper capsules 6.2 mm. in inside diameter, and weighed amounts of the priming charges were pressed down loosely on top. The weights of the priming charges were decreased until one failure occurred in 10 tests with the same weight of charge. In later series, the PETN was compressed at 2000 kilograms per square centimeter. When the priming charges were pressed loosely on the compressed PETN, considerably larger amounts were generally necessary. One gram of lead styphnate, however, was not able to initiate the explosion of the compressed PETN. When the priming charges were pressed, on top of the already compressed PETN, with pressures of 500, 1000, and 1500 kilograms per square centimeter, then it was found that the tetracene and the fulminate were dead-pressed but that the amounts of lead azide and silver azide which were needed were practically the same as in the first series when both the PETN and the priming charge were merely pressed loosely. Wallbaum reports the results which are tabulated below.

| Pressure on PETN, kg. per sq. cm. | 0 | 2000 | 2000 | 2000 | 2000 |
| Pressure on initiator, kg. per sq. cm. | 0 | 0 | 500 | 1000 | 1500 |
PRIMARY EXPLOSIVE	MINIMUM INITIATING CHARGE, GRAMS				
Tetracene	0.16	0.250	dead-pressed		
Mercury fulminate (gray)	0.30	0.330	"	"	
Mercury fulminate (white)	0.30	0.340	"	"	
Lead styphnate	0.55	No detonation with 1 g.			
Lead azide (technical)	0.04	0.170	0.05	0.05	0.04
Lead azide (pure)	0.015	0.100	0.01	0.01	0.01
Silver azide	0.005	0.110	0.005	0.005	0.005

Diazonium Salts

Every student of organic chemistry has worked with diazonium salts in solution. The substances are commonly not isolated in the solid state, for the dry materials are easily exploded by shock and by friction, and numerous laboratory accidents have resulted from their unintended crystallization and drying.

[53] Z. ges. Schiess- u. Sprengstoffw., **34**, 126, 161, 197 (1939).

The first volume of the *Mémorial des Poudres et Salpêtres* contains a report by Berthelot and Vieille [54] on the properties of benzenediazonium nitrate (diazobenzene nitrate). They prepared the material by passing nitrous gas into a cooled aqueous solution of aniline nitrate, diluting with an equal volume of alcohol, and precipitating in the form of white, voluminous flocks by the addition of an excess of ether.

$$2C_6H_5-NH_2 \cdot HNO_3 + N_2O_3 \longrightarrow 3H_2O + 2C_6H_5-\underset{\underset{N}{\vert\vert\vert}}{N}-NO_3$$

The product was washed with ether, pressed between pieces of filter paper, and dried in a vacuum desiccator. In dry air and in the dark it could be kept in good condition for many months. In the daylight it rapidly turned pink, and on longer keeping, especially in a moist atmosphere, it turned brown, took on an odor of phenol, and finally became black and swelled up with bubbles of gas.

Benzenediazonium nitrate detonates easily from the blow of a hammer or from any rubbing which is at all energetic. It explodes violently when heated to 90°. Its density at 15° is 1.37, but under strong compression gently applied it assumes an apparent density of 1.0. Its heat of formation is −47.4 Calories per mol, heat of explosion 114.8 Calories per mol.

m-Nitrobenzenediazonium perchlorate was patented by Herz [55] in 1911, and is reported to have been used in compound detonators with a high-explosive charge of nitromannite or other brisant nitric ester. It explodes spontaneously when heated to about 154°. It is sensitive to shock and to blow. Although it is very sparingly soluble in water and is stabilized to some extent by the nitro group on the nucleus, it is distinctly hygroscopic and is not exempt from the instability which appears to be characteristic of diazonium salts.

[54] *Mém. poudres*, **1**, 99 (1882–1883). Berthelot, *op. cit.*, Vol. 2, p. 35.
[55] Ger. Pat. 258,679 (1911).

Preparation of m-Nitrobenzenediazonium Perchlorate. Half a gram of *m*-nitroaniline is suspended in 5 cc. of water in a wide test tube, and 0.5 cc. of concentrated hydrochloric acid and 2.2 cc. of 20% perchloric acid solution are added. After the nitraniline has dissolved, 15 cc. of water is added and the solution is cooled by immersing the test tube in a beaker filled with a slurry of cracked ice. One-quarter of a gram of sodium nitrite dissolved in 1 or 2 cc. of water is added in 3 or 4 portions, the mixture being shaken after each addition or stirred with a stirring rod the end of which is covered with a short piece of rubber tubing. After standing in the cold for 5 minutes, the material is transferred to a filter, and the feltlike mass of pale yellow needles is washed with cold water, with alcohol, and with ether. The product is dried in several small portions on pieces of filter paper.

Diazodinitrophenol (DDNP, Dinol)

4,6-Dinitrobenzene-2-diazo-1-oxide, or diazodinitrophenol as it is more commonly called, occupies a place of some importance in the history of chemistry, for its discovery by Griess [56] led him to undertake his classic researches on the diazonium compounds and the diazo reaction. He prepared it by passing nitrous gas into an alcoholic solution of picramic acid, but it is more conveniently prepared by carrying out the diazotization in aqueous solution with sodium nitrite and hydrochloric acid.

Picric acid   Picramic acid   Diazodinitrophenol

Picramic acid, red needles, m. p. 169°, may be prepared by evaporating ammonium picrate in alcohol solution with ammonium sulfide.

Preparation of Diazodinitrophenol. Ten grams of picramic acid is suspended in 120 cc. of 5% hydrochloric acid in a beaker which stands in a basin of ice water, and the mixture is stirred rapidly with a mechanical stirrer. Sodium nitrite (3.6 grams) dissolved in 10 cc. of water is added all at once, and the stirring is continued for 20 minutes. The product is collected on a filter and washed thoroughly with ice

[56] *Ann.*, **106**, 123 (1858), **113**, 205 (1860).

water. The dark brown granular material may be used as such, or it may be dissolved in hot acetone and precipitated by the addition of a large volume of ice water to the rapidly agitated liquid, a treatment which converts it into a brilliant yellow amorphous powder.

L. V. Clark,[57] who has made an extensive study of the physical and explosive properties of diazodinitrophenol, reports that it has

FIGURE 103. Diazodinitrophenol Crystals (90×).

a true density at 25°/4° of 1.63. Its apparent density after being placed in a tube and tapped is only 0.27, but, when compressed in a detonator capsule at a pressure of 3400 pounds per square inch (239 kilograms per square centimeter), it has an apparent density of 0.86. It is not dead-pressed by a pressure of 130,000 pounds per square inch (9139 kilograms per square centimeter). It is soluble in nitrobenzene, acetone, aniline, pyridine, acetic acid, strong hydrochloric acid, and nitroglycerin at ordinary temperatures. Its solubility at 50° in 100 grams of solvent is: in ethyl acetate 2.45 grams, in methyl alcohol 1.25 grams, in ethyl

[57] *Ind. Eng. Chem.,* **25,** 663 (1933).

alcohol 2.43 grams, in benzene 0.23 gram, and in chloroform 0.11 gram.

Diazodinitrophenol is less sensitive to impact than mercury fulminate and lead azide. Its sensitivity to friction is about the same as that of lead azide, much less than that of mercury fulminate. It detonates when struck a sharp blow, but, if it is ignited when it is unconfined, it burns with a quick flash, like nitrocellulose, even in quantities of several grams. This burning produces little or no local shock, and will not initiate the explosion of a high explosive. Commercial detonators containing a high-explosive charge of nitromannite and a primary explosive charge of diazodinitrophenol explode if they are crimped to a piece of miner's fuse and the fuse is lighted, but a spark falling into the open end has been reported to cause only the flashing of the diazodinitrophenol. Likewise, if an open cap of this sort falls into a fire, the diazodinitrophenol may flash, the nitromannite may later melt and run out and burn with a flash, and the detonator may be destroyed without exploding. While it is not safe to expect that this will always happen, it is an advantage of diazodinitrophenol that it sometimes occurs.

Diazodinitrophenol is darkened rapidly by exposure to sunlight. It does not react with water at ordinary temperatures, but is desensitized by it. It is not exploded under water by a No. 8 blasting cap.

Clark reports experiments with diazodinitrophenol, mercury fulminate, and lead azide in which various weights of the explosives were introduced into No. 8 detonator capsules, pressed under reenforcing caps at 3400 pounds per square inch, and fired in the No. 2 sand test bomb. His results, tabulated below, show that diazodinitrophenol is much more powerful than mercury fulminate and lead azide. Other experiments by Clark showed

	Weight (Grams) of Sand Pulverized Finer than 30-Mesh by		
Weight (Grams) of Charge	Diazo-dinitro-phenol	Mercury Fulminate	Lead Azide
0.10	9.1	3.1	3.5
0.20	19.3	6.5	7.2
0.40	36.2	17.0	14.2
0.60	54.3	27.5	21.5
0.80	72.1	38.0	28.7
1.00	90.6	48.4	36.0

that diazodinitrophenol in the sand test has about the same strength as tetryl and hexanitrodiphenylamine.

Clark found that the initiatory power of diazodinitrophenol is about twice that of mercury fulminate and slightly less than that of lead azide. His experiments were made with 0.5-gram charges of the high explosives in No. 8 detonator capsules, with reenforcing caps, and with charges compressed under a pressure of 3400 pounds per square inch. He reported the results which are tabulated below.

HIGH EXPLOSIVE	MINIMUM INITIATING CHARGE (GRAMS) OF		
	Mercury Fulminate	Diazo-dinitrophenol	Lead Azide
Picric acid	0.225	0.115	0.12
Trinitrotoluene	0.240	0.163	0.16
Tetryl	0.165	0.075	0.03
Trinitroresorcinol	0.225	0.110	0.075
Trinitrobenzaldehyde	0.165	0.075	0.05
Tetranitroaniline	0.175	0.085	0.05
Hexanitrodiphenylamine	0.165	0.075	0.05

One gram of diazodinitrophenol in a No. 8 detonator capsule, compressed under a reenforcing cap at a pressure of 3400 pounds per square inch, and fired in a small Trauzl block, caused an expansion of 25 cc. Mercury fulminate under the same conditions caused an expansion of 8.1 cc., and lead azide one of 7.2 cc.

Clark determined the ignition temperature of diazodinitrophenol by dropping 0.02-gram portions of the material onto a heated bath of molten metal and noting the times which elapsed between the contacts with the hot metal and the explosions: 1 second at 200°, 2.5 seconds at 190°, 5 seconds at 185°, and 10.0 seconds at 180°. At 177° the material decomposed without an explosion.

Tetracene

1-Guanyl-4-nitrosoaminoguanyltetrazene, called tetracene for short, was first prepared by Hoffmann and Roth.[58] Hoffmann and his co-workers [59] studied its chemical reactions and determined

---

[58] *Ber.,* **43**, 682 (1910).

[59] Hoffmann, Hock, and Roth, *ibid.,* **43**, 1087 (1910); Hoffmann and Hock, *ibid.,* **43**, 1866 (1910), **44**, 2946 (1911); Hoffmann, Hock, and Kirmreuther, *Ann.,* **380**, 131 (1911).

its structure. It is formed by the action of nitrous acid on amino-guanidine, or, more exactly, by the interaction of an aminoguani-dine salt with sodium nitrite in the absence of free mineral acid.

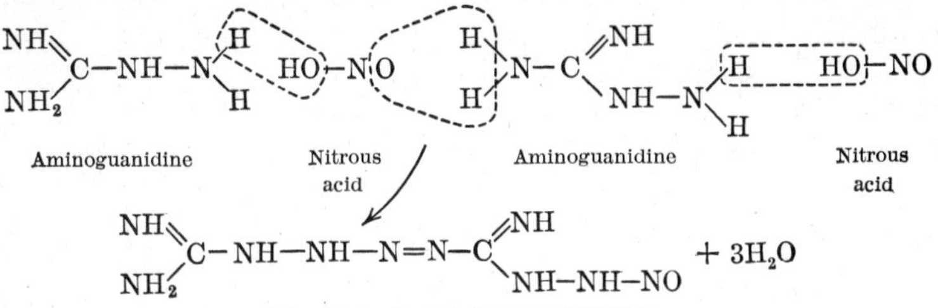

1-Guanyl-4-nitrosoaminoguanyltetrazene

Tetracene is a colorless or pale yellow, fluffy material which is practically insoluble in water, alcohol, ether, benzene, and carbon tetrachloride. It has an apparent density of only 0.45, but yields a pellet of density 1.05 when it is compressed under a pressure of 3000 pounds per square inch. Tetracene forms explosive salts, among which the perchlorate is especially interesting. It is soluble in strong hydrochloric acid; ether precipitates the hydrochloride from the solution, and this on treatment with sodium acetate or with ammonia gives tetracene again. With an excess of silver nitrate it yields the double salt, $C_2H_7N_{10}OAg \cdot AgNO_3 \cdot 3H_2O$. Tetracene is only slightly hygroscopic. It is stable at ordinary temperatures both wet and dry, but is decomposed by boiling water with the evolution of $2N_2$ per molecule. On hydrolysis with caustic soda it yields ammonia, cyanamide, and triazonitroso-aminoguanidine which can be isolated in the form of a bright blue precipitate of the explosive copper salt by the addition of copper acetate to the alkaline solution. The copper salt on treat-ment with acid yields tetrazolyl azide (5-azidotetrazole).[60]

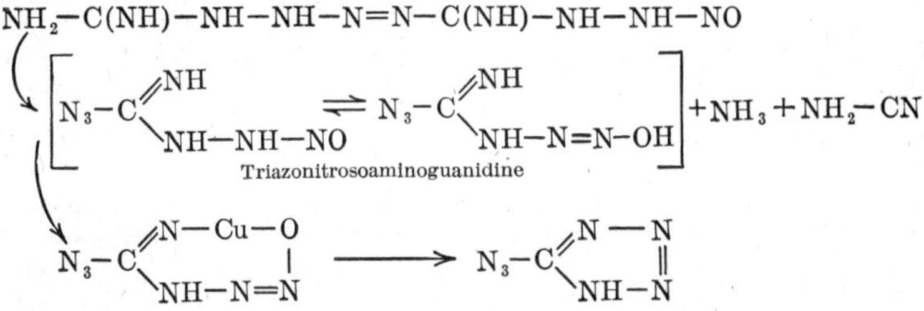

Triazonitrosoaminoguanidine

Tetrazolyl azide

[60] Cf. survey article by G. B. L. Smith, "The Chemistry of Aminoguani-dine and Related Substances," *Chem. Rev.*, **25**, 214 (1939).

In the presence of mineral acids, sodium nitrite reacts in a different manner with aminoguanidine, and guanyl azide is formed.

$$NH_2\text{---}C(NH)\text{---}NH\text{---}NH_2 + HONO \longrightarrow N_3\text{---}C\overset{\text{NH}}{\underset{\text{NH}_2}{\diagdown}} + 2H_2O$$

Guanyl azide

This substance forms salts with acids, and was first isolated in the form of its nitrate. The nitrate is not detonated by shock but undergoes a rapid decomposition with the production of light when it is heated. The picrate and the perchlorate explode violently from heat and from shock. Guanyl azide is not decomposed by boiling water. On hydrolysis with strong alkali, it yields the alkali metal salt of hydrazoic acid. It is hydrolyzed by ammoniacal silver nitrate in the cold with the formation of silver azide which remains in solution and of silver cyanamide which appears as a yellow precipitate. By treatment with acids or weak bases it is converted into 5-aminotetrazole.

$$N_3\text{---}C\overset{\text{NH}}{\underset{\text{NH}_2}{\diagdown}} \longrightarrow NH_2\text{---}C\overset{\text{N---N}}{\underset{\text{NH---N}}{\diagdown}}$$

5-Aminotetrazole

When the reaction between aminoguanidine and sodium nitrite occurs in the presence of an excess of acetic acid, still another product is formed, namely, 1,3-ditetrazolyltriazine, the genesis of which is easily understood from a consideration of the reactions already mentioned. 5-Aminotetrazole is evidently formed first; the amino group of one molecule of this substance is diazotized by the action of the nitrous acid, and the resulting diazonium salt in the acetic acid solution couples with a second molecule of the aminotetrazole.

$$\underset{\text{N---NH}}{\overset{\text{N---N}}{\diagup}}\!\!\diagdown C\text{---}NH_2 + HONO + CH_3\text{---}COOH \longrightarrow$$

$$\underset{\text{N---NH}}{\overset{\text{N---N}}{\diagup}}\!\!\diagdown C\text{---}N_2\text{---}O\text{---}CO\text{---}CH_3 + H_2O$$

$$\underset{\text{N---NH}}{\overset{\text{N---N}}{\diagup}}\!\!\diagdown C\text{---}N_2\text{---}O\text{---}CO\text{---}CH_3 + NH_2\text{---}C\overset{\text{N---N}}{\underset{\text{NH---N}}{\diagdown}} \longrightarrow$$

$$\underset{\text{N---NH}}{\overset{\text{N---N}}{\diagup}}\!\!\diagdown C\text{---}N\!\!=\!\!N\text{---}NH\text{---}C\overset{\text{N---N}}{\underset{\text{NH---N}}{\diagdown}} + CH_3\text{---}COOH$$

1,3-Ditetrazolyltriazine

Preparation of Tetracene. Thirty-four grams of aminoguanidine bi-carbonate, 2500 cc. of water, and 15.7 grams of glacial acetic acid are brought together in a 3-liter flask, and the mixture is warmed on the steam bath with occasional shaking until everything has gone into solution. The solution is filtered if need be, and cooled to 30° at the tap. Twenty-seven and sixth-tenths grams of solid sodium nitrite is added. The flask is swirled to make it dissolve, and is set aside at room temperature. After 3 or 4 hours, the flask is shaken to start precipitation of the product. It is allowed to stand for about 20 hours longer (22 to 24 hours altogether). The precipitate of tetracene is washed several times by decantation, transferred to a filter, and washed thoroughly with water. The product is dried at room temperature and is stored in a bottle which is closed by means of a cork or rubber stopper.

Tetracene explodes readily from flame without appreciable noise but with the production of much black smoke. Rinkenbach and Burton,[61] who have made an extended study of the explosive properties of tetracene, report that it explodes in 5 seconds at 160° (mercury fulminate 190°). They found that it is slightly more sensitive to impact than mercury fulminate; an 8-inch drop of an 8-ounce weight was needed to explode it, a drop of 9–10 inches to explode fulminate.

The brisance of tetracene, if it is used alone and is fired by a fuse, is greatest when the explosive is not compressed at all. Thus, 0.4 gram of tetracene, if uncompressed, crushed 13.1 grams of sand in the sand test; if compressed under a pressure of 250 pounds per square inch, 9.2 grams; if under 500 pounds per square inch, 7.5 grams; and, if under 3000 pounds per square inch, 2.0 grams. The data show the behavior of tetracene as it approaches the condition of being dead-pressed.

In another series of experiments, Rinkenbach and Burton used charges of 0.4 gram of tetracene, compressed under a pressure of 3000 pounds per square inch and initiated with varying amounts of fulminate (loaded under the same pressure), and found that the tetracene developed its maximum brisance (21.1 grams of sand crushed) when initiated with 0.4 gram of fulminate. A compound primer of 0.15 gram of tetryl initiated with 0.25 gram of mercury fulminate caused 0.4 gram of tetracene to crush 22.6 grams, or substantially the same amount, of sand. It appears

61 *Army Ordnance,* **12,** 120 (1931). See also Stettbacher, *Nitrocellulose,* **8,** 141 (1936); Grottanelli, *Chimica e industria,* **18,** 232 (1936).

then that tetracene is more brisant—and presumably explodes with a greater velocity of detonation—when initiated by fulminate or tetryl than when self-initiated by fire.

Tetracene is easily dead-pressed, its self-acceleration is low, and it is not suitable for use alone as an initiating explosive.

FIGURE 104. Tetracene Crystals (150×).

It is as efficient as fulminate only if it is externally initiated. It is used in detonators either initiated by another primary explosive and functioning as an intermediate booster or mixed with another primary explosive to increase the sensitivity of the latter to flame or heat. A recent patent [62] recommends the use of a mixture of tetracene and lead azide in explosive rivets. Tetracene is used in primer caps where as little as 2% in the composition results in an improved uniformity of percussion sensitivity.

[62] Brit. Pat. 528,299 (1940) to Dynamit-Aktien Gesellschaft vorm. Alfred Nobel & Co.

Hexamethylenetriperoxidediamine (HMTD)

Hexamethylenetriperoxidediamine is the only organic peroxide which has been considered seriously as an explosive. Its explosive properties commend it, but it is too reactive chemically and too unstable to be of practical use. It is most conveniently prepared by treating hexamethylenetetramine with hydrogen peroxide in the presence of citric acid which promotes the reaction by combining with the ammonia which is liberated.

$$C_6H_{12}N_4 + 3H_2O_2 \longrightarrow N \begin{array}{c} CH_2-O-O-CH_2 \\ CH_2-O-O-CH_2 \\ CH_2-O-O-CH_2 \end{array} N + 2NH_3$$

Hexamethylenetriperoxidediamine

Preparation of Hexamethylenetriperoxidediamine. Fourteen grams of hexamethylenetetramine is dissolved in 45 grams of 30% hydrogen peroxide solution which is stirred mechanically in a beaker standing in a freezing mixture of cracked ice with water and a little salt. To the solution 21 grams of powdered citric acid is added slowly in small portions at a time while the stirring is continued and the temperature of the mixture is kept at 0° or below. After all the citric acid has dissolved, the mixture is stirred for 3 hours longer while its temperature is kept at 0°. The cooling is then discontinued, the mixture is allowed to stand for 2 hours at room temperature, and the white crystalline product is filtered off, washed thoroughly with water, and rinsed with alcohol in order that it may dry out more quickly at ordinary temperatures.

Hexamethylenetriperoxidediamine is almost insoluble in water and in the common organic solvents at room temperature. It detonates when struck a sharp blow, but, when ignited, burns with a flash like nitrocellulose. Taylor and Rinkenbach [63] found its true density (20°/20°) to be 1.57, its apparent density after being placed in a tube and tapped 0.66, and its density after being compressed in a detonator capsule under a pressure of 2500 pounds per square inch only 0.91. They found that it required a 3-cm. drop of a 2-kilogram weight to make it explode, but that fulminate required a drop of only 0.25 cm. In the sand test it pulverized 2½ to 3 times as much sand as mercury fulminate, and slightly more sand than lead azide. It is not dead-pressed by a pressure of 11,000 pounds per square inch. It is considerably

[63] *Army Ordnance*, **5**, 463 (1924).

more effective than mercury fulminate as an initiator of detonation. Taylor and Rinkenbach, working with 0.4-gram portions of the high explosives and with varying weights of the primary explosives, compressed in detonator capsules under a pressure of 1000 pounds per square inch, found the minimum charges necessary to produce detonation to be as indicated in the following table.

	MINIMUM INITIATING CHARGE (GRAMS) OF		
	Fulminate with Reenforcing Cap	Hexamethylenetriperoxidediamine	
		With Reenforcing Cap	Without Reenforcing Cap
HIGH EXPLOSIVE			
Trinitrotoluene	0.26	0.08	0.10
Picric acid	0.21	0.05	0.06
Tetryl	0.24	0.05	0.06
Ammonium picrate	0.8–0.9	0.30	0.30
Tetranitroaniline	0.20	0.05	0.05
Guanidine picrate	0.30	0.13	0.15
Trinitroresorcinol	0.20	0.08	0.10
Hexanitrodiphenylamine	...	0.05	0.05
Trinitrobenzaldehyde	...	0.08	0.10

Taylor and Rinkenbach found that 0.05-gram portions of hexamethylenetriperoxidediamine, pressed in No. 8 detonator capsules under a pressure of 1000 pounds per square inch and fired by means of a black-powder fuse crimped in the usual way, caused the detonation of ordinary 40% nitroglycerin dynamite and of a gelatin dynamite which had become insensitive after storage of more than a year. The velocity of detonation of HMTD, loaded at a density of 0.88 in a column 0.22 inch in diameter, was found by the U. S. Bureau of Mines Explosives Testing Laboratory to be 4511 meters per second.

A small quantity of HMTD decomposed without exploding when dropped onto molten metal at 190°, but a small quantity detonated instantly when dropped onto molten metal at 200°. A 0.05-gram sample ignited in 3 seconds at 149°. At temperatures which are only moderately elevated the explosive shows signs of volatilizing and decomposing. Taylor and Rinkenbach report the results of experiments in which samples on watch glasses were heated in electric ovens at various temperatures, and weighed and examined from time to time, as shown below. The sample which had been heated at 60° showed no evidence of decomposition. The sample which had been heated at 75° was unchanged in color but had a faint odor of methylamine and appeared slightly moist. At 100° the substance gave off an amine odor. The residue which remained after 24 hours of heating at 100° consisted of a colorless liquid and needle crystals which were soluble in water.

% Weight Lost at	60°	75°	100°
In 2 hrs.	0.10	0.25	3.25
In 8 hrs.	0.35	0.60	29.60
In 24 hrs.	0.50	1.30	67.95
In 48 hrs.	0.50	2.25	....

When hexamethylenetriperoxidediamine is boiled with water, it disappears fairly rapidly, oxygen is given off, and the colorless solution is found to contain ammonia, formaldehyde, ethylene glycol, formic acid, and hexamethylenetetramine.

Friction Primers

Friction primers (friction tubes, friction igniters) are devices for the production of fire by the friction of the thrust, either push or pull, of a roughened rod or wire through a pellet of primer composition. They are used for firing artillery in circumstances where the propelling charge is loaded separately and is not enclosed in a brass case supplied with a percussion primer. They are sometimes crimped to an end of Bickford fuse for the purpose of lighting it. They are sometimes used for lighting flares, etc., which are thrown overboard from airplanes. For this use, the pull element of the primer is attached to the airplane by a length of twine or wire which the weight of the falling flare first pulls and then breaks off entirely.

The following table shows three compositions which have been widely used in friction primers for artillery. All the materials

Potassium chlorate	2	56.2	44.6
Antimony sulfide	1	24.6	44.6
Sulfur	..	9.0	3.6
Meal powder	..	...	3.6
Ground glass	..	10.2	3.6

are in the powdered condition except in the first mixture where half of the potassium chlorate is powdered and half of it is granular. The first mixture is probably the best. The sulfur which is contained in the second and third mixtures makes them more sensitive, but also makes them prone to turn sour after they have been wet-mixed, and these mixtures ought to be made up with a small amount of anti-acid (calcium carbonate, trimethylamine, etc., not mentioned in the table). All the mixtures are wet-mixed with 5% gum arabic solution, loaded wet, and dried out *in situ* to form pellets which do not crumble easily.

In a typical friction primer for an airplane flare, ignition is secured by pulling a loop of braided wire coated with red phosphorus and shellac through a pellet, made from potassium chlorate (14 parts) and charcoal (1.6 parts), hardened with dextrin (0.3 part).

Percussion Primers

Percussion primers produce fire or flame from the impact of the trigger or firing pin of a pistol, rifle, or cannon, or of the inertia-operated device in a fuze which functions when the projectile starts on its flight (the so-called concussion element, the primer of which is called a concussion primer) or of that which functions when the projectile strikes its target (the percussion element). A typical primer composition consists of a mixture of mercury fulminate (a primary explosive which produces the first explosion with heat and flame), antimony sulfide (a combustible material which maintains the flame for a longer time), and potassium chlorate (an oxidizing agent which supplies oxygen for the combustion). Sometimes no single primary explosive substance is present; the mixture itself is the primary explosive. Sometimes the compositions contain explosives such as TNT, tetryl, or PETN, which make them hotter, or ground glass which makes them more sensitive to percussion. Hot particles of solid (glass or heavy metal oxide) thrown out by a primer will set fire to black powder over a considerable distance, but they will fall onto smokeless powder without igniting it. The primers which produce the hottest gas are best suited for use with smokeless powder.

Primer compositions are usually mixed by hand on a glass-top table by a workman wearing rubber gloves and working alone in a small building remote from others. They are sometimes mixed dry, but in this country more commonly wet, with water or with water containing gum arabic or gum tragacanth, with alcohol alone or with an alcohol solution of shellac. The caps are loaded in much the same manner that blasting caps are loaded, the mixture is pressed down by machine and perhaps covered with a disc of tinfoil, the anvil is inserted and pressed into place (unless the primer is to be used in a cartridge or fuze of which the anvil is already an integral part), and the caps are finally dried in a dry-house and stored in small magazines until needed for loading.

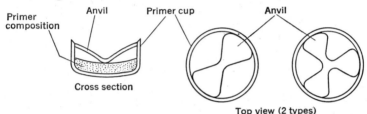

FIGURE 105. Primer Cap for Small Arms Cartridge.

For many years the standard mixture in France for all caps which were to be fired by the blow of a hammer was made from 2 parts of mercury fulminate, 1 of antimony sulfide, and 1 of saltpeter. This was mixed and loaded dry, and was considered to be safer to handle than similar mixtures containing potassium chlorate. Where a more sensitive primer was needed, the standard French composition for all concussion and percussion primers of fuzes was made from 5 parts of mercury fulminate and 9 parts each of antimony sulfide and potassium chlorate.

All the compositions listed in the following table (gum or shellac binder not included) have been used, in small arms primers or in fuze primers, by one or another of the great powers, and they illustrate the wide variations in the proportions of the ingredients which are possible or desirable according to the design of the device in which the primer is used.

Mercury fulminate	10.0	28.0	48.8	4	5	2	11.0	32	16.5	7	19.0
Potassium chlorate	37.0	35.5	24.4	2	9	3	52.5	45	50.0	21	33.0
Antimony sulfide	40.0	28.0	26.2	3	3	3	36.5	23	33.5	17	43.0
Sulfur											2.5
Meal powder											2.5
Ground glass	13.0	8.5		5						5	
Ground coke					1						
Tetryl					2						

A non-fulminate primer composition is probably somewhat safer to mix than one which contains fulminate. It contains no single substance which is a primary explosive, only the primary explosive mixture of the chlorate with the appropriate combustible material, or, more exactly, the explosive which exists at the point of contact between particles of the two substances. For a non-fulminate primer to perform properly, it is necessary that the composition should be mixed thoroughly and very uniformly in order that dissimilar particles may be found in contact with each other beneath the point of the anvil and may be crushed together by the blow of the trigger. It is not absolutely essential that fulminate compositions should be mixed with the same uniformity. Even if no fulminate happens to lie beneath the point of the anvil, the trigger blow sufficiently crushes the sensitive material in the neighborhood to make it explode. For mechanical reasons, the ingredients of primer composition ought not to be pulverized too finely.[64]

Several non-fulminate primer compositions are listed below.

Potassium chlorate	50	50.54	67	60	53
Antimony sulfide	20	26.31	..	30	17
Lead thiocyanate	..	...	..	..	25
Lead peroxide	25	...	..	..	..
Cuprous thiocyanate	..	...	15	3	..
TNT	5	...	..	..	5
Sulfur	..	8.76	16	7	..
Charcoal	..	...	2	..	..
Ground glass	..	12.39	..	..	...
Shellac	..	2.00	..	..	..

Sulfur ought not to be used in any primer composition, whether fulminate or non-fulminate, which contains chlorate unless an anti-acid is present. In a moist atmosphere, the sulfuric acid, which is inevitably present on the sulfur, attacks the chlorate, liberating chlorine dioxide which further attacks the sulfur, producing more sulfuric acid, and causing a self-catalyzed *souring* which results first in the primer becoming slow in its response to the trigger (hang fire) and later in its becoming inert (misfire). It is evident that the presence of fulminate in the composition will tend to nullify the effect of the souring, and that it

[64] Cf. Émile Monnin Chamot, "The Microscopy of Small Arms Primers," privately printed, Ithaca, New York, 1922.

is safest to avoid the use of sulfur with chlorate especially in non-fulminate mixtures. The second of the above-listed compositions is an undesirable one in this respect. In the third and fourth compositions, the cuprous thiocyanate serves both as a combustible and as an anti-acid, and it helps, particularly in the

$.30 = 7.63mm$
$.50 = 12.7 mm$

FIGURE 106. Longitudinal Sections of Military Rifle Ammunition of the First World War. (Courtesy Émile Monnin Chamot.) The cartridge at the bottom, French 9.0-mm. Lebel rifle, the one above it, German 7.9-mm. Mauser, and the one above that, Canadian .30 caliber, all have anvils of the Berdan type integrally one with the metal of the cartridge case.

third mixture, by supplying copper oxide which is a solid vehicle for the transfer of heat. The first and the last of the above-listed mixtures are the best. They contain no sulfur, and they contain lead enough to supply plenty of solid particles of hot material.

Gunnery experts ascribe a large part of the erosion of shotgun and rifle barrels to the action of the soluble salts which are produced from the materials of the primer compositions, particularly to the chlorides which come from the chlorate, and to the sulfates which result from the combustion of the antimony sulfide. The following table lists several non-chlorate, non-erosive primer compositions. They contain no compounds of chlorine. They con-

Mercury fulminate	36	40	25	20	39
Antimony sulfide	20	25	15	20	9
Barium nitrate	..	25	25	40	41
Lead peroxide	..	..	35	10	..
Lead chromate	40	..	..	..	..
Barium carbonate	..	6	..	..	..
Picric acid	..	..	..	..	5
Powdered glass	4	4	..	..	6
Calcium silicide	..	..	..	10	..

tain either lead or barium or both, and both of these metals form sulfates which are insoluble in water. Moreover, the soluble portions of the residues from the primers which contain barium nitrate are alkaline and are even capable of neutralizing any acidity which might arise from the smokeless powder.

INDEX OF NAMES

INDEX OF SUBJECTS

A

D

H

O